Occupational Health and Safety Act and Regulation for Construction Projects

Revised Statutes of Ontario, 1990
Chapter O.1, as amended

O. Reg. 213/91 as amended by
O. Reg. 631/94, O. Reg. 143/99,
O. Reg. 571/99, O. Reg. 145/00,
O. Reg. 527/00, O. Reg. 85/04,
O. Reg. 627/05, O. Reg. 628/05,
O. Reg. 443/09, O. Reg. 96/11,
O. Reg. 88/13.

Issue Date of this Edition:
July 2014

Occupational Health and Safety Act and Regulation for Construction Projects

This edition is prepared for convenience only. It is not intended to replace the OHSA or the regulations, and reference should always be made to the official version of the legislation. It is the responsibility of the workplace parties to ensure compliance with the legislation.

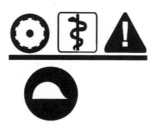

Issue Date of this Edition: July 2014

Copies of this publication and other publications relating to occupational health and safety may be purchased from ServiceOntario Publications.

Online at: www.serviceontario.ca/publications

By phone through the ServiceOntario Contact Centre
Monday to Friday, 8:30 AM to 5:00 PM

- 416 326-5300
- 416 325-3408 (TTY)
- 1 800 668-9938 Toll-free across Canada
- 1 800 268-7095 TTY Toll-free across Canada

CONTENTS

Appendices:

Notes on Amendments to the
Occupational Health and Safety Act
R.S.O. 1990, c. O.1.
[in force December 31, 1991]

1992, c. 14, s. 2 [in force June 25, 1992] added section 40.1 and repealed clauses 63 (1) (b) and (d).

1992, c. 21, s. 63 [in force January 1, 1993] amended subsection 50 (7).

1993, c. 27, Sched. [deemed in force December 31, 1991] amended subsection 1 (1) [definition of "committee"] and subsection 9 (4).

1994, c. 24, s. 35 [in force January 1, 1995] amended subsection 1 (1) [definition of "occupational illness"].

1994, c. 25, s. 83 (1) and (2) [in force April 1, 1995] amended subsection 1 (1) [definition of "licensee"] and subsection 24 (2).

1994, c. 27, s. 120 [in force December 9, 1994] added subsection 9 (3.1) and amended subsection 9 (5) and clause 26 (3) (c).

1995, c. 1, s. 84 [in force November 10, 1995] amended subsection 50 (7).

1995, c. 5, s. 28-32 [in force December 15, 1995] amended subsections 13 (2-8), subsection 14 (1), subsection 16 (9), and clause 6 (1) (b). It also repealed subsection 16 (8) and subsections 17 (5) and (6). [NOTE: Certain sections of this amending statute came into effect earlier than the date of Royal Assent.]

1997, c. 4, s. 84 [in force October 29, 1997] amended s. 43 (2) (b).

1997, c. 16, s. 2 [in force January 1, 1998] amended s. 1 (1), s. 12 (1), s. 22, s. 52, s. 65 (1) and s. 70 (2) 15. It also repealed s. 13-19.

1998, c. 8, s. 49-60 [in force June 29, 1998] amended s. 1 (1), s. 9 (36) and (37), s. 20 [new], s. 22.1 [new], s. 46, s. 47 (1) (a), s. 49, s. 50, s. 61, s. 65 (1) (c), and s. 70 (2) par. 48.

2001, c. 9, Sched. I, s. 3 [in force June 29, 2001] amended s. 4, s. 9 (3.2) [new], s. 9 (3.3) [new], s. 32.1 - 32.4 [new], s. 33 (6), s. 38 (1-3), s. 40 (1) (a), s. 43 (7), s. 52 (1), s. 57 (10), s. 60 and s. 68 (1). It also repealed s. 36 and s. 70 (2) 33.

2001, c. 13, s. 22 [in force June 29, 2001] amended s. 43 (2) (d) (i) and (ii).

2001, c. 26 [in force December 12, 2001] amended s. 54 (2), s. 56 (1-2), s. 56.1 [new]; s. 62 (1-3).

2004, c. 3, Sched. A, s. 93 [in force November 1, 2004] added s. 63 (6).

2006, c. 19, Sched. D, s. 14 and Sched. M, s. 5 [in force June 22, 2006] amended s. 43 (2) (c); s. 68.1 [new].

2006, c. 21, Sched. F, s. 136 (1) [in force July 25, 2007] amended s. 32.2 (3) and s. 61 (3.11).

2006, c. 34, Sched. C. s. 25 [in force April 1, 2007] amended s. 68.1 (3).

2006, c. 35, Sched. C, s. 93 [in force August 20, 2007] amended s. 5, s. 21 (2), s. 40.1 (1), (2); s. 50 (6), s. 65 (1) (a).

2007, c. 8, s. 221 [in force July 1, 2010] amended s. 43 (2) (d) (i)

2009, c. 23 [in force June 15, 2010] amended s. 1 (1) [definitions of "workplace harassment" and "workplace violence" - new]; s. 25 (3.1) [new]; s. 32.0.1 – 32.0.7 [new]; s. 43; s. 52 (1); s. 55.1, 55.2 [new]; s. 70 (2) 15, 33, 50, 51, 52 [new]; s. 71 [new].

2009, c. 33, Sched. 20, s. 3 [in force December 15, 2009] amended s. 1. (1), s. 55.

2011, c. 1, Sched. 7, s. 2 [in force March 30, 2011 OR by proclamation] amended s. 22.1; s. 25 (4); s. 31.0.1 (3); s. 37 (1), (3), (4), (5); 38 (1), (2), (3), (5), (6); s. 40 (1); s. 51 (1); s. 53; s. 55.1; s. 57 (8), (9); s. 61 (2) 4; s. 70 (2) 39, 40.

2011, c. 11 [in force on or before April 1, 2012] amended s. 1 (1) [definitions of "Building Code" (new), "certified member" (revised), "Chief Prevention Office" (new), "Office of the Employer Advisor" (new), "Office of the Worker Advisor" (new)]"; s. 4.1 [new]; s. 7.1 – 7.7 [new]; s. 8; s. 9 (19.1) [new]; 9 (20), (36); s. 22.2 – 22.4 [new]; s. 22.5 – 22.9 [new]; s. 25 (1) (e); s. 32.1; s. 32.2 (1); s. 32.4; s. 50 (2.1)-(2.3) [new]; s. 50 (3); s. 50 (4); s. 50 (4.1), (4.2) [new]; s. 50 (5) – (8); s. 50.1 [new]; s. 54 (1) (m); s. 63 (3.1) – (3.3) [new]; s. 65 (1), (2); s. 70 (2) 13.1, 13.2 [new]; s. 70 (2) 31.1 [new]; s. 70 (2) 53, 54, 55, 56 [new].

- - - - - - - - - -

The Occupational Health and Safety Act, and the regulations made under that Act, can be found on-line at the following website (all legislation is kept up-to-date within a week of any amendments): http://www.e-laws.gov.on.ca [click on the "O" under Current Consolidated Law]

- - - - - - - - - -

OCCUPATIONAL HEALTH AND SAFETY ACT

Definitions

1.   (1) In this Act,

"Board" means the Ontario Labour Relations Board; ("Commission")

"Building Code" means any version of the Ontario Building Code that was in force at any time since it was made under the Building Code Act, 1974, the Building Code Act of the Revised Statutes of Ontario, 1980, the Building Code Act of the Revised Statutes of Ontario, 1990, the Building Code Act, 1992 or a successor to the Building Code Act, 1992; ("code du bâtiment")

"certified member" means a committee member who is certified under section 7.6; ("membre agréé")

"Chief Prevention Officer" means the Chief Prevention Officer appointed under subsection 22.3 (1); ("directeur général de la prévention")

"committee" means a joint health and safety committee established under this Act; ("comité")

"competent person" means a person who

(a)   is qualified because of knowledge, training and experience to organize the work and its performance,

(b)   is familiar with this Act and the regulations that apply to the work, and

(c)   has knowledge of any potential or actual danger to health or safety in the workplace; ("personne compétente") "construction" includes erection, alteration, repair, dismantling, demolition, structural maintenance, painting, land clearing, earth moving, grading, excavating, trenching, digging, boring, drilling, blasting, or concreting, the installation of any machinery or plant, and any work or undertaking in connection with a project but does not include any work or undertaking underground in a mine; ("construction")

"constructor" means a person who undertakes a project for an owner and includes an owner who undertakes all or part of a project by himself or by more than one employer; ("constructeur")

"Deputy Minister" means the Deputy Minister of Labour; ("sous-ministre")

"designated substance" means a biological, chemical or physical agent or combination thereof prescribed as a designated substance to which the exposure of a worker is prohibited, regulated, restricted, limited or controlled; ("substance désignée")

"Director" means an inspector under this Act who is appointed as a Director for the purposes of this Act; ("directeur")

"employer" means a person who employs one or more workers or contracts for the services of one or more workers and includes a contractor or subcontractor who performs work or supplies services and a contractor or subcontractor who undertakes with an owner, constructor, contractor or subcontractor to perform work or supply services; ("employeur")

"engineer of the Ministry" means a person who is employed by the Ministry and who is licensed as a professional engineer under the Professional Engineers Act; ("ingénieur du ministère")

"factory" means,

(a) a building or place other than a mine, mining plant or place where homework is carried on, where,

    (i) any manufacturing process or assembling in connection with the manufacturing of any goods or products is carried on,

    (ii) in preparing, inspecting, manufacturing, finishing, repairing, warehousing, cleaning or adapting for hire or sale any substance, article or thing, energy is,

        (A) used to work any machinery or device, or

        (B) modified in any manner,

    (iii) any work is performed by way of trade or for the purposes of gain in or incidental to the making of any goods, substance, article or thing or part thereof,

    (iv) any work is performed by way of trade or for the purposes of gain in or incidental to the altering, demolishing, repairing, maintaining, ornamenting, finishing, storing, cleaning, washing or adapting for sale of any goods, substance, article or thing, or

    (v) aircraft, locomotives or vehicles used for private or public transport are maintained,

(b) a laundry including a laundry operated in conjunction with,

    (i) a public or private hospital,

      (ii)   a hotel, or

      (iii) a public or private institution for religious, charitable or educational purposes, and

  (c)   a logging operation; ("usine")

"hazardous material" means a biological or chemical agent named or described in the regulations as a hazardous material; ("matériau dangereux")

"hazardous physical agent" means a physical agent named or described in the regulations as a hazardous physical agent; ("agent physique dangereux")

"health and safety representative" means a health and safety representative selected under this Act; ("délégué à la santé et à la sécurité")

"homework" means the doing of any work in the manufacture, preparation, improvement, repair, alteration, assembly or completion of any article or thing or any part thereof by a person for wages in premises occupied primarily as living accommodation; ("travail à domicile")

"industrial establishment" means an office building, factory, arena, shop or office, and any land, buildings and structures appertaining thereto; ("établissement industriel")

"inspector" means an inspector appointed for the purposes of this Act and includes a Director; ("inspecteur")

"labour relations officer" means a labour relations officer appointed under the Labour Relations Act, 1995; ("agent des relations de travail") "licensee" means a person who holds a licence under Part III of the Crown Forest Sustainability Act, 1994; ("titulaire d'un permis")

"logging" means the operation of felling or trimming trees for commercial or industrial purposes or for the clearing of land, and includes the measuring, storing, transporting or floating of logs, the maintenance of haul roads, scarification, the carrying out of planned burns and the practice of silviculture; ("exploitation forestière")

"mine" means any work or undertaking for the purpose of opening up, proving, removing or extracting any metallic or non-metallic mineral or mineral-bearing substance, rock, earth, clay, sand or gravel; ("mine")

"mining plant" means any roasting or smelting furnace, concentrator, mill or place used for or in connection with washing, crushing, grinding, sifting, reducing, leaching, roasting, smelting, refining, treating or research on any substance mentioned in the definition of "mine"; ("installation minière")

"Minister" means the Minister of Labour; ("ministre")

"Ministry" means the Ministry of Labour; ("ministère")

"occupational illness" means a condition that results from exposure in a workplace to a physical, chemical or biological agent to the extent that the normal physiological mechanisms are affected and the health of the worker is impaired thereby and includes an occupational disease for which a worker is entitled to benefits under the Workplace Safety and Insurance Act, 1997; ("maladie professionnelle")

"Office of the Employer Adviser" means the office continued under subsection 176 (2) of the Workplace Safety and Insurance Act, 1997; ("Bureau des conseillers des employeurs")

"Office of the Worker Adviser" means the office continued under subsection 176 (1) of the Workplace Safety and Insurance Act, 1997; ("Bureau des conseillers des travailleurs")

"owner" includes a trustee, receiver, mortgagee in possession, tenant, lessee, or occupier of any lands or premises used or to be used as a workplace, and a person who acts for or on behalf of an owner as an agent or delegate; ("propriétaire")

"prescribed" means prescribed by a regulation made under this Act; ("prescrit")

"project" means a construction project, whether public or private, including,

(a) the construction of a building, bridge, structure, industrial establishment, mining plant, shaft, tunnel, caisson, trench, excavation, highway, railway, street, runway, parking lot, cofferdam, conduit, sewer, watermain, service connection, telegraph, telephone or electrical cable, pipe line, duct or well, or any combination thereof,

(b) the moving of a building or structure, and

(c) any work or undertaking, or any lands or appurtenances used in connection with construction; ("chantier")

"regulations" means the regulations made under this Act; ("règlements")

"shop" means a building, booth or stall or a part of such building, booth or stall where goods are handled, exposed or offered for sale or where services are offered for sale; ("magasin")

"supervisor" means a person who has charge of a workplace or authority over a worker; ("superviseur") "trade union" means a trade union as defined in the Labour Relations Act, 1995 that has the status of exclusive bargaining agent under that Act in respect of any bargaining unit or units in a workplace and includes an organization representing workers or persons to whom this Act applies where such organization has exclusive bargaining rights under any other Act in respect of such workers or persons; ("syndicat")

"worker" means a person who performs work or supplies services for monetary compensation but does not include an inmate of a correctional institution or like institution or facility who participates inside the institution or facility in a work project or rehabilitation program; ("travailleur")

"workplace" means any land, premises, location or thing at, upon, in or near which a worker works; ("lieu de travail")

"workplace harassment" means engaging in a course of vexatious comment or conduct against a worker in a workplace that is known or ought reasonably to be known to be unwelcome; ("harcèlement au travail")

"workplace violence" means,

(a)   the exercise of physical force by a person against a worker, in a workplace, that causes or could cause physical injury to the worker,

(b)   an attempt to exercise physical force against a worker, in a workplace, that could cause physical injury to the worker,

(c)   a statement or behaviour that it is reasonable for a worker to interpret as a threat to exercise physical force against the worker, in a workplace, that could cause physical injury to the worker. ("violence au travail") R.S.O. 1990, c. O.1, s. 1 (1); 1993, c. 27, Sched.; 1994, c. 24, s. 35; 1994, c. 25, s. 83 (1); 1997, c. 16, s. 2 (1-3); 1998, c. 8, s. 49; 2009, c. 23, s. 1; 2009, c. 33, Sched. 20, s. 3 (1); 2011, c. 11, s. 1.

Ship under repair

(2)   For the purposes of this Act and the regulations, a ship being manufactured or under repair shall be deemed to be a project. R.S.O. 1990, c. O.1, s. 1 (2).

Limitation

(3)   An owner does not become a constructor by virtue only of the fact that the owner has engaged an architect, professional engineer or other person solely to oversee quality control at a project. R.S.O. 1990, c. O.1, s. 1 (3).

PART I
APPLICATION

Crown and other Acts

Crown

2.   (1)   This Act binds the Crown and applies to an employee in the service of the Crown or an agency, board, commission or corporation that exercises any function assigned or delegated to it by the Crown.

Other Acts

(2)   Despite anything in any general or special Act, the provisions of this Act and the regulations prevail. R.S.O. 1990, c. O.1, s. 2.

Private residences, farming, teaching

Private residences

3.　(1)　This Act does not apply to work performed by the owner or occupant or a servant of the owner or occupant to, in or about a private residence or the lands and appurtenances used in connection therewith.

Farming operations

(2)　Except as is prescribed and subject to the conditions and limitations prescribed, this Act or a Part thereof does not apply to farming operations.

Teachers, etc.

(3)　Except as is prescribed and subject to the conditions and limitations prescribed, this Act or a Part thereof does not apply to,

(a)　a person who is employed as a teacher as defined in the Education Act; or

(b)　a person who is employed as a member or teaching assistant of the academic staff of a university or a related institution.　R.S.O. 1990, c. O.1, s. 3.

Self-employed persons

4.　Subsection 25 (1), clauses 26 (1) (c), (e), (f) and (g), subsection 33 (1) and sections 34, 37, 38, 39, 40, 41, 51, 52, 54, 57, 59, 60, 61, 62, 66, 67, 68 and 69, and the regulations in relation thereto, apply with necessary modifications to a self-employed person.　2001, c. 9, Sched. I, s. 3 (1).

PART II
ADMINISTRATION

Administration of Act

4.1 (1) The Minister is responsible for the administration of this Act. 2011, c. 11, s. 2.

Powers of Minister

(2) In administering this Act, the Minister's powers and duties include the following:

1. To promote occupational health and safety and to promote the prevention of workplace injuries and occupational diseases.

2. To promote public awareness of occupational health and safety.

3. To educate employers, workers and other persons about occupational health and safety.

4. To foster a commitment to occupational health and safety among employers, workers and others.

5. To make grants, in such amounts and on such terms as the Minister considers advisable, to support occupational health and safety. 2011, c. 11, s. 2.

Duty to consider

(3) In administering this Act, the Minister shall consider advice that is provided to the Minister under this Act. 2011, c. 11, s. 2.

Delegation of powers

5. Where under this Act or the regulations any power or duty is granted to or vested in the Minister or the Deputy Minister, the Minister or Deputy Minister may in writing delegate that power or duty from time to time to any employee in the Ministry subject to such limitations, restrictions, conditions and requirements as the Minister or Deputy Minister may set out in the delegation. R.S.O. 1990, c. O.1, s. 5; 2006, c. 35, Sched. C, s. 93 (1).

Appointment of inspectors and Directors

6. (1) Such persons as may be necessary to administer and enforce this Act and the regulations may be appointed as inspectors by the Deputy Minister and the Deputy Minister may designate one or more of the inspectors as a Director or Directors.

Director may act as inspector

(2) A Director may exercise any of the powers or perform any of the duties of an inspector under this Act or the regulations. R.S.O. 1990, c. O.1, s. 6.

Certificate of appointment

7. (1) The Deputy Minister shall issue a certificate of appointment, bearing his or her signature or a facsimile thereof, to every inspector.

Production of certificate

(2) Every inspector, in the exercise of any powers or duties under this Act, shall produce his or her certificate of appointment upon request. R.S.O. 1990, c. O.1, s. 7.

Standards – training programs

7.1 (1) The Chief Prevention Officer may establish standards for training programs required under this Act or the regulations. 2011, c. 11, s. 3.

Approval — training program

(2) The Chief Prevention Officer may approve a training program that is established before or after this subsection comes into force if

the training program meets the standards established under
subsection (1). 2011, c. 11, s. 3.

Standards – persons who provide training

7.2 (1) The Chief Prevention Officer may establish standards that a
person shall meet in order to become an approved training provider.
2011, c. 11, s. 3.

Approval – persons who provide training

(2) The Chief Prevention Officer may approve a person who
meets the standards described in subsection (1) as a training
provider with respect to one or more approved training programs.
2011, c. 11, s. 3.

Amendment of standard

7.3 (1) The Chief Prevention Officer may amend a standard
established under subsection 7.1 (1) or 7.2 (1). 2011, c. 11, s. 3.

Publication of standards

(2) The Chief Prevention Officer shall publish the standards
established under subsections 7.1 (1) and 7.2 (1) promptly after
establishing or amending them. 2011, c. 11, s. 3.

Time limit of approval

7.4 (1) An approval given under subsection 7.1 (2) or 7.2 (2) is valid
for the period that the Chief Prevention Officer specifies in the
approval. 2011, c. 11, s. 3.

Revocation, etc., of approval

(2) The Chief Prevention Officer may revoke or amend an
approval given under subsection 7.1 (2) or 7.2 (2). 2011, c. 11, s. 3.

Information to be provided to Chief Prevention Officer

(3) The Chief Prevention Officer may require any person who is
seeking an approval or is the subject of an approval under
subsection 7.1 (2) or 7.2 (2) to provide the Chief Prevention Officer

with whatever information, records or accounts he or she may require pertaining to the approval and the Chief Prevention Officer may make such inquiries and examinations as he or she considers necessary. 2011, c. 11, s. 3.

Collection and use of training information

7.5 (1) The Chief Prevention Officer may collect information about a worker's successful completion of an approved training program for the purpose of maintaining a record of workers who have successfully completed approved training programs. 2011, c. 11, s. 3.

Disclosure by training provider

(2) The Chief Prevention Officer may require an approved training provider to disclose to him or her the information described in subsection (1). 2011, c. 11, s. 3.

Same

(3) The Chief Prevention Officer may specify the time at which, and the form in which, the information shall be provided. 2011, c. 11, s. 3.

Disclosure by Chief Prevention Officer

(4) The Chief Prevention Officer may disclose information collected under subsection (1) to any person, including but not limited to a current or potential employer of a worker, if the worker consents to the disclosure. 2011, c. 11, s. 3.

Certification of members

7.6 (1) The Chief Prevention Officer may,

(a) establish training and other requirements that a committee member shall fulfil in order to become a certified member; and

    (b)   certify a committee member who fulfils the requirements described in clause (a). 2011, c. 11, s. 4.

Transition

(2)   A person who is certified under paragraph 5 of subsection 4 (1) of the Workplace Safety and Insurance Act, 1997 on the date section 20 of the Occupational Health and Safety Statute Law Amendment Act, 2011 comes into force is deemed to be certified under this section. 2011, c. 11, s. 4.

Delegation

7.7 The Chief Prevention Officer may in writing delegate from time to time his or her powers or duties under subsections 7.1 (2) and 7.2 (2), sections 7.4 and 7.5 and clause 7.6 (1) (b) to any employee in the Ministry, subject to such limitations, restrictions, conditions and requirements as the Chief Prevention Officer may set out in the delegation. 2011, c. 11, s. 5.

Mandatory selection of health and safety representative

8.   (1)   At a project or other workplace where no committee is required under section 9 and where the number of workers regularly exceeds five, the constructor or employer shall cause the workers to select at least one health and safety representative from among the workers at the workplace who do not exercise managerial functions. R.S.O. 1990, c. O.1, s. 8 (1).

Order appointing health and safety representatives

(2)   If no health and safety representative is required under subsection (1) and no committee is required under section 9 for a workplace, the Minister may, by order in writing, require a constructor or employer to cause the workers to select one or more health and safety representatives from among the workers at the workplace or part thereof who do not exercise managerial functions, and may provide in the order for the qualifications of such representatives. R.S.O. 1990, c. O.1, s. 8 (2).

Same

(3)   The Minister may from time to time give such directions as the Minister considers advisable concerning the carrying out of the functions of a health and safety representative. R.S.O. 1990, c. O.1, s. 8 (3).

What Minister shall consider

(4)   In exercising the power conferred by subsection (2), the Minister shall consider the matters set out in subsection 9 (5). R.S.O. 1990, c. O.1, s. 8 (4).

Selection of representatives

(5)   The selection of a health and safety representative shall be made by those workers who do not exercise managerial functions and who will be represented by the health and safety representative in the workplace, or the part or parts thereof, as the case may be, or, where there is a trade union or trade unions representing such workers, by the trade union or trade unions. R.S.O. 1990, c. O.1, s. 8 (5).

Note: On a day to be named by proclamation of the Lieutenant Governor, section 8 is amended by adding subsections (5.1), (5.2) and (5.3):

Training requirement

(5.1) Unless otherwise prescribed, a constructor or employer shall ensure that a health and safety representative selected under subsection (5) receives training to enable him or her to effectively exercise the powers and perform the duties of a health and safety representative. 2011, c. 11, s. 6.

Same

(5.2) The training described in subsection (5.1) shall meet such requirements as may be prescribed. 2011, c. 11, s. 6.

Entitlement to be paid

(5.3) A health and safety representative is deemed to be at work while he or she is receiving the training described in subsection (5.1), and the representative's employer shall pay the representative for the time spent, at the representative's regular or premium rate as may be proper. 2011, c. 11, s. 6.

Inspections

(6) Unless otherwise required by the regulations or by an order by an inspector, a health and safety representative shall inspect the physical condition of the workplace at least once a month. R.S.O. 1990, c. O.1, s. 8 (6).

Same

(7) If it is not practical to inspect the workplace at least once a month, the health and safety representative shall inspect the physical condition of the workplace at least once a year, inspecting at least a part of the workplace in each month. R.S.O. 1990, c. O.1, s. 8 (7).

Schedule of inspections

(8) The inspection required by subsection (7) shall be undertaken in accordance with a schedule agreed upon by the constructor or employer and the health and safety representative. R.S.O. 1990, c. O.1, s. 8 (8).

Inspections

(9) The constructor, employer and workers shall provide a health and safety representative with such information and assistance as the member may require for the purpose of carrying out an inspection of the workplace. R.S.O. 1990, c. O.1, s. 8 (9).

Same

(10) A health and safety representative has power to identify situations that may be a source of danger or hazard to workers and

to make recommendations or report his or her findings thereon to the employer, the workers and the trade union or trade unions representing the workers. R.S.O. 1990, c. O.1, s. 8 (10).

Powers of representative

(11) A health and safety representative has the power,

(a) to obtain information from the constructor or employer concerning the conducting or taking of tests of any equipment, machine, device, article, thing, material or biological, chemical or physical agent in or about a workplace for the purpose of occupational health and safety;

(b) to be consulted about, and be present at the beginning of, testing referred to in clause (a) conducted in or about the workplace if the representative believes his or her presence is required to ensure that valid testing procedures are used or to ensure that the test results are valid; and

(c) to obtain information from the constructor or employer respecting,

(i) the identification of potential or existing hazards of materials, processes or equipment, and

(ii) health and safety experience and work practices and standards in similar or other industries of which the constructor or employer has knowledge. R.S.O. 1990, c. O.1, s. 8 (11).

Response to recommendations

(12) A constructor or employer who receives written recommendations from a health and safety representative shall

respond in writing within twenty-one days. R.S.O. 1990, c. O.1, s. 8 (12).

Same

(13) A response of a constructor or employer under subsection (12) shall contain a timetable for implementing the recommendations the constructor or employer agrees with and give reasons why the constructor or employer disagrees with any recommendations that the constructor or employer does not accept. R.S.O. 1990, c. O.1, s. 8 (13).

Notice of accident, inspection by representative

(14) Where a person is killed or critically injured at a workplace from any cause, the health and safety representative may, subject to subsection 51 (2), inspect the place where the accident occurred and any machine, device or thing, and shall report his or her findings in writing to a Director. R.S.O. 1990, c. O.1, s. 8 (14).

Entitlement to time from work

(15) A health and safety representative is entitled to take such time from work as is necessary to carry out his or her duties under subsections (6) and (14) and the time so spent shall be deemed to be work time for which the representative shall be paid by his or her employer at the representative's regular or premium rate as may be proper. R.S.O. 1990, c. O.1, s. 8 (15).

Additional powers of certain health and safety representatives

(16) A health and safety representative or representatives of like nature appointed or selected under the provisions of a collective agreement or other agreement or arrangement between the constructor or the employer and the workers, has, in addition to his or her functions and powers under the provisions of the collective agreement or other agreement or arrangement, the functions and powers conferred upon a health and safety representative by this section. R.S.O. 1990, c. O.1, s. 8 (16).

Joint health and safety committee

Application

9. (1) Subject to subsection (3), this section does not apply,

   (a) to a constructor at a project at which work is expected to last less than three months; or

   (b) to a prescribed employer or workplace or class of employers or workplaces. R.S.O. 1990, c. O.1, s. 9 (1).

Joint health and safety committee

   (2) A joint health and safety committee is required,

   (a) at a workplace at which twenty or more workers are regularly employed;

   (b) at a workplace with respect to which an order to an employer is in effect under section 33; or

   (c) at a workplace, other than a construction project where fewer than twenty workers are regularly employed, with respect to which a regulation concerning designated substances applies. R.S.O. 1990, c. O.1, s. 9 (2).

Minister's order

   (3) Despite subsections (1) and (2), the Minister may, by order in writing, require a constructor or an employer to establish and maintain one or more joint health and safety committees for a workplace or a part thereof, and may, in such order, provide for the composition, practice and procedure of any committee so established. R.S.O. 1990, c. O.1, s. 9 (3).

Same

   (3.1) Despite subsections (1) and (2), the Minister may, by order in writing, permit a constructor or an employer to establish and maintain one joint health and safety committee for more than one workplace or parts thereof, and may, in the order, provide for the composition, practice and procedure of any committee so established. 1994, c. 27, s. 120 (1).

Same

(3.2) In an order under subsection (3.1), the Minister may,

    (a) provide that the members of a committee who represent workers may designate a worker at a workplace who is not a member of the committee to inspect the physical condition of the workplace under subsection 9 (23) and to exercise a committee member's rights and responsibilities under clause 43 (4) (a) and subsections 43 (7), (11) and (12); and

    (b) require the employer to provide training to the worker to enable the worker to adequately perform the tasks or exercise the rights and responsibilities delegated by the committee. 2001, c. 9, Sched. I, s. 3 (3).

Same

(3.3) If a worker is designated under clause (3.2) (a), the following apply:

    1. The designated worker shall comply with this section as if the worker were a committee member while exercising a committee member's rights and responsibilities.

    2. Subsections 9 (35) and 43 (13), section 55, clauses 62 (5) (a) and (b) and subsection 65 (1) apply to the designated worker as if the worker were a committee member while the worker exercises a committee member's rights and responsibilities.

3. The worker does not become a member of the committee as a result of the designation. 2001, c. 9, Sched. I, s. 3 (3).

Establishment of committee

(4) The constructor or employer shall cause a joint health and safety committee to be established and maintained at the workplace unless the Minister is satisfied that a committee of like nature or an arrangement, program or system in which the workers participate was, on the 1st day of October, 1979, established and maintained pursuant to a collective agreement or other agreement or arrangement and that such committee, arrangement, program or system provides benefits for the health and safety of the workers equal to, or greater than, the benefits to be derived under a committee established under this section. R.S.O. 1990, c. O.1, s. 9 (4); 1993, c. 27, Sched.

What Minister shall consider

(5) In exercising the power conferred by subsection (3) or (3.1), the Minister shall consider,

(a) the nature of the work being done;

(b) the request of a constructor, an employer, a group of the workers or the trade union or trade unions representing the workers in a workplace;

(c) the frequency of illness or injury in the workplace or in the industry of which the constructor or employer is a part;

(d) the existence of health and safety programs and procedures in the workplace and the effectiveness thereof; and

(e)   such other matters as the Minister considers advisable.
R.S.O. 1990, c. O.1, s. 9 (5); 1994, c. 27, s. 120 (2).

Composition of committee

(6)   A committee shall consist of,

(a)   at least two persons, for a workplace where fewer than
fifty workers are regularly employed; or

(b)   at least four persons or such greater number of people
as may be prescribed, for a workplace where fifty or
more workers are regularly employed. R.S.O. 1990,
c. O.1, s. 9 (6).

Same

(7)   At least half the members of a committee shall be workers
employed at the workplace who do not exercise managerial
functions. R.S.O. 1990, c. O.1, s. 9 (7).

Selection of members

(8)   The members of a committee who represent workers shall be
selected by the workers they are to represent or, if a trade union or
unions represent the workers, by the trade union or unions. R.S.O.
1990, c. O.1, s. 9 (8).

Same

(9)   The constructor or employer shall select the remaining
members of a committee from among persons who exercise
managerial functions for the constructor or employer and, to the
extent possible, who do so at the workplace. R.S.O. 1990, c. O.1,
s. 9 (9).

Requirement for committee membership

(10)   A member of the committee who ceases to be employed at the
workplace ceases to be a member of the committee. R.S.O. 1990,
c. O.1, s. 9 (10).

Committee to be co-chaired

(11) Two of the members of a committee shall co-chair the committee, one of whom shall be selected by the members who represent workers and the other of whom shall be selected by the members who exercise managerial functions. R.S.O. 1990, c. O.1, s. 9 (11).

Certification requirement

(12) Unless otherwise prescribed, a constructor or employer shall ensure that at least one member of the committee representing the constructor or employer and at least one member representing workers are certified members. R.S.O. 1990, c. O.1, s. 9 (12).

Same

(13) Subsection (12) does not apply with respect to a project where fewer than fifty workers are regularly employed or that is expected to last less than three months. R.S.O. 1990, c. O.1, s. 9 (13).

Designation of member to be certified

(14) If no member representing workers is a certified member, the workers or the trade unions who selected the members representing workers shall select from among them one or more who are to become certified. R.S.O. 1990, c. O.1, s. 9 (14).

Designation of certified members

(15) If there is more than one certified member representing workers, the workers or the trade unions who selected the members representing workers shall designate one or more certified members who then become solely entitled to exercise the rights and required to perform the duties under this Act of a certified member representing workers. R.S.O. 1990, c. O.1, s. 9 (15).

Same

(16) If there is more than one certified member representing the constructor or employer, the constructor or employer shall

designate one or more of them who then become solely entitled to exercise the rights and required to perform the duties under this Act of a certified member representing a constructor or an employer. R.S.O. 1990, c. O.1, s. 9 (16).

Replacement of certified member

(17) If a certified member resigns or is unable to act, the constructor or employer shall, within a reasonable time, take all steps necessary to ensure that the requirement set out in subsection (12) is met. R.S.O. 1990, c. O.1, s. 9 (17).

Powers of committee

(18) It is the function of a committee and it has power to,

    (a)   identify situations that may be a source of danger or hazard to workers;

    (b)   make recommendations to the constructor or employer and the workers for the improvement of the health and safety of workers;

    (c)   recommend to the constructor or employer and the workers the establishment, maintenance and monitoring of programs, measures and procedures respecting the health or safety of workers;

    (d)   obtain information from the constructor or employer respecting,

        (i)   the identification of potential or existing hazards of materials, processes or equipment, and

        (ii)   health and safety experience and work practices and standards in similar or other industries of which the constructor or employer has knowledge;

(e)   obtain information from the constructor or employer concerning the conducting or taking of tests of any equipment, machine, device, article, thing, material or biological, chemical or physical agent in or about a workplace for the purpose of occupational health and safety; and

(f)   be consulted about, and have a designated member representing workers be present at the beginning of, testing referred to in clause (e) conducted in or about the workplace if the designated member believes his or her presence is required to ensure that valid testing procedures are used or to ensure that the test results are valid. R.S.O. 1990, c. O.1, s. 9 (18).

Same

(19) The members of the committee who represent workers shall designate one of them who is entitled to be present at the beginning of testing described in clause (18) (f). R.S.O. 1990, c. O.1, s. 9 (19).

Powers of co-chairs

(19.1) If the committee has failed to reach consensus about making recommendations under subsection (18) after attempting in good faith to do so, either co-chair of the committee has the power to make written recommendations to the constructor or employer. 2011, c. 11, s. 7 (1).

Response to recommendations

(20) A constructor or employer who receives written recommendations from a committee or co-chair shall respond in writing within twenty-one days. R.S.O. 1990, c. O.1, s. 9 (20); 2011, c. 11, s. 7 (2).

Same

(21) A response of a constructor or employer under subsection (20) shall contain a timetable for implementing the recommendations the constructor or employer agrees with and give reasons why the constructor or employer disagrees with any recommendations that the constructor or employer does not accept. R.S.O. 1990, c. O.1, s. 9 (21).

Minutes of proceedings

(22) A committee shall maintain and keep minutes of its proceedings and make the same available for examination and review by an inspector. R.S.O. 1990, c. O.1, s. 9 (22).

Inspections

(23) Subject to subsection (24), the members of a committee who represent workers shall designate a member representing workers to inspect the physical condition of the workplace. R.S.O. 1990, c. O.1, s. 9 (23).

Same

(24) If possible, the member designated under subsection (23) shall be a certified member. R.S.O. 1990, c. O.1, s. 9 (24).

Same

(25) The members of a committee are not required to designate the same member to perform all inspections or to perform all of a particular inspection. R.S.O. 1990, c. O.1, s. 9 (25).

Same

(26) Unless otherwise required by the regulations or by an order by an inspector, a member designated under subsection (23) shall inspect the physical condition of the workplace at least once a month. R.S.O. 1990, c. O.1, s. 9 (26).

Same

(27) If it is not practical to inspect the workplace at least once a month, the member designated under subsection (23) shall inspect the physical condition of the workplace at least once a year, inspecting at least a part of the workplace in each month. R.S.O. 1990, c. O.1, s. 9 (27).

Schedule of inspections

(28) The inspection required by subsection (27) shall be undertaken in accordance with a schedule established by the committee. R.S.O. 1990, c. O.1, s. 9 (28).

Inspections

(29) The constructor, employer and the workers shall provide a member designated under subsection (23) with such information and assistance as the member may require for the purpose of carrying out an inspection of the workplace. R.S.O. 1990, c. O.1, s. 9 (29).

Information reported to the committee

(30) The member shall inform the committee of situations that may be a source of danger or hazard to workers and the committee shall consider such information within a reasonable period of time. R.S.O. 1990, c. O.1, s. 9 (30).

Same

(31) The members of a committee who represent workers shall designate one or more such members to investigate cases where a worker is killed or critically injured at a workplace from any cause and one of those members may, subject to subsection 51 (2), inspect the place where the accident occurred and any machine, device or thing, and shall report his or her findings to a Director and to the committee. R.S.O. 1990, c. O.1, s. 9 (31).

Posting of names and work locations

(32) A constructor or an employer required to establish a committee under this section shall post and keep posted at the workplace the names and work locations of the committee members in a conspicuous place or places where they are most likely to come to the attention of the workers. R.S.O. 1990, c. O.1, s. 9 (32).

Meetings

(33) A committee shall meet at least once every three months at the workplace and may be required to meet by order of the Minister. R.S.O. 1990, c. O.1, s. 9 (33).

Entitlement to time from work

(34) A member of a committee is entitled to,

    (a)   one hour or such longer period of time as the committee determines is necessary to prepare for each committee meeting;

    (b)   such time as is necessary to attend meetings of the committee; and

    (c)   such time as is necessary to carry out the member's duties under subsections (26), (27) and (31). R.S.O. 1990, c. O.1, s. 9 (34).

Entitlement to be paid

(35) A member of a committee shall be deemed to be at work during the times described in subsection (34) and the member's employer shall pay the member for those times at the member's regular or premium rate as may be proper. R.S.O. 1990, c. O.1, s. 9 (35).

Same

(36) A member of a committee shall be deemed to be at work while the member is fulfilling the requirements for becoming a certified

member and the member's employer shall pay the member for the time spent at the member's regular or premium rate as may be proper. R.S.O. 1990, c. O.1, s. 9 (36); 1998, c. 8, s. 50 (1); 2011, c. 11, s. 7 (3).

Exception

(37) Subsection (36) does not apply with respect to workers who are paid by the Workplace Safety and Insurance Board for the time spent fulfilling the requirements for becoming certified. R.S.O. 1990, c. O.1, s. 9 (37); 1998, c. 8, s. 50 (2).

Additional powers of certain committees

(38) Any committee of a like nature to a committee established under this section in existence in a workplace under the provisions of a collective agreement or other agreement or arrangement between a constructor or an employer and the workers has, in addition to its functions and powers under the provisions of the collective agreement or other agreement or arrangement, the functions and powers conferred upon a committee by this section. R.S.O. 1990, c. O.1, s. 9 (38).

Dispute resolution

(39) Where a dispute arises as to the application of subsection (2), or the compliance or purported compliance therewith by a constructor or an employer, the dispute shall be decided by the Minister after consulting the constructor or the employer and the workers or the trade union or trade unions representing the workers. R.S.O. 1990, c. O.1, s. 9 (39).

Worker trades committee

10. (1) If a committee is required at a project, other than a project where fewer than fifty workers are regularly employed or that is expected to last less than three months, the committee shall establish a worker trades committee for the project.

Committee membership

(2)   The members of a worker trades committee shall represent workers employed in each of the trades at the workplace.

Selection of members

(3)   The members of a worker trades committee shall be selected by the workers employed in the trades the members are to represent or, if a trade union represents the workers, by the trade union.

Function of worker trades committee

(4)   It is the function of a worker trades committee to inform the committee at the workplace of the health and safety concerns of the workers employed in the trades at the workplace.

Entitlement to time from work

(5)   Subject to subsection (6), a member of a worker trades committee is entitled to such time from work as is necessary to attend meetings of the worker trades committee and the time so spent shall be deemed to be work time for which the member shall be paid by the employer at the member's regular or premium rate as may be proper.

Committee to determine maximum entitlement

(6)   The committee for a workplace shall determine the maximum amount of time for which members of a worker trades committee for the workplace are entitled to be paid under subsection (5) for each meeting of the worker trades committee. R.S.O. 1990, c. O.1, s. 10.

Consultation on industrial hygiene testing

11. (1)   The constructor or employer at a workplace shall consult a health and safety representative or the committee with respect to proposed testing strategies for investigating industrial hygiene at the workplace.

Information

(2) The constructor or employer shall provide information to a health and safety representative or the committee concerning testing strategies to be used to investigate industrial hygiene at the workplace.

Attendance at testing

(3) A health and safety representative or a designated committee member representing workers at a workplace is entitled to be present at the beginning of testing conducted with respect to industrial hygiene at the workplace if the representative or member believes his or her presence is required to ensure that valid testing procedures are used or to ensure that the test results are valid.

Designation of member

(4) The committee members representing workers shall designate one of them for the purpose of subsection (3). R.S.O. 1990, c. O.1, s. 11.

Summary to be furnished

12. (1) For workplaces to which the insurance plan established under the Workplace Safety and Insurance Act, 1997 applies, the Workplace Safety and Insurance Board, upon the request of an employer, a worker, committee, health and safety representative or trade union, shall send to the employer, and to the worker, committee, health and safety representative or trade union requesting the information an annual summary of data relating to the employer in respect of the number of work accident fatalities, the number of lost work day cases, the number of lost work days, the number of non-fatal cases that required medical aid without lost work days, the incidence of occupational illnesses, the number of occupational injuries, and such other data as the Board may consider necessary or advisable. R.S.O. 1990, c. O.1, s. 12 (1); 1997, c. 16, s. 2 (4).

Posting of copy of summary

(2)   Upon receipt of the annual summary, the employer shall cause a copy thereof to be posted in a conspicuous place or places at the workplace where it is most likely to come to the attention of the workers.

Director to provide information

(3)   A Director shall, in accordance with the objects and purposes of this Act, ensure that persons and organizations concerned with the purposes of this Act are provided with information and advice pertaining to its administration and to the protection of the occupational health and occupational safety of workers generally. R.S.O. 1990, c. O.1, s. 12 (2, 3).

13. Repealed: 1997, c. 16, s. 2 (5).

14. Repealed: 1997, c. 16, s. 2 (6).

15. Repealed: 1997, c. 16, s. 2 (7).

16. Repealed: 1997, c. 16, s. 2 (8).

17. Repealed: 1997, c. 16, s. 2 (9).

18. Repealed: 1997, c. 16, s. 2 (10).

19. Repealed: 1997, c. 16, s. 2 (10).

Testimony in civil proceedings, etc.

20.   (1)   Except with the consent of the Board, no member of the Board, nor its registrar, nor any of its other officers, nor any of its clerks or servants shall be required to give testimony in any civil proceeding or in any proceeding before the Board or in any proceeding before any other tribunal respecting information obtained in the discharge of their duties or while acting within the scope of their employment under this Act.

Non-disclosure

(2)   No information or material furnished to or received by a labour relations officer under this Act shall be disclosed except to the Board or as authorized by the Board. 1998, c. 8, s. 51.

Advisory committees

21.   (1)   The Minister may appoint committees, which are not committees as defined in subsection 1 (1), or persons to assist or advise the Minister on any matter arising under this Act or to inquire into and report to the Minister on any matter that the Minister considers advisable. R.S.O. 1990, c. O.1, s. 21 (1).

Remuneration and expenses

(2)   Any person appointed under subsection (1) who is not a public servant within the meaning of the Public Service of Ontario Act, 2006 may be paid such remuneration and expenses as may be from time to time fixed by the Lieutenant Governor in Council. R.S.O. 1990, c. O.1, s. 21 (2); 2006, c. 35, Sched. C, s. 93 (2).

Contribution to defray cost

22.   (1)   The Workplace Safety and Insurance Board shall require Schedule 1 and Schedule 2 employers under the Workplace Safety and Insurance Act, 1997 to make payments to defray the cost of administering this Act and the regulations. The Lieutenant Governor in Council may fix the total payment to be made by all employers for that purpose.

Same

(2)   The Workplace Safety and Insurance Board shall remit the money collected from employers under this section to the Minister of Finance. 1997, c. 16, s. 2 (11).

Powers under federal legislation

22.1 (1)   If a regulation under the Canada Labour Code incorporates by reference all or part of this Act or the regulations made under it, the

Board and any person having powers under this Act may exercise any powers conferred by the regulation under the Canada Labour Code. 2011, c. 1, Sched. 7, s. 2 (1).

Same

(2) If a regulation under section 44 of the Nuclear Safety and Control Act (Canada) requires an employer to whom this Act applies to comply with all or part of this Act or the regulations made under it, the Board and any person having powers under this Act may exercise any powers conferred by the regulation under the Nuclear Safety and Control Act (Canada). 2011, c. 1, Sched. 7, s. 2 (1).

PART II.1
PREVENTION COUNCIL, CHIEF PREVENTION OFFICER AND DESIGNATED ENTITIES

Prevention Council

Prevention Council

22.2 (1) The Minister shall establish a council to be known as the Prevention Council in English and Conseil de la prévention in French. 2011, c. 11, s. 8 (1).

Composition

(2) The Council shall be composed of such members as the Minister may appoint, and shall include representatives from each of the following groups:

1. Trade unions and provincial labour organizations.

2. Employers.

3. Non-unionized workers, the Workplace Safety and Insurance Board and persons with occupational health and safety expertise. 2011, c. 11, s. 8 (1).

Same

(3) In appointing members of the Council, the Minister shall ensure that,

(a) an equal number of members are appointed to represent the groups described in paragraphs 1 and 2 of subsection (2); and

(b) the group described in paragraph 3 of subsection (2) is represented by not more than one-third of the members of the Council. 2011, c. 11, s. 8 (1).

Appointment of members

(4) The members of the Council shall be appointed for such term as may be determined by the Minister. 2011, c. 11, s. 8 (1).

Chair

(5) The members of the Council shall choose a chair from among themselves by the date fixed by the Minister; if they fail to do so, the Minister shall designate a member as chair. 2011, c. 11, s. 8 (1).

Same

(6) Subsection (5) applies on the first appointment of members and thereafter whenever the office of chair is vacant. 2011, c. 11, s. 8 (1).

Functions

(7) The Council shall,

(a) provide advice to the Minister on the appointment of a Chief Prevention Officer;

(b) provide advice to the Chief Prevention Officer,

(i) on the prevention of workplace injuries and occupational diseases,

> > (ii) for the purposes of the provincial occupational health and safety strategy and the annual report under section 22.3, and
> >
> > (iii) on any significant proposed changes to the funding and delivery of services for the prevention of workplace injuries and occupational diseases;
>
> (c) provide advice on any other matter specified by the Minister; and
>
> (d) perform such other functions as may be specified by the Minister. 2011, c. 11, s. 8 (1).

Advice

(8) For the purposes of subsection (7), any advice provided by the Council shall be communicated by the chair of the Council. 2011, c. 11, s. 8 (1).

Remuneration and expenses

(9) Any member of the Council who is not a public servant within the meaning of the Public Service of Ontario Act, 2006 may be paid such remuneration and expenses as may be from time to time fixed by the Lieutenant Governor in Council. 2011, c. 11, s. 8 (1).

Chief Prevention Officer

Functions

22.3 (1) The Minister shall appoint a Chief Prevention Officer to,

> (a) develop a provincial occupational health and safety strategy;
>
> (b) prepare an annual report on occupational health and safety;

(c) exercise any power or duty delegated to him or her by the Minister under this Act;

(d) provide advice to the Minister on the prevention of workplace injuries and occupational diseases;

(e) provide advice to the Minister on any proposed changes to the funding and delivery of services for the prevention of workplace injuries and occupational diseases;

(f) provide advice to the Minister on the establishment of standards for designated entities under section 22.5;

(g) exercise the powers and perform the duties with respect to training that are set out in sections 7.1 to 7.5;

(h) establish requirements for the certification of persons for the purposes of this Act and certify persons under section 7.6 who meet those requirements;

(i) exercise the powers and perform the duties set out in section 22.7; and

(j) exercise such other powers and perform such other duties as may be assigned to the Chief Prevention Officer under this Act. 2011, c. 11, s. 8 (1).

Appointment

(2) The Chief Prevention Officer may be appointed for a term not exceeding five years and may be reappointed for successive terms not exceeding five years each. 2011, c. 11, s. 8 (1).

Occupational health and safety strategy

(3) The Chief Prevention Officer shall develop a written provincial occupational health and safety strategy that includes,

(a) a statement of occupational health and safety goals;

(b) key performance indicators for measuring the achievement of the goals; and

(c) any other matter specified by the Minister. 2011, c. 11, s. 8 (1).

Advice of Prevention Council

(4) The Chief Prevention Officer shall consult with the Prevention Council and shall consider its advice in developing the strategy. 2011, c. 11, s. 8 (1).

Strategy provided to Minister

(5) The Chief Prevention Officer shall provide the strategy to the Minister on or before a day specified by the Minister. 2011, c. 11, s. 8 (1).

Minister's approval

(6) The Minister may approve the strategy or refer it back to the Chief Prevention Officer for further consideration. 2011, c. 11, s. 8 (1).

Publication

(7) After approving the strategy, the Minister shall publish it promptly. 2011, c. 11, s. 8 (1).

Annual report

(8) The Chief Prevention Officer shall provide an annual written report to the Minister on occupational health and safety that includes a measurement of the achievement of the goals established in the strategy, and that contains such other information as the Minister may require. 2011, c. 11, s. 8 (1).

Advice of Prevention Council

(9)   The Chief Prevention Officer shall consult with the Prevention Council and shall consider its advice in developing the report. 2011, c. 11, s. 8 (1).

Report provided to Minister

(10) The Chief Prevention Officer shall provide the annual report to the Minister on or before a day specified by the Minister. 2011, c. 11, s. 8 (1).

Publication

(11) The Minister shall publish the Chief Prevention Officer's report promptly. 2011, c. 11, s. 8 (1).

Changes to Funding and Delivery of Services

If Minister proposes change

22.4 (1)   If the Minister is considering a proposed change to the funding and delivery of services for the prevention of workplace injuries and occupational diseases, the Minister shall determine whether the proposed change would be a significant change. 2011, c. 11, s. 8 (1).

If proposed change significant

(2)   If the Minister determines that the proposed change is significant, the Minister shall seek advice from the Chief Prevention Officer with respect to the proposed change. 2011, c. 11, s. 8 (1).

If Chief Prevention Officer advising on change

(3)   If the Chief Prevention Officer is considering providing advice to the Minister concerning a proposed change to the funding and delivery of services for the prevention of workplace injuries and occupational diseases, the Chief Prevention Officer shall determine whether the proposed change would be a significant change. 2011, c. 11, s. 8 (1).

Prevention Council endorsement

(4)   If the Minister asks the Chief Prevention Officer for advice under subsection (2) or if the Chief Prevention Officer determines under subsection (3) that a proposed change would be a significant change, the Chief Prevention Officer shall,

(a)   ask the chair of the Prevention Council to state whether the Council endorses the proposed change; and

(b)   include that statement in the advice to the Minister. 2011, c. 11, s. 8 (1).

Matters to consider in determining if change is significant

(5)   The Minister and the Chief Prevention Officer shall consider such matters as may be prescribed when determining whether a proposed change to the funding and delivery of services for the prevention of workplace injuries and occupational diseases would be a significant change. 2011, c. 11, s. 8 (1).

Regulation

(6)   On the recommendation of the Minister, the Lieutenant Governor in Council may make regulations prescribing matters to be considered when determining whether a proposed change to the funding and delivery of services for the prevention of workplace injuries and occupational diseases would be a significant change. 2011, c. 11, s. 8 (1).

Same

(7)   Before recommending to the Lieutenant Governor in Council that a regulation be made under subsection (6), the Minister shall seek the advice of the Chief Prevention Officer and require the Chief Prevention Officer to seek the advice of the Prevention Council with respect to the matters to be prescribed. 2011, c. 11, s. 8 (1).

Designated Entities

Eligible for grant

22.5 (1)   An entity that is designated under this section is eligible for a grant from the Ministry. 2011, c. 11, s. 8 (2).

Designation by Minister

(2)   The Minister may designate an entity as a safe workplace association or as a medical clinic or training centre specializing in occupational health and safety matters if the entity meets the standards established by the Minister. 2011, c. 11, s. 8 (2).

Standards

(3)   The Minister may establish standards that an entity shall meet before it is eligible to be designated. 2011, c. 11, s. 8 (2).

Same

(4)   The standards established under subsection (3) may address any matter the Minister considers appropriate, including governance, objectives, functions and operations. 2011, c. 11, s. 8 (2).

Same

(5)   The Minister may establish different standards for associations, clinics or centres serving different industries or groups. 2011, c. 11, s. 8 (2).

Duty to comply

(6)   A designated entity shall operate in accordance with the standards established under subsection (3) that apply to it, and in accordance with any other requirements imposed on it under section 22.6. 2011, c. 11, s. 8 (2).

Amendment of standard

(7)   The Minister may amend a standard established under subsection (3). 2011, c. 11, s. 8 (2).

Date for compliance with amended standard

(8)   If the Minister amends a standard established under subsection (3), the Minister shall establish a date by which designated entities to which the amended standard applies are required to comply with it. 2011, c. 11, s. 8 (2).

Publication of standards

(9)   The Minister shall promptly publish,

(a)   the standards established under subsection (3); and

(b)   standards amended under subsection (7), together with the compliance date described in subsection (8). 2011, c. 11, s. 8 (2).

Transition

(10) When the Minister establishes and publishes standards under subsections (3) and (9) for the first time after the coming into force of subsection 8 (2) of the Occupational Health and Safety Statute Law Amendment Act, 2011, the Minister shall establish a date for the purposes of subsections (11) and (12) and shall publish it together with the standards. 2011, c. 11, s. 8 (2).

Same

(11) An entity that is designated as a safe workplace association or as a medical clinic or training centre specializing in occupational health and safety matters under section 6 of the Workplace Safety and Insurance Act, 1997 on the date section 20 of the Occupational Health and Safety Statute Law Amendment Act, 2011 comes into force is deemed to be designated for the purposes of this Act until the date established by the Minister under subsection (10). 2011, c. 11, s. 8 (2).

Same

(12) The standards that are in place under section 6 of
the Workplace Safety and Insurance Act, 1997 on the date section
20 of the Occupational Health and Safety Statute Law Amendment
Act, 2011 comes into force continue to apply, with necessary
modifications, and are deemed to be standards for the purposes of
this section, until the date established by the Minister under
subsection (10). 2011, c. 11, s. 8 (2).

Effect of designation - Directions

22.6 (1)   The Minister may direct a designated entity to take such
actions as the Minister considers appropriate. 2011, c. 11, s. 8 (2).

Government directives

(2)   In addition to the directions the Minister may issue under
subsection (1), the Minister may direct an entity to comply with such
government directives as the Minister specifies. 2011, c. 11,
s. 8 (2).

Failure to comply

(3)   If an entity has committed any failure described in paragraphs
1 to 3 of subsection 22.7 (3), the Minister may,

    (a)   reduce or suspend grants to the entity while the non-
compliance continues;

    (b)   assume control of the entity and responsibility for its
affairs and operations;

    (c)   revoke the designation and cease to provide grants to
the entity; or

    (d)   take such other steps as he or she considers
appropriate. 2011, c. 11, s. 8 (2).

Compliance and monitoring of designated entities

22.7 (1)   The Chief Prevention Officer shall monitor the operation of designated entities and,

    (a)   may require a designated entity to provide such information, records or accounts as the Chief Prevention Officer specifies; and

    (b)   may make such inquiries and examinations as he or she considers necessary. 2011, c. 11, s. 8 (2).

Report to Minister

(2)   The Chief Prevention Officer shall report to the Minister on the compliance of designated entities with the standards established under section 22.5 and with any directions given by the Minister under section 22.6. 2011, c. 11, s. 8 (2).

Advice to Minister

(3)   Where the Chief Prevention Officer determines that any of the following have occurred, the Chief Prevention Officer shall report that determination to the Minister and may advise the Minister with respect to any action the Minister may decide to take under section 22.6:

1.   A designated entity has failed to operate in accordance with a standard established under section 22.5 that applies to it.

2.   A designated entity has failed to comply with a direction given by the Minister under section 22.6 or a requirement of the Chief Prevention Officer under clause (1) (a).

3.   A designated entity has failed to co-operate in an inquiry or examination conducted by the Chief Prevention Officer under clause (1) (b). 2011, c. 11, s. 8 (2).

Appointment of administrator

22.8 (1)   For the purposes of assuming control of an entity and responsibility for its affairs and operations under clause 22.6 (3) (b), the Minister may appoint an administrator. 2011, c. 11, s. 8 (2).

Term of appointment

(2)   The appointment of the administrator remains valid until it is terminated by the Minister. 2011, c. 11, s. 8 (2).

Powers and duties of administrator

(3)   The administrator has the exclusive right to exercise the powers and perform the duties of the board of directors and its officers and exercise the powers of its members. 2011, c. 11, s. 8 (2).

Same

(4)   In the appointment, the Minister may specify the powers and duties of the administrator and the terms and conditions governing those powers and duties. 2011, c. 11, s. 8 (2).

Additional power of administrator

(5)   The board of directors and officers may continue to act to the extent authorized by the Minister, but any such act is valid only if approved, in writing, by the administrator. 2011, c. 11, s. 8 (2).

Report, directions

(6)   The administrator shall report to the Minister as required by him or her and shall carry out his or her directions. 2011, c. 11, s. 8 (2).

Meeting of members

(7)   Before the termination of an administrator's appointment, the administrator may call a meeting of the members to elect a board of directors in accordance with the Corporations Act. 2011, c. 11, s. 8 (2).

Note: On the later of (a) the earlier of April 1, 2012 and a day to be named by
proclamation of the Lieutenant Governor and (b) the day section 24 of the
Not-For-Profit Corporations Act, 2010 comes into force, subsection (7) is
amended by striking out "Corporations Act" and substituting "Not-For-
Profit Corporations Act, 2010".

Unincorporated entity

(8) This section applies, with necessary modifications, to an entity
that is not incorporated. 2011, c. 11, s. 8 (2).

Delegation of powers and duties

22.9 Despite section 5, the Minister may delegate his or her powers or
duties under sections 22.5, 22.6 and 22.8 only to the Chief
Prevention Officer. 2011, c. 11, s. 8 (2).

PART III
DUTIES OF EMPLOYERS AND OTHER PERSONS

Duties of constructor

23. (1) A constructor shall ensure, on a project undertaken by the
constructor that,

(a) the measures and procedures prescribed by this Act and
the regulations are carried out on the project;

(b) every employer and every worker performing work on the
project complies with this Act and the regulations; and

(c) the health and safety of workers on the project is
protected.

Notice of project

(2) Where so prescribed, a constructor shall, before commencing
any work on a project, give to a Director notice in writing of the
project containing such information as may be prescribed. R.S.O.
1990, c. O.1, s. 23.

Duties of licensees

24. (1) A licensee shall ensure that,

    (a) the measures and procedures prescribed by this Act and the regulations are carried out with respect to logging in the licensed area;

    (b) every employer performing logging in the licensed area for the licensee complies with this Act and the regulations; and

    (c) the health and safety of workers employed by employers referred to in clause (b) is protected. R.S.O. 1990, c. O.1, s. 24 (1).

Definition

    (2) In this section,

"licensed area" means the lands on which the licensee is authorized to harvest or use forest resources. R.S.O. 1990, c. O.1, s. 24 (2); 1994, c. 25, s. 83 (2).

Duties of employers

25. (1) An employer shall ensure that,

    (a) the equipment, materials and protective devices as prescribed are provided;

    (b) the equipment, materials and protective devices provided by the employer are maintained in good condition;

    (c) the measures and procedures prescribed are carried out in the workplace;

    (d) the equipment, materials and protective devices provided by the employer are used as prescribed; and

    (e)   a building, structure, or any part thereof, or any other part of a workplace, whether temporary or permanent, is capable of supporting any loads that may be applied to it,

        (i)   as determined by the applicable design requirements established under the version of the Building Code that was in force at the time of its construction,

        (ii)   in accordance with such other requirements as may be prescribed, or

        (iii)   in accordance with good engineering practice, if subclauses (i) and (ii) do not apply. R.S.O. 1990, c. O.1, s. 25 (1); 2011, c. 11, s. 9.

Same

(2)   Without limiting the strict duty imposed by subsection (1), an employer shall,

    (a)   provide information, instruction and supervision to a worker to protect the health or safety of the worker;

    (b)   in a medical emergency for the purpose of diagnosis or treatment, provide, upon request, information in the possession of the employer, including confidential business information, to a legally qualified medical practitioner and to such other persons as may be prescribed;

    (c)   when appointing a supervisor, appoint a competent person;

    (d)   acquaint a worker or a person in authority over a worker with any hazard in the work and in the handling, storage, use, disposal and transport of any article, device, equipment or a biological, chemical or physical agent;

(e) afford assistance and co-operation to a committee and a health and safety representative in the carrying out by the committee and the health and safety representative of any of their functions;

(f) only employ in or about a workplace a person over such age as may be prescribed;

(g) not knowingly permit a person who is under such age as may be prescribed to be in or about a workplace;

(h) take every precaution reasonable in the circumstances for the protection of a worker;

(i) post, in the workplace, a copy of this Act and any explanatory material prepared by the Ministry, both in English and the majority language of the workplace, outlining the rights, responsibilities and duties of workers;

(j) prepare and review at least annually a written occupational health and safety policy and develop and maintain a program to implement that policy;

(k) post at a conspicuous location in the workplace a copy of the occupational health and safety policy;

(l) provide to the committee or to a health and safety representative the results of a report respecting occupational health and safety that is in the employer's possession and, if that report is in writing, a copy of the portions of the report that concern occupational health and safety; and

(m) advise workers of the results of a report referred to in clause (l) and, if the report is in writing, make available to them on request copies of the portions of the report that concern occupational health and safety. R.S.O. 1990, c. O.1, s. 25 (2).

Same

(3) For the purposes of clause (2) (c), an employer may appoint himself or herself as a supervisor where the employer is a competent person. R.S.O. 1990, c. O.1, s. 25 (3).

Same

(3.1) Any explanatory material referred to under clause (2) (i) may be published as part of the poster required under section 2 of the Employment Standards Act, 2000. 2009, c. 23, s. 2.

Same

(4) Clause (2) (j) does not apply with respect to a workplace at which five or fewer workers are regularly employed. R.S.O. 1990, c. O.1, s. 25 (4); 2011, c. 1, Sched. 7, s. 2 (2).

Additional duties of employers

26. (1) In addition to the duties imposed by section 25, an employer shall,

(a) establish an occupational health service for workers as prescribed;

(b) where an occupational health service is established as prescribed, maintain the same according to the standards prescribed;

(c) keep and maintain accurate records of the handling, storage, use and disposal of biological, chemical or physical agents as prescribed;

(d) accurately keep and maintain and make available to the worker affected such records of the exposure of a worker to biological, chemical or physical agents as may be prescribed;

(e) notify a Director of the use or introduction into a workplace of such biological, chemical or physical agents as may be prescribed;

(f) monitor at such time or times or at such interval or intervals the levels of biological, chemical or physical agents in a workplace and keep and post accurate records thereof as prescribed;

(g) comply with a standard limiting the exposure of a worker to biological, chemical or physical agents as prescribed;

(h) establish a medical surveillance program for the benefit of workers as prescribed;

(i) provide for safety-related medical examinations and tests for workers as prescribed;

(j) where so prescribed, only permit a worker to work or be in a workplace who has undergone such medical examinations, tests or x-rays as prescribed and who is found to be physically fit to do the work in the workplace;

(k) where so prescribed, provide a worker with written instructions as to the measures and procedures to be taken for the protection of a worker; and

(l) carry out such training programs for workers, supervisors and committee members as may be prescribed.

Same

(2)   For the purposes of clause (1) (a), a group of employers, with the approval of a Director, may act as an employer. R.S.O. 1990, c. O.1, s. 26 (1, 2).

Same

(3)   If a worker participates in a prescribed medical surveillance program or undergoes prescribed medical examinations or tests, his or her employer shall pay,

(a)   the worker's costs for medical examinations or tests required by the medical surveillance program or required by regulation;

(b)   the worker's reasonable travel costs respecting the examinations or tests; and

(c)   the time the worker spends to undergo the examinations or tests, including travel time, which shall be deemed to be work time for which the worker shall be paid at his or her regular or premium rate as may be proper. R.S.O. 1990, c. O.1, s. 26 (3); 1994, c. 27, s. 120 (3).

Duties of supervisor

27.   (1)   A supervisor shall ensure that a worker,

(a)   works in the manner and with the protective devices, measures and procedures required by this Act and the regulations; and

(b)   uses or wears the equipment, protective devices or clothing that the worker's employer requires to be used or worn.

Additional duties of supervisor

(2)   Without limiting the duty imposed by subsection (1), a supervisor shall,

(a)   advise a worker of the existence of any potential or actual danger to the health or safety of the worker of which the supervisor is aware;

(b)   where so prescribed, provide a worker with written instructions as to the measures and procedures to be taken for protection of the worker; and

(c)   take every precaution reasonable in the circumstances for the protection of a worker.   R.S.O. 1990, c. O.1, s. 27.

Duties of workers

28.   (1)   A worker shall,

(a)   work in compliance with the provisions of this Act and the regulations;

(b)   use or wear the equipment, protective devices or clothing that the worker's employer requires to be used or worn;

(c)   report to his or her employer or supervisor the absence of or defect in any equipment or protective device of which the worker is aware and which may endanger himself, herself or another worker; and

(d)   report to his or her employer or supervisor any contravention of this Act or the regulations or the existence of any hazard of which he or she knows.

Same

(2)   No worker shall,

(a) remove or make ineffective any protective device required by the regulations or by his or her employer, without providing an adequate temporary protective device and when the need for removing or making ineffective the protective device has ceased, the protective device shall be replaced immediately;

(b) use or operate any equipment, machine, device or thing or work in a manner that may endanger himself, herself or any other worker; or

(c) engage in any prank, contest, feat of strength, unnecessary running or rough and boisterous conduct.

Consent to medical surveillance

(3) A worker is not required to participate in a prescribed medical surveillance program unless the worker consents to do so. R.S.O. 1990, c. O.1, s. 28.

Duties of owners

29. (1) The owner of a workplace that is not a project shall,

(a) ensure that,

(i) such facilities as are prescribed are provided,

(ii) any facilities prescribed to be provided are maintained as prescribed,

(iii) the workplace complies with the regulations, and

(iv) no workplace is constructed, developed, reconstructed, altered or added to except in compliance with this Act and the regulations; and

(b) where so prescribed, furnish to a Director any drawings, plans or specifications of any workplace as prescribed.

Mine plans

(2) The owner of a mine shall cause drawings, plans or specifications to be maintained and kept up to date not more than six months last past on such scale and showing such matters or things as may be prescribed.

Plans of workplaces

(3) Where so prescribed, an owner or employer shall,

(a) not begin any construction, development, reconstruction, alteration, addition or installation to or in a workplace until the drawings, layout and specifications thereof and any alterations thereto have been filed with the Ministry for review by an engineer of the Ministry for compliance with this Act and the regulations; and

(b) keep a copy of the drawings as reviewed in a convenient location at or near the workplace and such drawings shall be produced by the owner or employer upon the request of an inspector for his or her examination and inspection.

Additional information

(4) An engineer of the Ministry may require the drawings, layout and specifications to be supplemented by the owner or employer with additional information.

Fees

(5) Fees as prescribed for the filing and review of drawings, layout or specifications shall become due and payable by the owner or employer upon filing. R.S.O. 1990, c. O.1, s. 29.

Duty of project owners

30. (1) Before beginning a project, the owner shall determine whether any designated substances are present at the project site and shall prepare a list of all designated substances that are present at the site.

Tenders

(2)   If any work on a project is tendered, the person issuing the tenders shall include, as part of the tendering information, a copy of the list referred to in subsection (1).

Same

(3)   An owner shall ensure that a prospective constructor of a project on the owner's property has received a copy of the list referred to in subsection (1) before entering into a binding contract with the constructor.

Duty of constructors

(4)   The constructor for a project shall ensure that each prospective contractor and subcontractor for the project has received a copy of the list referred to in subsection (1) before the prospective contractor or subcontractor enters into a binding contract for the supply of work on the project.

Liability

(5)   An owner who fails to comply with this section is liable to the constructor and every contractor and subcontractor who suffers any loss or damages as the result of the subsequent discovery on the project of a designated substance that the owner ought reasonably to have known of but that was not on the list prepared under subsection (1).

Same

(6)   A constructor who fails to comply with this section is liable to every contractor and subcontractor who suffers any loss or damages as the result of the subsequent discovery on the project of a designated substance that was on the list prepared under subsection (1). R.S.O. 1990, c. O.1, s. 30.

Duties of suppliers

31. (1)   Every person who supplies any machine, device, tool or equipment under any rental, leasing or similar arrangement for use in or about a workplace shall ensure,

      (a)   that the machine, device, tool or equipment is in good condition;

      (b)   that the machine, device, tool or equipment complies with this Act and the regulations; and

      (c)   if it is the person's responsibility under the rental, leasing or similar arrangement to do so, that the machine, device, tool or equipment is maintained in good condition.

Architects and engineers

(2)   An architect as defined in the Architects Act, and a professional engineer as defined in the Professional Engineers Act, contravenes this Act if, as a result of his or her advice that is given or his or her certification required under this Act that is made negligently or incompetently, a worker is endangered. R.S.O. 1990, c. O.1, s. 31.

Duties of directors and officers of a corporation

32. Every director and every officer of a corporation shall take all reasonable care to ensure that the corporation complies with,

      (a)   this Act and the regulations;

      (b)   orders and requirements of inspectors and Directors; and

      (c)   orders of the Minister. R.S.O. 1990, c. O.1, s. 32.

PART III.0.1
VIOLENCE AND HARASSMENT

Policies, violence and harassment

32.0.1(1) An employer shall,

    (a)   prepare a policy with respect to workplace violence;

    (b)   prepare a policy with respect to workplace harassment; and

    (c)   review the policies as often as is necessary, but at least annually. 2009, c. 23, s. 3.

Written form, posting

(2) The policies shall be in written form and shall be posted at a conspicuous place in the workplace. 2009, c. 23, s. 3.

Exception

(3) Subsection (2) does not apply if the number of workers regularly employed at the workplace is five or fewer, unless an inspector orders otherwise. 2009, c. 23, s. 3; 2011, c. 1, Sched. 7, s. 2 (3).

Program, violence

32.0.2(1) An employer shall develop and maintain a program to implement the policy with respect to workplace violence required under clause 32.0.1 (1) (a). 2009, c. 23, s. 3.

Contents

(2) Without limiting the generality of subsection (1), the program shall,

  (a) include measures and procedures to control the risks identified in the assessment required under subsection 32.0.3 (1) as likely to expose a worker to physical injury;

  (b) include measures and procedures for summoning immediate assistance when workplace violence occurs or is likely to occur;

  (c) include measures and procedures for workers to report incidents of workplace violence to the employer or supervisor;

  (d) set out how the employer will investigate and deal with incidents or complaints of workplace violence; and

  (e) include any prescribed elements. 2009, c. 23, s. 3.

Assessment of risks of violence

32.0.3(1) An employer shall assess the risks of workplace violence that may arise from the nature of the workplace, the type of work or the conditions of work. 2009, c. 23, s. 3.

Considerations

 (2) The assessment shall take into account,

  (a) circumstances that would be common to similar workplaces;

  (b) circumstances specific to the workplace; and

  (c) any other prescribed elements. 2009, c. 23, s. 3.

Results

 (3) An employer shall,

(a) advise the committee or a health and safety representative, if any, of the results of the assessment, and provide a copy if the assessment is in writing; and

(b) if there is no committee or health and safety representative, advise the workers of the results of the assessment and, if the assessment is in writing, provide copies on request or advise the workers how to obtain copies. 2009, c. 23, s. 3.

Reassessment

(4) An employer shall reassess the risks of workplace violence as often as is necessary to ensure that the related policy under clause 32.0.1 (1) (a) and the related program under subsection 32.0.2 (1) continue to protect workers from workplace violence. 2009, c. 23, s. 3.

Same

(5) Subsection (3) also applies with respect to the results of the reassessment. 2009, c. 23, s. 3.

Domestic violence

32.0.4 If an employer becomes aware, or ought reasonably to be aware, that domestic violence that would likely expose a worker to physical injury may occur in the workplace, the employer shall take every precaution reasonable in the circumstances for the protection of the worker. 2009, c. 23, s. 3.

Duties re violence

32.0.5 (1) For greater certainty, the employer duties set out in section 25, the supervisor duties set out in section 27, and the worker duties set out in section 28 apply, as appropriate, with respect to workplace violence. 2009, c. 23, s. 3.

Information

(2) An employer shall provide a worker with,

(a)   information and instruction that is appropriate for the worker on the contents of the policy and program with respect to workplace violence; and

(b)   any other prescribed information or instruction. 2009, c. 23, s. 3.

Provision of information

(3)   An employer's duty to provide information to a worker under clause 25 (2) (a) and a supervisor's duty to advise a worker under clause 27 (2) (a) include the duty to provide information, including personal information, related to a risk of workplace violence from a person with a history of violent behaviour if,

(a)   the worker can be expected to encounter that person in the course of his or her work; and

(b)   the risk of workplace violence is likely to expose the worker to physical injury. 2009, c. 23, s. 3.

Limit on disclosure

(4)   No employer or supervisor shall disclose more personal information in the circumstances described in subsection (3) than is reasonably necessary to protect the worker from physical injury. 2009, c. 23, s. 3.

Program, harassment

32.0.6(1)   An employer shall develop and maintain a program to implement the policy with respect to workplace harassment required under clause 32.0.1 (1) (b). 2009, c. 23, s. 3.

Contents

(2)   Without limiting the generality of subsection (1), the program shall,

(a)   include measures and procedures for workers to report incidents of workplace harassment to the employer or supervisor;

(b)   set out how the employer will investigate and deal with incidents and complaints of workplace harassment; and

(c)   include any prescribed elements. 2009, c. 23, s. 3.

Information and instruction, harassment
32.0.7 An employer shall provide a worker with,

(a)   information and instruction that is appropriate for the worker on the contents of the policy and program with respect to workplace harassment; and

(b)   any other prescribed information. 2009, c. 23, s. 3.

PART III.1
CODES OF PRACTICE

Definition
32.1 In this Part,

"legal requirement" means a requirement imposed by a provision of this Act or by a regulation made under this Act. 2011, c. 11, s. 10.

Approval of code of practice
32.2 (1)   The Minister may approve a code of practice and the approved code of practice may be followed to comply with a legal requirement specified in the approval. 2011, c. 11, s. 11.

Same
(1.1) An approval made under subsection (1) may be subject to such terms and conditions as the Minister considers appropriate

and may be general or particular in its application. 2011, c. 11, s. 11.

Withdrawal of approval

(2)   The Minister may withdraw an approval under subsection (1). 2001, c. 9, Sched. I, s. 3 (4).

Legislation Act, 2006, Part III

(3)   Part III (Regulations) of the Legislation Act, 2006 does not apply with respect to an approval under this section or the withdrawal of such an approval. 2001, c. 9, Sched. I, s. 3 (4); 2006, c. 21, Sched. F, s. 136 (1).

Delegation

(4)   The Minister may delegate the Minister's power under this section to the Deputy Minister. 2001, c. 9, Sched. I, s. 3 (4).

Publication of approval, etc.

32.3 (1)   An approval or a withdrawal of an approval under section 32.2 shall be published in The Ontario Gazette. 2001, c. 9, Sched. I, s. 3 (4).

Effect of publication

(2)   Publication of an approval or withdrawal of approval in The Ontario Gazette,

(a)   is, in the absence of evidence to the contrary, proof of the approval or withdrawal of approval; and

(b)   shall be deemed to be notice of the approval or withdrawal of approval to everyone affected by it. 2001, c. 9, Sched. I, s. 3 (4).

Judicial notice

(3)   Judicial notice shall be taken of an approval or withdrawal of approval published in The Ontario Gazette. 2001, c. 9, Sched. I, s. 3 (4).

Effect of approved code of practice

32.4 The following apply if a code of practice is approved under section 32.2:

1.   Subject to any terms or conditions set out in the approval, compliance with the approved code of practice is deemed to be compliance with the legal requirement.

2.   A failure to comply with the approved code of practice is not, in itself, a breach of the legal requirement. 2011, c. 11, s. 12.

PART IV
TOXIC SUBSTANCES

Orders of Director

33.   (1)   Where a biological, chemical or physical agent or combination of such agents is used or intended to be used in the workplace and its presence in the workplace or the manner of its use is in the opinion of a Director likely to endanger the health of a worker, the Director shall by notice in writing to the employer order that the use, intended use, presence or manner of use be,

(a)   prohibited;

(b)   limited or restricted in such manner as the Director specifies; or

(c)   subject to such conditions regarding administrative control, work practices, engineering control and time limits for compliance as the Director specifies. R.S.O. 1990, c. O.1, s. 33 (1).

Contents of order

(2)   Where a Director makes an order to an employer under subsection (1), the order shall,

(a)   identify the biological, chemical or physical agent, or combination of such agents, and the manner of use that is the subject-matter of the order; and

(b)   state the opinion of the Director as to the likelihood of the danger to the health of a worker, and the Director's reasons in respect thereof, including the matters or causes which give rise to his or her opinion. R.S.O. 1990, c. O.1, s. 33 (2).

Posting of order

(3)   The employer shall provide a copy of an order made under subsection (1) to the committee, health and safety representative and trade union, if any, and shall cause a copy of the order to be posted in a conspicuous place in the workplace where it is most likely to come to the attention of the workers who may be affected by the use, presence or intended use of the biological, chemical or physical agent or combination of agents. R.S.O. 1990, c. O.1, s. 33 (3).

Appeal to Minister

(4)   Where the employer, a worker or a trade union considers that he, she or it is aggrieved by an order made under subsection (1), the employer, worker or trade union may by notice in writing given within fourteen days of the making of the order appeal to the Minister. R.S.O. 1990, c. O.1, s. 33 (4).

Delegation

(5)   The Minister may, having regard to the circumstances, direct that an appeal under subsection (4) be determined on his or her

behalf by a person appointed by the Minister for that purpose.
R.S.O. 1990, c. O.1, s. 33 (5).

Procedure

(6)   The Minister or, where a person has been appointed under
subsection (5), the person so appointed, may give such directions
and issue such orders as he or she considers proper or necessary
concerning the procedures to be adopted or followed and shall have
all the powers of a chair of a board of arbitration under subsection
48 (12) of the Labour Relations Act, 1995. R.S.O. 1990, c. O.1,
s. 33 (6); 2001, c. 9, Sched. I, s. 3 (5).

Substitution of findings

(7)   On an appeal, the Minister or, where a person has been
appointed under subsection (5), the person so appointed, may
substitute his or her findings for those of the Director and may
rescind or affirm the order appealed from or make a new order in
substitution therefor and such order shall stand in the place of and
have the like effect under this Act and the regulations as the order
of the Director, and such order shall be final and not subject to
appeal under this section. R.S.O. 1990, c. O.1, s. 33 (7).

Matters to be considered

(8)   In making a decision or order under subsection (1) or (7), a
Director, the Minister or, where a person has been appointed under
subsection (5), the person so appointed shall consider as relevant
factors,

(a)   the relation of the agent, combination of agents or by-
product to a biological or chemical agent that is known to
be a danger to health;

(b)   the quantities of the agent, combination of agents or by-
product used or intended to be used or present;

(c)   the extent of exposure;

    (d)   the availability of other processes, agents or equipment for use or intended use;

    (e)   data regarding the effect of the process or agent on health; and

    (f)   any criteria or guide with respect to the exposure of a worker to a biological, chemical or physical agent or combination of such agents that are adopted by a regulation. R.S.O. 1990, c. O.1, s. 33 (8).

Suspension of order by Minister, etc., pending disposition of appeal

(9)   On an appeal under subsection (4), the Minister or, where a person has been appointed under subsection (5), the person so appointed may suspend the operation of the order appealed from pending the disposition of the appeal. R.S.O. 1990, c. O.1, s. 33 (9).

Remuneration of appointee

(10) A person appointed under subsection (5) shall be paid such remuneration and expenses as the Minister, with the approval of the Lieutenant Governor in Council, determines. R.S.O. 1990, c. O.1, s. 33 (10).

Application

(11) This section does not apply to designated substances. R.S.O. 1990, c. O.1, s. 33 (11).

No hearing required prior to issuing order

(12) A Director is not required to hold or afford to an employer or any other person an opportunity for a hearing before making an order under subsection (1). R.S.O. 1990, c. O.1, s. 33 (12).

New biological or chemical agents

34. (1)   Except for purposes of research and development, no person shall,

> (a)   manufacture;
>
> (b)   distribute; or
>
> (c)   supply,

for commercial or industrial use in a workplace any new biological or chemical agent unless the person first submits to a Director notice in writing of the person's intention to manufacture, distribute or supply such new agent and the notice shall include the ingredients of such new agent and their common or generic name or names and the composition and properties thereof.

Report on assessment

(2)   Where in the opinion of the Director, which opinion shall be made promptly, the introduction of the new biological or chemical agent referred to in subsection (1) may endanger the health or safety of the workers in a workplace, the Director shall require the manufacturer, distributor or supplier, as the case may be, to provide, at the expense of the manufacturer, distributor or supplier, a report or assessment, made or to be made by a person possessing such special, expert or professional knowledge or qualifications as are specified by the Director, of the agent intended to be manufactured, distributed or supplied and the manner of use including the matters referred to in subclauses 54 (1) (o) (i) to (vii).

Interpretation

(3)   For the purpose of this section, a biological or chemical agent is not considered to be new if, before a person manufactures, distributes or supplies the agent, it was used in a workplace other than the person's workplace or it is included in an inventory compiled or adopted by the Minister. R.S.O. 1990, c. O.1, s. 34.

Designation of substances

35. Prior to a substance being designated under paragraph 23 of subsection 70 (2), the Minister,

    (a) shall publish in The Ontario Gazette a notice stating that the substance may be designated and calling for briefs or submissions in relation to the designation; and

    (b) shall publish in The Ontario Gazette a notice setting forth the proposed regulation relating to the designation of the substance at least sixty days before the regulation is filed with the Registrar of Regulations. R.S.O. 1990, c. O.1, s. 35.

36. Repealed: 2001, c. 9, Sched. I, s. 3 (7).

Hazardous material identification and data sheets

37. (1) An employer,

    (a) shall ensure that all hazardous materials present in the workplace are identified in the prescribed manner;

    (b) shall obtain or prepare, as may be prescribed, an unexpired material safety data sheet for all hazardous materials present in the workplace; and

Note: On a day to be named by proclamation of the Lieutenant Governor, clause (b) is amended by striking out "material safety" and substituting "safety". See: 2011, c. 1, Sched. 7, ss. 2 (12), 4 (2).

    (c) shall ensure that the identification required by clause (a) and material safety data sheets required by clause (b) are available in English and such other languages as may be prescribed. R.S.O. 1990, c. O.1, s. 37 (1).

Note: On a day to be named by proclamation of the Lieutenant Governor, clause (c) is amended by striking out "material safety" and substituting "safety". See: 2011, c. 1, Sched. 7, ss. 2 (12), 4 (2).

Prohibition

(2) No person shall remove or deface the identification described in clause (1) (a) for a hazardous material. R.S.O. 1990, c. O.1, s. 37 (2).

Hazardous material not to be used

(3) An employer shall ensure that a hazardous material is not used, handled or stored at a workplace unless the prescribed requirements concerning identification, material safety data sheets and worker instruction and training are met. R.S.O. 1990, c. O.1, s. 37 (3).

Note: On a day to be named by proclamation of the Lieutenant Governor, subsection (3) is amended by striking out "material safety" and substituting "safety". See: 2011, c. 1, Sched. 7, ss. 2 (12), 4 (2).

Notice to Director

(4) An employer shall advise a Director in writing if the employer, after making reasonable efforts, is unable to obtain a label or material safety data sheet required by subsection (1). R.S.O. 1990, c. O.1, s. 37 (4).

Note: On a day to be named by proclamation of the Lieutenant Governor, subsection (4) is amended by striking out "material safety" and substituting "safety". See: 2011, c. 1, Sched. 7, ss. 2 (12), 4 (2).

Expiry of material safety data sheet

(5) A material safety data sheet expires three years after the date of its publication. R.S.O. 1990, c. O.1, s. 37 (5).

Note: On a day to be named by proclamation of the Lieutenant Governor, subsection (5) is amended by striking out "material safety" and substituting "safety". See: 2011, c. 1, Sched. 7, ss. 2 (12), 4 (2).

Material safety data sheets to be made available

38. (1) A copy of every unexpired material safety data sheet required by this Part in respect of hazardous materials in a workplace shall be,

Note: On a day to be named by proclamation of the Lieutenant Governor, subsection (1) is amended by striking out "material safety" in the portion before clause (a) and substituting "safety". See: 2011, c. 1, Sched. 7, ss. 2 (12), 4 (2).

    (a) made available by the employer in the workplace in such a manner as to allow examination by the workers;

    (b) furnished by the employer to the committee or health and safety representative, if any, for the workplace or to a worker selected by the workers to represent them, if there is no committee or health and safety representative;

    (c) furnished by the employer on request or if so prescribed to the medical officer of health of the health unit in which the workplace is located;

    (d) furnished by the employer on request or if so prescribed to the fire department which serves the location in which the workplace is located; and

    (e) filed by the employer with a Director on request or if so prescribed. 2001, c. 9, Sched. I, s. 3 (8).

Public access

(2) The medical officer of health, at the request of any person, shall request an employer to furnish a copy of an unexpired material safety data sheet. 2001, c. 9, Sched. I, s. 3 (9).

72

Note: On a day to be named by proclamation of the Lieutenant Governor, subsection (2) is amended by striking out "material safety" and substituting "safety". See: 2011, c. 1, Sched. 7, ss. 2 (12), 4 (2).

Same

(3)   At the request of any person, the medical officer of health shall make available to the person for inspection a copy of any material safety data sheet requested by the person and in the possession of the medical officer of health. 2001, c. 9, Sched. I, s. 3 (9).

Note: On a day to be named by proclamation of the Lieutenant Governor, subsection (3) is amended by striking out "material safety" and substituting "safety". See: 2011, c. 1, Sched. 7, ss. 2 (12), 4 (2).

Same

(4)   A medical officer of health shall not disclose the name of any person who makes a request under subsection (2) or (3). R.S.O. 1990, c. O.1, s. 38 (4).

Additional requirement

(5)   In addition to the requirements imposed under subsection (1), a copy of every material safety data sheet required by subsection (1) shall be made available by the employer in the workplace in such a manner that it is readily accessible by all workers who may be exposed to the hazardous material to which it relates. R.S.O. 1990, c. O.1, s. 38 (5).

Note: On a day to be named by proclamation of the Lieutenant Governor, subsection (5) is amended by striking out "material safety" and substituting "safety". See: 2011, c. 1, Sched. 7, ss. 2 (12), 4 (2).

Same

(6)   An employer who makes a material safety data sheet readily accessible on a computer terminal at a workplace,

Note: On a day to be named by proclamation of the Lieutenant Governor, subsection (6) is amended by striking out "material safety" in the portion before clause (a) and substituting "safety". See: 2011, c. 1, Sched. 7, ss. 2 (12), 4 (2).

    (a)   shall take all reasonable steps necessary to keep the terminal in working order;

    (b)   shall give a worker upon request a copy of the material safety data sheet; and

Note: On a day to be named by proclamation of the Lieutenant Governor, clause (b) is amended by striking out "material safety" and substituting "safety". See: 2011, c. 1, Sched. 7, ss. 2 (12), 4 (2).

    (c)   shall teach all workers who work with or in proximity to hazardous materials, the health and safety representative, if any, at the workplace and the members of the committee how to retrieve the material safety data sheet on the computer terminal. R.S.O. 1990, c. O.1, s. 38 (6).

Note: On a day to be named by proclamation of the Lieutenant Governor, clause (c) is amended by striking out "material safety" and substituting "safety". See: 2011, c. 1, Sched. 7, ss. 2 (12), 4 (2).

Assessment for hazardous materials

39. (1)   Where so prescribed, an employer shall assess all biological and chemical agents produced in the workplace for use therein to determine if they are hazardous materials.

Assessments to be made available

  (2)   The assessment required by subsection (1) shall be in writing and a copy of it shall be,

    (a)   made available by the employer in the workplace in such a manner as to allow examination by the workers;

(b) furnished by the employer to the committee or health and safety representative, if any, for the workplace or to a worker selected by the workers to represent them, if there is no committee or health and safety representative. R.S.O. 1990, c. O.1, s. 39.

Confidential business information

40. (1) An employer may file a claim with the claims board for an exemption from disclosing,

(a) information required under this Part in a label or material safety data sheet; or

Note: On a day to be named by proclamation of the Lieutenant Governor, clause (a) is amended by striking out "material safety" and substituting "safety". See: 2011, c. 1, Sched. 7, ss. 2 (12), 4 (2).

(b) the name of a toxicological study used by the employer to prepare a material safety data sheet,

Note: On a day to be named by proclamation of the Lieutenant Governor, clause (b) is amended by striking out "material safety" and substituting "safety". See: 2011, c. 1, Sched. 7, ss. 2 (12), 4 (2).

on the grounds that it is confidential business information. R.S.O. 1990, c. O.1, s. 40 (1); 2001, c. 9, Sched. I, s. 3 (10).

Same

(2) An application under subsection (1) shall be made only in respect of such types of confidential business information as may be prescribed. R.S.O. 1990, c. O.1, s. 40 (2).

Powers and duties of the claims board

(3) The claims board shall exercise the powers and perform the functions of the Hazardous Materials Information Review Commission under sections 11 to 18 and 20 to 27 of the Hazardous

Materials Information Review Act (Canada). R.S.O. 1990, c. O.1, s. 40 (3).

Appeal

(4)   The employer or any worker of the employer or any trade union representing the workers of the employer may, in accordance with the regulations, appeal a determination made under subsection (3). R.S.O. 1990, c. O.1, s. 40 (4).

Determination of claim

(5)   The claims board, in accordance with its procedures, shall determine every appeal under subsection (4). R.S.O. 1990, c. O.1, s. 40 (5).

Effect of claim

(6)   Information that an employer considers to be confidential business information is exempt from disclosure from the time a claim is filed under subsection (1) until the claim is finally determined and for three years thereafter, if the claim is found to be valid. R.S.O. 1990, c. O.1, s. 40 (6).

Federal agency

(7)   Where the Parliament of Canada establishes an agency that has the power to determine whether information related to any hazardous material is confidential business information, the Lieutenant Governor in Council may by regulation name that agency as the claims board and adopt its procedures for the purposes of this section. R.S.O. 1990, c. O.1, s. 40 (7).

Definition

(8)   In this section,

"claims board" means an agency designated by the regulations as the claims board. R.S.O. 1990, c. O.1, s. 40 (8).

Information privileged

40.1 (1) Subject to subsection (2), all information obtained by an employee in the Ministry from the Hazardous Materials Information Review Commission under subsection 46 (2) of the Hazardous Materials Information Review Act (Canada) is privileged and no employee in the Ministry shall knowingly, without the consent in writing of the Commission,

  (a) communicate or allow to be communicated to any person any information obtained under that section;

  (b) allow any person to inspect or to have access to any part of a book, record, writing or other document containing any information obtained under that section. 1992, c. 14, s. 2 (1); 2006, c. 35, Sched. C, s. 93 (3).

Exception

(2) An employee in the Ministry may communicate or allow to be communicated information described in subsection (1) or allow inspection of or access to any part of a book, record, writing or other document containing any such information to or by,

  (a) another employee in the Ministry for the purpose of administering or enforcing this Act; or

  (b) a physician or a medical professional prescribed under the Hazardous Materials Information Review Act (Canada) who requests that information for the purpose of making a medical diagnosis of, or rendering medical treatment to, a person in an emergency. 1992, c. 14, s. 2 (1); 2006, c. 35, Sched. C, s. 93 (4).

Conditions

(3) No person who obtains any information under subsection (2) shall knowingly disclose that information to any other person or knowingly allow any other person to have access to that information

except as may be necessary for the purposes mentioned in that subsection. 1992, c. 14, s. 2 (1).

Non-disclosure prevails

(4) Despite subsection 63 (1), the requirements in this section that information received from the Hazardous Materials Information Review Commission not be disclosed prevail over any other law. 1992, c. 14, s. 2 (1).

Hazardous physical agents

41. (1) A person who distributes or supplies, directly or indirectly, or manufactures, produces or designs a thing for use in a workplace that causes, emits or produces a hazardous physical agent when the thing is in use or operation shall ensure that such information as may be prescribed is readily available respecting the hazardous physical agent and the proper use or operation of the thing.

Duty of employer

(2) Where an employer has a thing described in subsection (1) in the workplace, the employer shall ensure that the information referred to in that subsection has been obtained and is,

    (a) made available in the workplace for workers who use or operate the thing or who are likely to be exposed to the hazardous physical agent; and

    (b) furnished by the employer to the committee or health and safety representative, if any, for the workplace or a worker selected by the workers to represent them, if there is no committee or health and safety representative.

Notices

(3) An employer to whom subsection (2) applies shall post prominent notices identifying and warning of the hazardous physical

agent in the part of the workplace in which the thing is used or operated or is to be used or operated.

Same

(4)   Notices required by subsection (3) shall contain such information as may be prescribed and shall be in English and such other language or languages as may be prescribed. R.S.O. 1990, c. O.1, s. 41.

Instruction and training

42.   (1)   In addition to providing information and instruction to a worker as required by clause 25 (2) (a), an employer shall ensure that a worker exposed or likely to be exposed to a hazardous material or to a hazardous physical agent receives, and that the worker participates in, such instruction and training as may be prescribed.

Consultation

(2)   The instruction and training to be given under subsection (1) shall be developed and implemented by the employer in consultation with the committee or health and safety representative, if any, for the workplace.

Review

(3)   An employer shall review, in consultation with the committee or health and safety representative, if any, for the workplace, the training and instruction provided to a worker and the worker's familiarity therewith at least annually.

Same

(4)   The review described in subsection (3) shall be held more frequently than annually, if,

(a)   the employer, on the advice of the committee or health and safety representative, if any, for the workplace, determines that such reviews are necessary; or

(b)   there is a change in circumstances that may affect the health or safety of a worker. R.S.O. 1990, c. O.1, s. 42.

PART V
RIGHT TO REFUSE OR TO STOP WORK WHERE HEALTH OR SAFETY IN DANGER

Refusal to work

Non-application to certain workers

43.   (1)   This section does not apply to a worker described in subsection (2),

(a)   when a circumstance described in clause (3) (a), (b), (b.1) or (c) is inherent in the worker's work or is a normal condition of the worker's employment; or

(b)   when the worker's refusal to work would directly endanger the life, health or safety of another person. R.S.O. 1990, c. O.1, s. 43 (1); 2009, c. 23, s. 4 (1).

Same

(2)   The worker referred to in subsection (1) is,

(a)   a person employed in, or a member of, a police force to which the Police Services Act applies;

(b)   a firefighter as defined in subsection 1 (1) of the Fire Protection and Prevention Act, 1997;

(c)   a person employed in the operation of,

(i)   a correctional institution or facility,

(ii)   a place of secure custody designated under section 24.1 of the Young Offenders Act (Canada), whether in accordance with section 88 of the Youth Criminal Justice Act (Canada) or otherwise,

(iii) a place of temporary detention under the Youth Criminal Justice Act (Canada), or

(iv) a similar institution, facility or place;

(d) a person employed in the operation of,

(i) a hospital, sanatorium, long-term care home, psychiatric institution, mental health centre or rehabilitation facility,

(ii) a residential group home or other facility for persons with behavioural or emotional problems or a physical, mental or developmental disability,

(iii) an ambulance service or a first aid clinic or station,

(iv) a laboratory operated by the Crown or licensed under the Laboratory and Specimen Collection Centre Licensing Act, or

(v) a laundry, food service, power plant or technical service or facility used in conjunction with an institution, facility or service described in subclause (i) to (iv). R.S.O. 1990, c. O.1, s. 43 (2); 1997, c. 4, s. 84; 2001, c. 13, s. 22; 2006, c. 19, Sched. D, s. 14; 2007, c. 8, s. 221.

Refusal to work

(3) A worker may refuse to work or do particular work where he or she has reason to believe that,

    (a)   any equipment, machine, device or thing the worker is to use or operate is likely to endanger himself, herself or another worker;

    (b)   the physical condition of the workplace or the part thereof in which he or she works or is to work is likely to endanger himself or herself;

    (b.1) workplace violence is likely to endanger himself or herself; or

    (c)   any equipment, machine, device or thing he or she is to use or operate or the physical condition of the workplace or the part thereof in which he or she works or is to work is in contravention of this Act or the regulations and such contravention is likely to endanger himself, herself or another worker. R.S.O. 1990, c. O.1, s. 43 (3); 2009, c. 23, s. 4 (2).

Report of refusal to work

(4)   Upon refusing to work or do particular work, the worker shall promptly report the circumstances of the refusal to the worker's employer or supervisor who shall forthwith investigate the report in the presence of the worker and, if there is such, in the presence of one of,

    (a)   a committee member who represents workers, if any;

    (b)   a health and safety representative, if any; or

    (c)   a worker who because of knowledge, experience and training is selected by a trade union that represents the worker, or if there is no trade union, is selected by the workers to represent them, who shall be made available and who shall attend without delay. R.S.O. 1990, c. O.1, s. 43 (4).

Worker to remain in safe place and available for investigation

(5) Until the investigation is completed, the worker shall remain,

(a) in a safe place that is as near as reasonably possible to his or her work station; and

(b) available to the employer or supervisor for the purposes of the investigation. 2009, c. 23, s. 4 (3).

Refusal to work following investigation

(6) Where, following the investigation or any steps taken to deal with the circumstances that caused the worker to refuse to work or do particular work, the worker has reasonable grounds to believe that,

(a) the equipment, machine, device or thing that was the cause of the refusal to work or do particular work continues to be likely to endanger himself, herself or another worker;

(b) the physical condition of the workplace or the part thereof in which he or she works continues to be likely to endanger himself or herself;

(b.1) workplace violence continues to be likely to endanger himself or herself; or

(c) any equipment, machine, device or thing he or she is to use or operate or the physical condition of the workplace or the part thereof in which he or she works or is to work is in contravention of this Act or the regulations and such contravention continues to be likely to endanger himself, herself or another worker, the worker may refuse to work or do the particular work and the employer or the worker or a person on behalf of the employer or worker shall cause an inspector to be notified thereof. R.S.O. 1990, c. O.1, s. 43 (6); 2009, c. 23, s. 4 (4).

Investigation by inspector

(7)   An inspector shall investigate the refusal to work in consultation with the employer or a person representing the employer, the worker, and if there is such, the person mentioned in clause (4) (a), (b) or (c). 2001, c. 9, Sched. I, s. 3 (11).

Decision of inspector

(8)   The inspector shall, following the investigation referred to in subsection (7), decide whether a circumstance described in clause (6) (a), (b), (b.1) or (c) is likely to endanger the worker or another person. 2009, c. 23, s. 4 (5).

Same

(9)   The inspector shall give his or her decision, in writing, as soon as is practicable, to the employer, the worker, and, if there is such, the person mentioned in clause (4) (a), (b) or (c). R.S.O. 1990, c. O.1, s. 43 (9).

Worker to remain in safe place and available for investigation

(10) Pending the investigation and decision of the inspector, the worker shall remain, during the worker's normal working hours, in a safe place that is as near as reasonably possible to his or her work station and available to the inspector for the purposes of the investigation. 2009, c. 23, s. 4 (6).

Exception

(10.1) Subsection (10) does not apply if the employer, subject to the provisions of a collective agreement, if any,

    (a)   assigns the worker reasonable alternative work during the worker's normal working hours; or

    (b)   subject to section 50, where an assignment of reasonable alternative work is not practicable, gives other directions to the worker. 2009, c. 23, s. 4 (6).

Duty to advise other workers

(11) Pending the investigation and decision of the inspector, no worker shall be assigned to use or operate the equipment, machine, device or thing or to work in the workplace or in the part of the workplace being investigated unless, in the presence of a person described in subsection (12), the worker has been advised of the other worker's refusal and of his or her reasons for the refusal. R.S.O. 1990, c. O.1, s. 43 (11).

Same

(12) The person referred to in subsection (11) must be,

    (a)   a committee member who represents workers and, if possible, who is a certified member;

    (b)   a health and safety representative; or

    (c)   a worker who because of his or her knowledge, experience and training is selected by the trade union that represents the worker or, if there is no trade union, by the workers to represent them. R.S.O. 1990, c. O.1, s. 43 (12).

Entitlement to be paid

(13) A person shall be deemed to be at work and the person's employer shall pay him or her at the regular or premium rate, as may be proper,

(a) for the time spent by the person carrying out the duties under subsections (4) and (7) of a person mentioned in clause (4) (a), (b) or (c); and

(b) for time spent by the person carrying out the duties under subsection (11) of a person described in subsection (12). R.S.O. 1990, c. O.1, s. 43 (13).

Definition and non-application

Definition

44. (1) In sections 45 to 48,

"dangerous circumstances" means a situation in which,

(a) a provision of this Act or the regulations is being contravened,

(b) the contravention poses a danger or a hazard to a worker, and

(c) the danger or hazard is such that any delay in controlling it may seriously endanger a worker.

Non-application

(2) Sections 45 to 49 do not apply to,

(a) a workplace at which workers described in clause 43 (2) (a), (b) or (c) are employed; or

(b) a workplace at which workers described in clause 43 (2) (d) are employed if a work stoppage would directly endanger the life, health or safety of another person. R.S.O. 1990, c. O.1, s. 44.

Bilateral work stoppage

45. (1)   A certified member who has reason to believe that dangerous circumstances exist at a workplace may request that a supervisor investigate the matter and the supervisor shall promptly do so in the presence of the certified member.

Investigation by second certified member

(2)   The certified member may request that a second certified member representing the other workplace party investigate the matter if the first certified member has reason to believe that dangerous circumstances continue after the supervisor's investigation and remedial actions, if any.

Same

(3)   The second certified member shall promptly investigate the matter in the presence of the first certified member.

Direction following investigation

(4)   If both certified members find that the dangerous circumstances exist, the certified members may direct the constructor or employer to stop the work or to stop the use of any part of a workplace or of any equipment, machine, device, article or thing.

Constructor's or employer's duties

(5)   The constructor or employer shall immediately comply with the direction and shall ensure that compliance is effected in a way that does not endanger a person.

Investigation by inspector

(6)   If the certified members do not agree whether dangerous circumstances exist, either certified member may request that an inspector investigate the matter and the inspector shall do so and provide the certified members with a written decision.

Cancellation of direction

(7)   After taking steps to remedy the dangerous circumstances, the constructor or employer may request the certified members or an inspector to cancel the direction.

Same

(8)   The certified members who issued a direction may jointly cancel it or an inspector may cancel it.

Delegation by certified member

(9)   In such circumstances as may be prescribed, a certified member who represents the constructor or employer shall designate a person to act under this section in his or her stead when the certified member is not available at the workplace. R.S.O. 1990, c. O.1, s. 45.

Declaration against constructor, etc.

46.   (1)   A certified member at a workplace or an inspector who has reason to believe that the procedure for stopping work set out in section 45 will not be sufficient to protect a constructor's or employer's workers at the workplace from serious risk to their health or safety may apply to the Board for a declaration or recommendation described in subsection (5), or both. R.S.O. 1990, c. O.1, s. 46 (1); 1998, c. 8, s. 53 (1).

(2) **Repealed:** 1998, c. 8, s. 53 (2).

Minister a party

(3)   The Minister is entitled to be a party to a proceeding before the Board. R.S.O. 1990, c. O.1, s. 46 (3); 1998, c. 8, s. 53 (3).

Board procedure, etc.

(4)   Subsections 61 (2) to (3.13) and subsection 61 (8) apply, with necessary modifications, with respect to applications under this section. 1998, c. 8, s. 53 (4).

Declaration and recommendation

(5) If the Board finds that the procedure for stopping work set out in section 45 will not be sufficient to protect the constructor's or employer's workers at the workplace from serious risk to their health or safety, the Board,

   (a) may issue a declaration that the constructor or employer is subject to the procedure for stopping work set out in section 47 for the period specified; and

   (b) may recommend to the Minister that an inspector be assigned to oversee the health and safety practices of the constructor or employer at the workplace on a full-time or part-time basis for a specified period. R.S.O. 1990, c. O.1, s. 46 (5); 1998, c. 8, s. 53 (5).

Criteria

(6) In making a finding under subsection (5), the Board shall determine, using the prescribed criteria, whether the constructor or employer has demonstrated a failure to protect the health and safety of workers and shall consider such other matters as may be prescribed. R.S.O. 1990, c. O.1, s. 46 (6); 1998, c. 8, s. 53 (6).

Decision final

(7) The decision of the Board on an application is final. R.S.O. 1990, c. O.1, s. 46 (7); 1998, c. 8, s. 53 (7).

Costs of inspector

(8) The employer shall reimburse the Province of Ontario for the wages, benefits and expenses of an inspector assigned to the employer as recommended by the Board. 1998, c. 8, s. 53 (8).

Unilateral work stoppage

47. (1) This section applies, and section 45 does not apply, to a constructor or an employer,

(a) against whom the Board has issued a declaration under section 46; or

(b) who advises the committee at a workplace in writing that the constructor or employer adopts the procedures set out in this section respecting work stoppages. R.S.O. 1990, c. O.1, s. 47 (1); 1998, c. 8, s. 54.

Direction re work stoppage

(2) A certified member may direct the constructor or employer to stop specified work or to stop the use of any part of a workplace or of any equipment, machine, device, article or thing if the certified member finds that dangerous circumstances exist.

Constructor's or employer's duties

(3) The constructor or employer shall immediately comply with the direction and shall ensure that compliance is effected in a way that does not endanger a person.

Investigation by constructor, etc.

(4) After complying with the direction, the constructor or employer shall promptly investigate the matter in the presence of the certified member.

Investigation by inspector

(5) If the certified member and the constructor or employer do not agree whether dangerous circumstances exist, the constructor or employer or the certified member may request that an inspector investigate the matter and the inspector shall do so and provide them with a written decision.

Cancellation of direction

(6) After taking steps to remedy the dangerous circumstances, the constructor or employer may request the certified member or an inspector to cancel the direction.

Same

(7)   The certified member who made the direction or an inspector may cancel it. R.S.O. 1990, c. O.1, s. 47 (2-7).

Entitlement to investigate

48.   (1)   A certified member who receives a complaint that dangerous circumstances exist is entitled to investigate the complaint.

Entitlement to be paid

(2)   The time spent by a certified member in exercising powers and carrying out duties under this section and sections 45 and 47 shall be deemed to be work time for which the member's employer shall pay the member at the regular or premium rate as may be proper. R.S.O. 1990, c. O.1, s. 48.

Complaint re direction to stop work

49.   (1)   A constructor, an employer, a worker at the workplace or a representative of a trade union that represents workers at the workplace may file a complaint with the Board if he, she or it has reasonable grounds to believe that a certified member at the workplace recklessly or in bad faith exercised or failed to exercise a power under section 45 or 47. R.S.O. 1990, c. O.1, s. 49 (1); 1998, c. 8, s. 55 (1).

Limitation

(2)   A complaint must be filed not later than 30 days after the event to which the complaint relates. R.S.O. 1990, c. O.1, s. 49 (2); 1998, c. 8, s. 55 (2).

Minister a party

(3)   The Minister is entitled to be a party to a proceeding before the Board. R.S.O. 1990, c. O.1, s. 49 (3); 1998, c. 8, s. 55 (3).

Board procedure, etc.

(3.1) Subsections 61 (2) to (3.13) and subsection 61 (8) apply, with necessary modifications, with respect to complaints under this section. 1998, c. 8, s. 55 (4).

Determination of complaint

(4) The Board shall make a decision respecting the complaint and may make such order as it considers appropriate in the circumstances including an order decertifying a certified member. 1998, c. 8, s. 55 (5).

Decision final

(5) The decision of the Board is final. R.S.O. 1990, c. O.1, s. 49 (5); 1998, c. 8, s. 55 (6).

PART VI
REPRISALS BY EMPLOYER PROHIBITED

No discipline, dismissal, etc., by employer

50. (1) No employer or person acting on behalf of an employer shall,

(a) dismiss or threaten to dismiss a worker;

(b) discipline or suspend or threaten to discipline or suspend a worker;

(c) impose any penalty upon a worker; or

(d) intimidate or coerce a worker,

because the worker has acted in compliance with this Act or the regulations or an order made thereunder, has sought the enforcement of this Act or the regulations or has given evidence in a proceeding in respect of the enforcement of this Act or the regulations or in an inquest under the Coroners Act. R.S.O. 1990, c. O.1, s. 50 (1).

Arbitration

(2)   Where a worker complains that an employer or person acting on behalf of an employer has contravened subsection (1), the worker may either have the matter dealt with by final and binding settlement by arbitration under a collective agreement, if any, or file a complaint with the Board in which case any rules governing the practice and procedure of the Board apply with all necessary modifications to the complaint. 1998, c. 8, s. 56 (1).

Referral by inspector

(2.1) Where the circumstances warrant, an inspector may refer a matter to the Board if the following conditions are met:

1.   The worker has not had the matter dealt with by final and binding settlement by arbitration under a collective agreement or filed a complaint with the Board under subsection (2).

2.   The worker consents to the referral. 2011, c. 11, s. 13 (1).

Same

(2.2) Any rules governing the practice and procedure of the Board apply with all necessary modifications to a referral made under subsection (2.1). 2011, c. 11, s. 13 (1).

Referral not an order

(2.3) A referral made under subsection (2.1) is not an order or decision for the purposes of section 61. 2011, c. 11, s. 13 (1).

Inquiry by Board

(3)   The Board may inquire into any complaint filed under subsection (2) or referral made under subsection (2.1) and section

96 of the Labour Relations Act, 1995, except subsection (5), applies
with all necessary modifications as if such section, except
subsection (5), is enacted in and forms part of this Act. 1998, c. 8,
s. 56 (1); 2011, c. 11, s. 13 (2).

Same

(4)   On an inquiry by the Board into a complaint filed under
subsection (2) or a referral made under subsection (2.1), sections
110, 111, 114 and 116 of the Labour Relations Act, 1995 apply with
all necessary modifications. 1998, c. 8, s. 56 (1); 2011, c. 11,
s. 13 (3).

Rules to expedite proceedings

(4.1) The chair of the Board may make rules under subsection
110 (18) of the Labour Relations Act, 1995 to expedite proceedings
relating to a complaint filed under subsection (2) or a referral made
under subsection (2.1). 2011, c. 11, s. 13 (4).

Same

(4.2) Subsections 110 (19), (20), (21) and (22) of the Labour
Relations Act, 1995 apply, with necessary modifications, to rules
made under subsection (4.1). 2011, c. 11, s. 13 (4).

Onus of proof

(5)   On an inquiry by the Board into a complaint filed under
subsection (2) or a referral made under subsection (2.1), the burden
of proof that an employer or person acting on behalf of an employer
did not act contrary to subsection (1) lies upon the employer or the
person acting on behalf of the employer. R.S.O. 1990, c. O.1,
s. 50 (5); 1998, c. 8, s. 56 (2); 2011, c. 11, s. 13 (5).

Jurisdiction when complaint by public servant

(6)   The Board shall exercise jurisdiction under this section when a
complaint filed under subsection (2) or a referral made under
subsection (2.1) is in respect of a worker who is a public servant

within the meaning of the Public Service of Ontario Act, 2006.
2011, c. 11, s. 13 (6).

Board may substitute penalty

(7)   Where on an inquiry by the Board into a complaint filed under
subsection (2) or a referral made under subsection (2.1), the Board
determines that a worker has been discharged or otherwise
disciplined by an employer for cause and the contract of
employment or the collective agreement, as the case may be, does
not contain a specific penalty for the infraction, the Board may
substitute such other penalty for the discharge or discipline as to the
Board seems just and reasonable in all the circumstances. 1995,
c. 1, s. 84 (1); 1998, c. 8, s. 56 (4); 2011, c. 11, s. 13 (7).

Exception

(8)   Despite subsections (2) and (2.1), a person who is subject to a
rule or code of discipline under the Police Services Act shall have
his or her complaint in relation to an alleged contravention of
subsection (1) dealt with under that Act. R.S.O. 1990, c. O.1,
s. 50 (8); 2011, c. 11, s. 13 (8).

Offices of the Worker and Employer Advisers

Office of the Worker Adviser

50.1 (1)   In addition to the functions set out in section 176 of
the Workplace Safety and Insurance Act, 1997, the Office of the
Worker Adviser has the functions prescribed for the purposes of this
Part, with respect to workers who are not members of a trade union.
2011, c. 11, s. 14.

Office of the Employer Adviser

(2)   In addition to the functions set out in section 176 of
the Workplace Safety and Insurance Act, 1997, the Office of the
Employer Adviser has the functions prescribed for the purposes of
this Part, with respect to employers that have fewer than 100

employees or such other number as may be prescribed. 2011, c. 11, s. 14.

Costs

(3)   In determining the amount of the costs that may be incurred by each office under subsection 176 (3) of the Workplace Safety and Insurance Act, 1997, the Minister shall take into account any functions prescribed for the purposes of this Part. 2011, c. 11, s. 14.

PART VII
NOTICES

Notice of death or injury

51.   (1)   Where a person is killed or critically injured from any cause at a workplace, the constructor, if any, and the employer shall notify an inspector, and the committee, health and safety representative and trade union, if any, immediately of the occurrence by telephone or other direct means and the employer shall, within forty-eight hours after the occurrence, send to a Director a written report of the circumstances of the occurrence containing such information and particulars as the regulations prescribe. R.S.O. 1990, c. O.1, s. 51 (1); 2011, c. 1, Sched. 7, s. 2 (7).

Preservation of wreckage

(2)   Where a person is killed or is critically injured at a workplace, no person shall, except for the purpose of,

(a)   saving life or relieving human suffering;

(b)   maintaining an essential public utility service or a public transportation system; or

(c)   preventing unnecessary damage to equipment or other property, interfere with, disturb, destroy, alter or carry away any wreckage, article or thing at the scene of or connected with the occurrence until permission so to do has been given by an inspector. R.S.O. 1990, c. O.1, s. 51 (2).

Notice of accident, explosion, fire or violence causing injury

52. (1) If a person is disabled from performing his or her usual work or requires medical attention because of an accident, explosion, fire or incident of workplace violence at a workplace, but no person dies or is critically injured because of that occurrence, the employer shall, within four days of the occurrence, give written notice of the occurrence containing the prescribed information and particulars to the following:

1. The committee, the health and safety representative and the trade union, if any.

2. The Director, if an inspector requires notification of the Director. 2001, c. 9, Sched. I, s. 3 (12); 2009, c. 23, s. 5.

Notice of occupational illness

(2) If an employer is advised by or on behalf of a worker that the worker has an occupational illness or that a claim in respect of an occupational illness has been filed with the Workplace Safety and Insurance Board by or on behalf of the worker, the employer shall give notice in writing, within four days of being so advised, to a Director, to the committee or a health and safety representative and to the trade union, if any, containing such information and particulars as are prescribed. R.S.O. 1990, c. O.1, s. 52 (2); 1997, c. 16, s. 2 (12).

Same

(3) Subsection (2) applies with all necessary modifications if an employer is advised by or on behalf of a former worker that the worker has or had an occupational illness or that a claim in respect

of an occupational illness has been filed with the Workplace Safety and Insurance Board by or on behalf of the worker. R.S.O. 1990, c. O.1, s. 52 (3); 1997, c. 16, s. 2 (13).

Accident, etc., at project site or mine

53. If an accident, premature or unexpected explosion, fire, flood or inrush of water, failure of any equipment, machine, device, article or thing, cave-in, subsidence, rockburst, or other prescribed incident occurs at a project site, mine or mining plant, the constructor of the project or the owner of the mine or mining plant shall, within two days after the occurrence, give notice in writing with the prescribed information and particulars,

      (a)   to the committee, health and safety representative and trade union, if any; and

      (b)   to a Director, unless a report under section 51 or a notice under section 52 has already been given to a Director. 2011, c. 1, Sched. 7, s. 2 (8).

PART VIII
ENFORCEMENT

Powers of inspector

54. (1)   An inspector may, for the purposes of carrying out his or her duties and powers under this Act and the regulations,

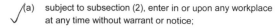

      (a)   subject to subsection (2), enter in or upon any workplace at any time without warrant or notice;

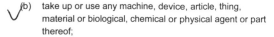

      (b)   take up or use any machine, device, article, thing, material or biological, chemical or physical agent or part thereof;

(c) require the production of any drawings, specifications, licence, document, record or report, and inspect, examine and copy the same;

(d) upon giving a receipt therefor, remove any drawings, specifications, licence, document, record or report inspected or examined for the purpose of making copies thereof or extracts therefrom, and upon making copies thereof or extracts therefrom, shall promptly return the same to the person who produced or furnished them;

(e) conduct or take tests of any equipment, machine, device, article, thing, material or biological, chemical or physical agent in or about a workplace and for such purposes, take and carry away such samples as may be necessary;

(f) require in writing an employer to cause any tests described in clause (e) to be conducted or taken, at the expense of the employer, by a person possessing such special expert or professional knowledge or qualifications as are specified by the inspector and to provide, at the expense of the employer, a report or assessment by that person;

(g) in any inspection, examination, inquiry or test, be accompanied and assisted by or take with him or her any person or persons having special, expert or professional knowledge of any matter, take photographs, and take with him or her and use any equipment or materials required for such purpose;

(h) make inquiries of any person who is or was in a workplace either separate and apart from another person or in the presence of any other person that are or may be relevant to an inspection, examination, inquiry or test;

(i) require that a workplace or part thereof not be disturbed for a reasonable period of time for the purposes of carrying out an examination, investigation or test;

(j) require that any equipment, machine, device, article, thing or process be operated or set in motion or that a system or procedure be carried out that may be relevant to an examination, inquiry or test;

(k) require in writing an employer to have equipment, machinery or devices tested, at the expense of the employer, by a professional engineer and to provide, at the expense of the employer, a report bearing the seal and signature of the professional engineer stating that the equipment, machine or device is not likely to endanger a worker;

(l) require in writing that any equipment, machinery or device not be used pending testing described in clause (k);

(m) require in writing an owner, constructor or employer to provide, at the expense of the owner, constructor or employer, a report bearing the seal and signature of a professional engineer stating,

(i) the load limits of a building, structure, or any part thereof, or any other part of a workplace, whether temporary or permanent,

(ii) that a building, structure, or any part thereof, or any other part of a workplace, whether temporary or permanent, is capable of supporting or withstanding the loads being applied to it or likely to be applied to it, or

      (iii)   that a building, structure, or any part thereof, or any other part of a workplace, whether temporary or permanent, is capable of supporting any loads that may be applied to it,

          (A)   as determined by the applicable design requirements established under the version of the Building Code that was in force at the time of its construction,

          (B)   in accordance with such other requirements as may be prescribed, or

          (C)   in accordance with good engineering practice, if sub-subclauses (A) and (B) do not apply;

(n)   require in writing an owner of a mine or part thereof to provide, at the owner's expense, a report in writing bearing the seal and signature of a professional engineer stating that the ground stability of, the mining methods and the support or rock reinforcement used in the mine or part thereof is such that a worker is not likely to be endangered;

(o)   require in writing, within such time as is specified, a person who is an employer, manufacturer, producer, importer, distributor or supplier to produce records or information, or to provide, at the expense of the person, a report or evaluation made or to be made by a person or organization having special, expert or professional knowledge or qualifications as are specified by the inspector of any process or biological, chemical or physical agents or combination of such agents present, used or intended for use in a workplace and the manner of use, including,

      (i)   the ingredients thereof and their common or generic name or names,

      (ii)   the composition and the properties thereof,

      (iii) the toxicological effect thereof,

      (iv) the effect of exposure thereto whether by contact, inhalation or ingestion,

      (v)   the protective measures used or to be used in respect thereof,

      (vi) the emergency measures used or to be used to deal with exposure in respect thereof, and

      (vii) the effect of the use, transport and disposal thereof; and

(p)   require the production of any materials concerning the content, frequency and manner of instruction of any training program and inspect, examine and copy the materials and attend any such program. R.S.O. 1990, c. O.1, s. 54 (1); 2011, c. 11, s. 15.

Entry to dwellings

(2)   An inspector may only enter a dwelling or that part of a dwelling actually being used as a workplace with the consent of the occupier or under the authority of a warrant issued under this Act or the Provincial Offences Act. 2001, c. 26, s. 1.

Representative to accompany inspector

(3)   Where an inspector makes an inspection of a workplace under the powers conferred upon him or her under subsection (1), the constructor, employer or group of employers shall afford a committee member representing workers or a health and safety

representative, if any, or a worker selected by a trade union or trade unions, if any, because of knowledge, experience and training, to represent it or them and, where there is no trade union, a worker selected by the workers because of knowledge, training and experience to represent them, the opportunity to accompany the inspector during his or her physical inspection of a workplace, or any part or parts thereof. R.S.O. 1990, c. O.1, s. 54 (3).

Consultation with workers

(4)   Where there is no committee member representing workers, no health and safety representative or worker selected under subsection (3), the inspector shall endeavour to consult during his or her physical inspection with a reasonable number of the workers concerning matters of health and safety at their work. R.S.O. 1990, c. O.1, s. 54 (4).

Entitlement to time from work

(5)   The time spent by a committee member representing workers, a health and safety representative or a worker selected in accordance with subsection (3) in accompanying an inspector during his or her physical inspection, shall be deemed to be work time for which he or she shall be paid by his or her employer at his or her regular or premium rate as may be proper. R.S.O. 1990, c. O.1, s. 54 (5).

Order for inspections

55. Subject to subsections 8 (6) and 9 (26), an inspector may in writing direct a health and safety representative or a member designated under subsection 9 (23) to inspect the physical condition of all or part of a workplace at specified intervals. R.S.O. 1990, c. O.1, s. 55; 2009, c. 33, Sched. 20, s. 3 (2).

Order for written policies

55.1 In the case of a workplace at which the number of workers regularly
employed is five or fewer, an inspector may in writing order that the
policies with respect to workplace violence and workplace
harassment required under section 32.0.1 be in written form and
posted at a conspicuous place in the workplace. 2009, c. 23, s. 6;
2011, c. 1, Sched. 7, s. 2 (9).

Order for written assessment, etc.

55.2 An inspector may in writing order that the following be in written
form:

1. The assessment of the risks of workplace violence
    required under subsection 32.0.3 (1).

2. A reassessment required under subsection 32.0.3 (4).
    2009, c. 23, s. 6.

Warrants – investigative techniques, etc.

56. (1)   On application without notice, a justice of the peace or a
provincial judge may issue a warrant authorizing an inspector,
subject to this section, to use any investigative technique or
procedure or to do any thing described in the warrant if the justice of
the peace or provincial judge, as the case may be, is satisfied by
information under oath that there are reasonable grounds to believe
that an offence against this Act or the regulations has been or is
being committed and that information and other evidence
concerning the offence will be obtained through the use of the
technique or procedure or the doing of the thing. 2001, c. 26, s. 2.

Expert help

(1.1) The warrant may authorize persons who have special, expert
or professional knowledge to accompany and assist the inspector in
the execution of the warrant. 2001, c. 26, s. 2.

Terms and conditions of warrant

(1.2) The warrant shall authorize the inspector to enter and search the place for which the warrant was issued and, without limiting the powers of the justice of the peace or the provincial judge under subsection (1), the warrant may, in respect of the alleged offence, authorize the inspector to,

(a) seize or examine and copy any drawings, specifications, licence, document, record or report;

(b) seize or examine any equipment, machine, device, article, thing, material or biological, chemical or physical agent;

(c) require a person to produce any item described in clause (a) or (b);

(d) conduct or take tests of any equipment, machine, device, article, thing, material or biological, chemical or physical agent, and take and carry away samples from the testing;

(e) take measurements of and record by any means the physical circumstances of the workplace; and

(f) make inquiries of any person either separate and apart from another person or in the presence of any other person. 2001, c. 26, s. 2.

Duration

(1.3) The warrant is valid for 30 days or for such shorter period as may be specified in it. 2001, c. 26, s. 2.

Other terms and conditions

(1.4) The warrant may contain terms and conditions in addition to those provided for in subsections (1) to (1.3) as the justice of the peace or provincial judge, as the case may be, considers advisable in the circumstances. 2001, c. 26, s. 2.

Further warrants

(1.5) A justice of the peace or provincial judge may issue further warrants under subsection (1). 2001, c. 26, s. 2.

Powers, duties not restricted

(1.6) Nothing in this section restricts any power or duty of an inspector under this Act or the regulations. 2001, c. 26, s. 2.

Possession

(2) The inspector may remove any thing seized under a warrant from the place from which it was seized or may detain it in that place. 2001, c. 26, s. 2.

Notice and receipt

(3) The inspector shall inform the person from whom the thing is seized as to the reason for the seizure and shall give the person a receipt for it. R.S.O. 1990, c. O.1, s. 56 (3).

Report to justice

(4) The inspector shall bring a thing seized under the authority of this section before a provincial judge or justice of the peace or, if that is not reasonably possible, shall report the seizure to a provincial judge or justice of the peace. R.S.O. 1990, c. O.1, s. 56 (4).

Procedure

(5) Sections 159 and 160 of the Provincial Offences Act apply with necessary modifications in respect of a thing seized under the authority of this section. R.S.O. 1990, c. O.1, s. 56 (5).

Power of inspector to seize

56.1 (1)   An inspector who executes a warrant issued under section 56 may seize or examine and copy any drawings, specifications, licence, document, record or report or seize or examine any equipment, machine, device, article, thing, material or biological, chemical or physical agent, in addition to those mentioned in the warrant, that he or she believes on reasonable grounds will afford evidence in respect of an offence under this Act or the regulations. 2001, c. 26, s. 3.

Searches in exigent circumstances

(2)   Although a warrant issued under section 56 would otherwise be required, an inspector may exercise any of the powers described in subsection 56 (1) without a warrant if the conditions for obtaining the warrant exist but by reason of exigent circumstances it would be impracticable to obtain the warrant. 2001, c. 26, s. 3.

Report to justice, etc.

(3)   Subsections 56 (3), (4) and (5) apply with necessary modifications to a thing seized under this section. 2001, c. 26, s. 3.

Orders by inspectors where non-compliance

57. (1)   Where an inspector finds that a provision of this Act or the regulations is being contravened, the inspector may order, orally or in writing, the owner, constructor, licensee, employer, or person whom he or she believes to be in charge of a workplace or the person whom the inspector believes to be the contravener to comply with the provision and may require the order to be carried out forthwith or within such period of time as the inspector specifies. R.S.O. 1990, c. O.1, s. 57 (1).

Same

(2)   Where an inspector makes an oral order under subsection (1), the inspector shall confirm the order in writing before leaving the workplace. R.S.O. 1990, c. O.1, s. 57 (2).

Contents of order

(3)   An order made under subsection (1) shall indicate generally the nature of the contravention and where appropriate the location of the contravention. R.S.O. 1990, c. O.1, s. 57 (3).

Compliance plan

(4)   An order made under subsection (1) may require a constructor, a licensee or an employer to submit to the Ministry a compliance plan prepared in the manner and including such items as required by the order. R.S.O. 1990, c. O.1, s. 57 (4).

Same

(5)   The compliance plan shall specify what the constructor, licensee or employer plans to do to comply with the order and when the constructor, licensee or employer intends to achieve compliance. R.S.O. 1990, c. O.1, s. 57 (5).

Orders by inspector where worker endangered

(6)   Where an inspector makes an order under subsection (1) and finds that the contravention of this Act or the regulations is a danger or hazard to the health or safety of a worker, the inspector may,

(a)   order that any place, equipment, machine, device, article or thing or any process or material shall not be used until the order is complied with;

(b)   order that the work at the workplace as indicated in the order shall stop until the order to stop work is withdrawn or cancelled by an inspector after an inspection;

(c)   order that the workplace where the contravention exists be cleared of workers and isolated by barricades, fencing or any other means suitable to prevent access thereto by a worker until the danger or hazard to the health or safety of a worker is removed. R.S.O. 1990, c. O.1, s. 57 (6).

Resumption of work pending inspection

(7)   Despite clause (6) (b), a constructor, a licensee or an employer who gives notice to an inspector of compliance with an order made under subsection (6) may resume work pending an inspection and decision by an inspector respecting compliance with the order if, before the resumption of work, a committee member representing workers or a health and safety representative, as the case may be, advises an inspector that in his or her opinion the order has been complied with. R.S.O. 1990, c. O.1, s. 57 (7).

Additional orders

(8)   In addition to the orders that may be made under subsection (6), where an inspector makes an order under subsection (1) for a contravention of section 37 or 41 or a Director has been advised of an employer's inability to obtain an unexpired material safety data sheet, the inspector may order that the hazardous material shall not be used or that the thing that causes, emits or produces the hazardous physical agent not be used or operated until the order is withdrawn or cancelled. R.S.O. 1990, c. O.1, s. 57 (8).

Note: On a day to be named by proclamation of the Lieutenant Governor, subsection (8) is amended by striking out "material safety" and substituting "safety". See: 2011, c. 1, Sched. 7, ss. 2 (12), 4 (2).

Posting of notice

(9)   Where an inspector makes an order under this section, he or she may affix to the workplace, or to any equipment, machine, device, article or thing, a copy thereof or a notice of the order, in a form obtained from the Ministry, and no person, except an inspector, shall remove such copy or notice unless authorized to do so by an inspector. R.S.O. 1990, c. O.1, s. 57 (9); 2011, c. 1, Sched. 7, s. 2 (10).

Same

(10) Where an inspector makes an order in writing or issues a report of his or her inspection to an owner, constructor, licensee, employer or person in charge of the workplace,

    (a)   the owner, constructor, licensee, employer or person in charge of the workplace shall forthwith cause a copy or copies of it to be posted in a conspicuous place or places at the workplace where it is most likely to come to the attention of the workers and shall furnish a copy of the order or report to the health and safety representative and the committee, if any; and

    (b)   if the order or report resulted from a complaint of a contravention of this Act or the regulations and the person who made the complaint requests a copy of it, the inspector shall cause a copy of it to be furnished to that person. 2001, c. 9, Sched. I, s. 3 (13).

No hearing required prior to making order

(11) An inspector is not required to hold or afford to an owner, constructor, licensee, employer or any other person an opportunity for a hearing before making an order. R.S.O. 1990, c. O.1, s. 57 (11).

Entry into barricaded area

58. Where an order is made under clause 57 (6) (c), no owner, constructor, employer or supervisor shall require or permit a worker to enter the workplace except for the purpose of doing work that is necessary or required to remove the danger or hazard and only where the worker is protected from the danger or hazard. R.S.O. 1990, c. O.1, s. 58.

Notice of compliance

59. (1) Within three days after a constructor or employer who has received an order under section 57 believes that compliance with the order has been achieved, the constructor or employer shall submit to the Ministry a notice of compliance.

Same

(2) The notice shall be signed by the constructor or employer and shall be accompanied by,

(a) a statement of agreement or disagreement with the contents of the notice, signed by a member of the committee representing workers or by a health and safety representative, as the case may be; or

(b) a statement that the member or representative has declined to sign the statement referred to in clause (a).

Same

(3) The constructor or employer shall post the notice and the order issued under section 57 for a period of fourteen days following its submission to the Ministry in a place or places in the workplace where it is most likely to come to the attention of workers.

Compliance achieved

(4) Despite the submission of a notice of compliance, a constructor or employer achieves compliance with an order under section 57 when an inspector determines that compliance has been achieved. R.S.O. 1990, c. O.1, s. 59.

Injunction proceedings

60. In addition to any other remedy or penalty therefor, where an order made under subsection 57 (6) is contravened, such contravention may be restrained upon an application made without notice to a judge of the Superior Court of Justice made at the instance of a Director. R.S.O. 1990, c. O.1, s. 60; 2001, c. 9, Sched. I, s. 3 (14).

Appeals from order of an inspector

61. (1)   Any employer, constructor, licensee, owner, worker or trade union which considers himself, herself or itself aggrieved by any order made by an inspector under this Act or the regulations may appeal to the Board within 30 days after the making of the order. 1998, c. 8, s. 57 (1).

Parties

(2)   The following are parties to the appeal:

1.   The appellant.

2.   In the case of an appeal by an employer, the employer's workers and each trade union representing any of the workers.

3.   In the case of an appeal by a worker or trade union representing a worker, the worker's employer.

4.   A Director.

5.   Such other persons as the Board may specify.   1998, c. 8, s. 57 (2); 2011, c. 1, Sched. 7, s. 2 (11).

Inquiry by labour relations officer

(3)   The Board may authorize a labour relations officer to inquire into an appeal. 1998, c. 8, s. 57 (2).

Same

(3.1) The labour relations officer shall forthwith inquire into the appeal and endeavour to effect a settlement of the matters raised in the appeal. 1998, c. 8, s. 57 (2).

Report to Board

(3.2) The labour relations officer shall report the results of his or her inquiry and endeavours to the Board. 1998, c. 8, s. 57 (2).

Hearings

(3.3) Subject to the rules made under subsection (3.8), the Board shall hold a hearing to consider the appeal unless the Board makes an order under subsection (3.4). 1998, c. 8, s. 57 (2).

Orders after consultation

(3.4) The Board may make any interim or final order it considers appropriate after consulting with the parties. 1998, c. 8, s. 57 (2).

Same

(3.5) The Statutory Powers Procedure Act does not apply with respect to a consultation the Board makes under subsection (3.4). 1998, c. 8, s. 57 (2).

Practice and procedure

(3.6) The Board shall determine its own practice and procedure but shall give full opportunity to the parties to present their evidence and to make their submissions. 1998, c. 8, s. 57 (2).

Rules of practice

(3.7) The chair may make rules governing the Board's practice and procedure and the exercise of its powers and prescribing such forms as the chair considers advisable. 1998, c. 8, s. 57 (2).

Expedited appeals

(3.8) The chair of the Board may make rules to expedite appeals and such rules,

    (a)   may provide that the Board is not required to hold a hearing; and

    (b)   may limit the extent to which the Board is required to give full opportunity to the parties to present their evidence and to make their submissions. 1998, c. 8, s. 57 (2).

Effective date of rules

(3.9) Rules made under subsection (3.8) come into force on such dates as the Lieutenant Governor in Council may by order determine. 1998, c. 8, s. 57 (2).

Conflict with Statutory Powers Procedure Act

(3.10) Rules made under this section apply despite anything in the Statutory Powers Procedure Act. 1998, c. 8, s. 57 (2).

Rules not regulations

(3.11) Rules made under this section are not regulations within the meaning of Part III (Regulations) of the Legislation Act, 2006. 1998, c. 8, s. 57 (2); 2006, c. 21, Sched. F, s. 136 (1).

Quorum

(3.12) The chair or a vice-chair of the Board constitutes a quorum for the purposes of this section and is sufficient for the exercise of the jurisdiction and powers of the Board under this section. 1998, c. 8, s. 57 (2).

Entering premises

(3.13) For the purposes of an appeal under this section, the Board may enter any premises where work is being or has been done by workers or in which the employer carries on business, whether or not the premises are those of the employer, and inspect and view any work, material, machinery, appliance or article therein, and interrogate any person respecting any matter and post therein any notice that the Board considers necessary to bring to the attention of persons having an interest in the appeal. 1998, c. 8, s. 57 (2).

Powers of the Board

(4)   On an appeal under this section, the Board may substitute its findings for those of the inspector who made the order appealed from and may rescind or affirm the order or make a new order in substitution therefor, and for such purpose has all the powers of an

inspector and the order of the Board shall stand in the place of and have the like effect under this Act and the regulations as the order of the inspector. 1998, c. 8, s. 57 (2).

Order, extended meaning

(5)   In this section, an order of an inspector under this Act or the regulations includes any order or decision made or given or the imposition of any terms or conditions therein by an inspector under the authority of this Act or the regulations or the refusal to make an order or decision by an inspector. R.S.O. 1990, c. O.1, s. 61 (5).

Decision of adjudicator final

(6)   A decision of the Board under this section is final. R.S.O. 1990, c. O.1, s. 61 (6); 1998, c. 8, s. 57 (3).

Suspension of order by adjudicator pending disposition of appeal

(7)   On an appeal under subsection (1), the Board may suspend the operation of the order appealed from pending the disposition of the appeal. R.S.O. 1990, c. O.1, s. 61 (7); 1998, c. 8, s. 57 (4).

Reconsideration

(8)   The Board may at any time, if it considers it advisable to do so, reconsider any decision, order, direction, declaration or ruling made by it under this section and may vary or revoke any such decision, order, direction, declaration or ruling. 1998, c. 8, s. 57 (5).

Obstruction of inspector

62.   (1)   No person shall hinder, obstruct, molest or interfere with or attempt to hinder, obstruct, molest or interfere with an inspector in the exercise of a power or the performance of a duty under this Act or the regulations or in the execution of a warrant issued under this Act or the Provincial Offences Act with respect to a matter under this Act or the regulations. 2001, c. 26, s. 4.

Assistance

(2) Every person shall furnish all necessary means in the person's power to facilitate any entry, search, inspection, investigation, examination, testing or inquiry by an inspector,

    (a) in the exercise of his or her powers or the performance of his or her duties under this Act or the regulations; or

    (b) in the execution of a warrant issued under this Act or the Provincial Offences Act with respect to a matter under this Act or the regulations. 2001, c. 26, s. 4.

False information, etc.

(3) No person shall knowingly furnish an inspector with false information or neglect or refuse to furnish information required by an inspector,

    (a) in the exercise of his or her powers or the performance of his or her duties under this Act or the regulations; or

    (b) in the execution of a warrant issued under this Act or the Provincial Offences Act with respect to a matter under this Act or the regulations. 2001, c. 26, s. 4.

Monitoring devices

(4) No person shall interfere with any monitoring equipment or device in a workplace. R.S.O. 1990, c. O.1, s. 62 (4).

Obstruction of committee, etc.

(5) No person shall knowingly,

    (a) hinder or interfere with a committee, a committee member or a health and safety representative in the exercise of a power or performance of a duty under this Act;

    (b)   furnish a committee, a committee member or a health and safety representative with false information in the exercise of a power or performance of a duty under this Act; or

    (c)   hinder or interfere with a worker selected by a trade union or trade unions or a worker selected by the workers to represent them in the exercise of a power or performance of a duty under this Act. R.S.O. 1990, c. O.1, s. 62 (5).

Information confidential

63. (1) Except for the purposes of this Act and the regulations or as required by law,

    (a)   an inspector, a person accompanying an inspector or a person who, at the request of an inspector, makes an examination, test or inquiry, shall not publish, disclose or communicate to any person any information, material, statement, report or result of any examination, test or inquiry acquired, furnished, obtained, made or received under the powers conferred under this Act or the regulations;

    (b)   **Repealed:** 1992, c. 14, s. 2 (2).

    (c)   no person shall publish, disclose or communicate to any person any secret manufacturing process or trade secret acquired, furnished, obtained, made or received under the provisions of this Act or the regulations;

    (d)   **Repealed:** 1992, c. 14, s. 2 (3).

    (e)   no person to whom information is communicated under this Act and the regulations shall divulge the name of the informant to any person; and

(f)   no person shall disclose any information obtained in any medical examination, test or x-ray of a worker made or taken under this Act except in a form calculated to prevent the information from being identified with a particular person or case. R.S.O. 1990, c. O.1, s. 63 (1); 1992, c. 14, s. 2 (2, 3).

Employer access to health records

(2)   No employer shall seek to gain access, except by an order of the court or other tribunal or in order to comply with another statute, to a health record concerning a worker without the worker's written consent. R.S.O. 1990, c. O.1, s. 63 (2).

Compellability, civil suit

(3)   An inspector or a person who, at the request of an inspector, accompanies an inspector, or a person who makes an examination, test, inquiry or takes samples at the request of an inspector, is not a compellable witness in a civil suit or any proceeding, except an inquest under the Coroners Act, respecting any information, material, statement or test acquired, furnished, obtained, made or received under this Act or the regulations. R.S.O. 1990, c. O.1, s. 63 (3).

Compellability of witnesses

(3.1) Persons employed in the Office of the Worker Adviser or the Office of the Employer Adviser are not compellable witnesses in a civil suit or any proceeding respecting any information or material furnished to or obtained, made or received by them under this Act while acting within the scope of their employment. 2011, c. 11, s. 16.

Exception

(3.2) If the Office of the Worker Adviser or the Office of the Employer Adviser is a party to a proceeding, a person employed in the relevant Office may be determined to be a compellable witness. 2011, c. 11, s. 16.

Production of documents

(3.3) Persons employed in the Office of the Worker Adviser or the Office of the Employer Adviser are not required to produce, in a proceeding in which the relevant Office is not a party, any information or material furnished to or obtained, made or received by them under this Act while acting within the scope of their employment. 2011, c. 11, s. 16.

Power of Director to disclose

(4) A Director may communicate or allow to be communicated or disclosed information, material, statements or the result of a test acquired, furnished, obtained, made or received under this Act or the regulations. R.S.O. 1990, c. O.1, s. 63 (4).

Medical emergencies

(5) Subsection (1) does not apply so as to prevent any person from providing any information in the possession of the person, including confidential business information, in a medical emergency for the purpose of diagnosis or treatment. R.S.O. 1990, c. O.1, s. 63 (5).

Conflict

(6) This section prevails despite anything to the contrary in the Personal Health Information Protection Act, 2004. 2004, c. 3, Sched. A, s. 93.

Copies of reports

64. A Director may, upon receipt of a request in writing from the owner of a workplace who has entered into an agreement to sell the same and upon payment of the fee or fees prescribed, furnish to the owner or a person designated by the owner copies of reports or orders of an inspector made under this Act in respect of the workplace as to its compliance with subsection 29 (1). R.S.O. 1990, c. O.1, s. 64.

Immunity

65. (1) No action or other proceeding for damages, prohibition or mandamus shall be instituted respecting any act done in good faith in the execution or intended execution of a person's duties under this Act or in the exercise or intended exercise of a person's powers under this Act or for any alleged neglect or default in the execution or performance in good faith of the person's duties or powers if the person is,

    (a) an employee in the Ministry or a person who acts as an advisor for the Ministry;

    (b) an employee in the Office of the Worker Adviser or the Office of the Employer Adviser;

    (c) the Board or a labour relations officer;

    (d) a health and safety representative or a committee member; or

    (e) a worker selected by a trade union or trade unions or by workers to represent them. R.S.O. 1990, c. O.1, s. 65 (1); 1995, c. 5, s. 32; 1997, c. 16, s. 2 (14, 15); 1998, c. 8, s. 58; 2006, c. 35, Sched. C, s. 93 (6); 2011, c. 11, s. 17 (1).

Liability of Crown

(2)　Subsection (1) does not, by reason of subsections 5 (2) and (4) of the Proceedings Against the Crown Act, relieve the Crown of liability in respect of a tort committed by a Director, the Chief Prevention Officer, an inspector or an engineer of the Ministry to which it would otherwise be subject and the Crown is liable under that Act for any such tort in a like manner as if subsection (1) had not been enacted.　R.S.O. 1990, c. O.1, s. 65 (2); 2011, c. 11, s. 17 (2).

PART IX
OFFENCES AND PENALTIES

Penalties

66.　(1)　Every person who contravenes or fails to comply with,

(a)　a provision of this Act or the regulations;

(b)　an order or requirement of an inspector or a Director; or

(c)　an order of the Minister,

is guilty of an offence and on conviction is liable to a fine of not more than $25,000 or to imprisonment for a term of not more than twelve months, or to both.

Same

(2)　If a corporation is convicted of an offence under subsection (1), the maximum fine that may be imposed upon the corporation is $500,000 and not as provided therein.

Defence

(3)   On a prosecution for a failure to comply with,

(a)   subsection 23 (1);

(b)   clause 25 (1) (b), (c) or (d); or

(c)   subsection 27 (1),

it shall be a defence for the accused to prove that every precaution reasonable in the circumstances was taken.

Accused liable for acts or neglect of managers, agents, etc.

(4)   In a prosecution of an offence under any provision of this Act, any act or neglect on the part of any manager, agent, representative, officer, director or supervisor of the accused, whether a corporation or not, shall be the act or neglect of the accused. R.S.O. 1990, c. O.1, s. 66.

Certified copies of documents, etc., as evidence

67.   (1)   In any proceeding or prosecution under this Act,

(a)   a copy of an order or decision purporting to have been made under this Act or the regulations and purporting to have been signed by the Minister or an inspector;

(b)   a document purporting to be a copy of a notice, drawing, record or other document, or any extract therefrom given or made under this Act or the regulations and purporting to be certified by an inspector;

(c)   a document purporting to certify the result of a test or an analysis of a sample of air and setting forth the concentration or amount of a biological, chemical or physical agent in a workplace or part thereof and purporting to be certified by an inspector; or

(d)   a document purporting to certify the result of a test or an analysis of any equipment, machine, device, article, thing or substance and purporting to be certified by an inspector,

is evidence of the order, decision, writing or document, and the facts appearing in the order, decision, writing or document without proof of the signature or official character of the person appearing to have signed the order or the certificate and without further proof.

Service of orders and decisions

(2)   In any proceeding or prosecution under this Act, a copy of an order or decision purporting to have been made under this Act or the regulations and purporting to have been signed by the Minister, a Director or an inspector may be served,

(a)   personally in the case of an individual or in case of a partnership upon a partner, and in the case of a corporation, upon the president, vice-president, secretary, treasurer or a director, or upon the manager or person in charge of the workplace; or

(b)   by registered letter addressed to a person or corporation mentioned in clause (a) at the last known place of business of the person or corporation,

and the same shall be deemed to be good and sufficient service thereof. R.S.O. 1990, c. O.1, s. 67.

Place of trial

68.   (1)   An information in respect of an offence under this Act may, at the election of the informant, be heard, tried and determined by the Ontario Court of Justice sitting in the county or district in which the accused is resident or carries on business although the subject-matter of the information did not arise in that county or district. R.S.O. 1990, c. O.1, s. 68 (1); 2001, c. 9, Sched. I, s. 3 (15).

Provincial judge required

(2)   The Attorney General or an agent for the Attorney General may by notice to the clerk of the court having jurisdiction in respect of an offence under this Act require that a provincial judge preside over the proceeding. R.S.O. 1990, c. O.1, s. 68 (2).

Publication re convictions

68.1 (1)   If a person, including an individual, is convicted of an offence under this Act, a Director may publish or otherwise make available to the general public the name of the person, a description of the offence, the date of the conviction and the person's sentence. 2006, c. 19, Sched. M, s. 5.

Internet publication

(2)   Authority to publish under subsection (1) includes authority to publish on the Internet. 2006, c. 19, Sched. M, s. 5.

Disclosure

(3)   Any disclosure made under subsection (1) shall be deemed to be in compliance with clause 42 (1) (e) of the Freedom of Information and Protection of Privacy Act. 2006, c. 19, Sched. M, s. 5; 2006, c. 34, Sched. C, s. 25.

Limitation on prosecutions

69.   No prosecution under this Act shall be instituted more than one year after the last act or default upon which the prosecution is based occurred. R.S.O. 1990, c. O.1, s. 69.

PART X
REGULATIONS

Regulations

70. (1)   The Lieutenant Governor in Council may make such regulations as are advisable for the health or safety of persons in or about a workplace. R.S.O. 1990, c. O.1, s. 70 (1).

Same

(2)   Without limiting the generality of subsection (1), the Lieutenant Governor in Council may make regulations,

1.   defining any word or expression used in this Act or the regulations that is not defined in this Act;

2.   designating or defining any industry, workplace, employer or class of workplaces or employers for the purposes of this Act, a part of this Act, or the regulations or any provision thereof;

3.   exempting any workplace, industry, activity, business, work, trade, occupation, profession, constructor, employer or any class thereof from the application of a regulation or any provision thereof;

4.   limiting or restricting the application of a regulation or any provision thereof to any workplace, industry, activity, business, work, trade, occupation, profession, constructor, employer or any class thereof;

5.   exempting an employer from the requirements of clause 37 (1) (a) or (b) with respect to a hazardous material;

6.   respecting any matter or thing that is required or permitted to be regulated or prescribed under this Act;

7.   respecting any matter or thing, where a provision of this Act requires that the matter or thing be done, used or carried out or provided as prescribed;

8.   respecting any matter or thing, where it is a condition precedent that a regulation be made prescribing the matter or thing before this Act or a provision of this Act has any effect;

9. providing for and prescribing fees and the payment or refund of fees;

10. prescribing classes of workplaces for which and circumstances under which a committee shall consist of more than four persons and in each case prescribing the number of persons;

11. prescribing employers or workplaces or classes thereof for the purposes of clause 9 (1) (b);

12. exempting any workplace, industry, activity, business, work, trade, occupation, profession, constructor or employer or any class thereof from the application of subsection 9 (2);

13. respecting the conditions for eligibility, qualifications, selection and term of committee members, including certified members, and the operation of the committee;

Note: On a day to be named by proclamation of the Lieutenant Governor, subsection (2) is amended by adding the following paragraphs 13.1 and 13.2. See: 2011, c. 11, ss. 18 (1), 29 (2).

13.1 exempting any class of workplaces from the requirement set out in subsection 8 (5.1);

13.2 requiring that the training of health and safety representatives under subsection 8 (5.1) meet such requirements as may be prescribed;

14. exempting any class of workplaces from the requirement set out in subsection 9 (12);

15. prescribing elements that any policy required under this Act must contain;

16. regulating or prohibiting the installation or use of any machine, device or thing or any class thereof;

17. requiring that any equipment, machine, device, article or thing used bear the seal of approval of an organization designated by the regulations to test and approve the equipment, machine, device, article or thing and designating organizations for such purposes;

18. prescribing classes of employers who shall establish and maintain a medical surveillance program in which workers may volunteer to participate;

19. governing medical surveillance programs;

20. respecting the reporting by physicians and others of workers affected by any biological, chemical or physical agents or combination thereof;

21. regulating or prohibiting atmospheric conditions to which any worker may be exposed in a workplace;

22. prescribing methods, standards or procedures for determining the amount, concentration or level of any atmospheric condition or any biological, chemical or physical agent or combination thereof in a workplace;

23. prescribing any biological, chemical or physical agent or combination thereof as a designated substance;

24. prohibiting, regulating, restricting, limiting or controlling the handling of, exposure to, or the use and disposal of any designated substance;

25. adopting by reference, in whole or in part, with such changes as the Lieutenant Governor in Council

considers necessary, any code or standard and requiring compliance with any code or standard that is so adopted;

26. adopting by reference any criteria or guide in relation to the exposure of a worker to any biological, chemical or physical agent or combination thereof;

27. enabling a Director by notice in writing to designate that any part of a project shall be an individual project for the purposes of this Act and the regulations and prescribing to whom notice shall be given;

28. permitting the Minister to approve laboratories for the purpose of carrying out and performing sampling, analyses, tests and examinations, and requiring that sampling, analyses, examinations and tests be carried out and performed by a laboratory approved by the Minister;

29. requiring and providing for the registration of employers of workers;

30. providing for the establishment, equipment, operation and maintenance of mine rescue stations, as the Minister may direct, and providing for the payment of the cost thereof and the recovery of such cost from the mining industry;

31. prescribing training programs that employers shall provide;

31.1 requiring that training programs provided by employers meet such requirements as may be prescribed;

32. increasing the number of certified members required on a committee;

33. prescribing restrictions, prohibitions or conditions with respect to workers or workplaces relating to the risks of workplace violence;

34. prescribing forms and notices and providing for their use;

35. prescribing building standards for industrial establishments;

36. prescribing by name or description any biological or chemical agent as a hazardous material and any physical agent as a hazardous physical agent;

37. prohibiting an employer from altering a label on a hazardous material in prescribed circumstances;

38. prescribing the criteria to be used by the claims board to determine whether information is confidential business information in an application under subsection 40 (1);

39. requiring an employer to disclose to such persons as may be prescribed the source of toxicological data used by the employer to prepare a material safety data sheet;

Note: On a day to be named by proclamation of the Lieutenant Governor, paragraph 39 is amended by striking out "material safety" and substituting "safety". See: 2011, c. 1, Sched. 7, ss. 2 (12), 4 (2).

40. prescribing the format and contents of a material safety data sheet;

Note: On a day to be named by proclamation of the Lieutenant Governor, paragraph 40 is amended by striking out "material safety" and substituting "safety". See: 2011, c. 1, Sched. 7, ss. 2 (12), 4 (2).

41. prescribing by class of employer the intervals at which a health and safety representative or a committee member

designated under subsection 9 (23) shall inspect all or part of a workplace;

42. establishing criteria for determining, for the purpose of section 51, whether a person is critically injured;

43. prescribing first aid requirements to be met and first aid services to be provided by employers and constructors;

44. prescribing, for the purpose of clause 26 (1) (i), medical examinations and tests that a worker is required to undergo to ensure that the worker's health will not affect his or her ability to perform his or her job in a manner that might endanger others;

45. prescribing classes of workplace with respect to which section 45 does not apply;

46. prescribing the qualifications of persons whom a certified member may designate under subsection 45 (9);

47. prescribing, for the purpose of subsection 46 (6), criteria for determining whether a constructor or employer has demonstrated a failure to protect the health and safety of workers;

48. prescribing matters to be considered by the Board in deciding upon an application under section 46;

49. prescribing classes of workplace with respect to which section 47 does not apply;

50. requiring an employer to designate a person in a workplace to act as a workplace co-ordinator with respect to workplace violence and workplace

harassment, and prescribing the functions and duties of the co-ordinator;

51. in the case of a worker described in subsection 43 (2), specifying situations in which a circumstance described in clause 43 (3) (a), (b), (b.1) or (c) shall be considered, for the purposes of clause 43 (1) (a), to be inherent in the worker's work or a normal condition of employment;

52. varying or supplementing subsections 43 (4) to (13) with respect to the following workers, in circumstances when section 43 applies to them:

    i. workers to whom section 43 applies by reason of a regulation made for the purposes of subsection 3 (3), and

    ii. workers described in subsection 43 (2);

53. providing for such transitional matters as the Lieutenant Governor in Council considers necessary or advisable in connection with the implementation of section 22.5;

54. prescribing the functions of the Office of the Worker Adviser for the purposes of Part VI;

55. prescribing the functions of the Office of the Employer Adviser for the purposes of Part VI;

56. prescribing a number of employees for the purposes of subsection 50.1 (2). R.S.O. 1990, c. O.1, s. 70 (2); 1997, c. 16, s. 2 (16); 1998, c. 8, s. 59; 2001, c. 9, Sched. I, s. 3 (16); 2009, c. 23, s. 7; 2011, c. 11, s. 18 (2-4).

Regulations, taxi industry

71. (1) The Lieutenant Governor in Council may make regulations governing the application of the duties and rights set out in Part III.0.1 to the taxi industry. 2009, c. 23, s. 8.

Same

(2) Without limiting the generality of subsection (1), the Lieutenant Governor in Council may make regulations,

    (a) specifying that all or any of the duties set out in Part III.0.1 apply for the purposes of the regulations, with such modifications as may be necessary in the circumstances;

    (b) specifying who shall be considered an employer for the purposes of the regulations and requiring that person to carry out the specified duties;

    (c) specifying who shall be considered a worker for the purposes of the regulations;

    (d) specifying what shall be considered a workplace for the purposes of the regulations. 2009, c. 23, s. 8.

REGULATION MADE UNDER THE
OCCUPATIONAL HEALTH AND SAFETY ACT

Construction Projects

TABLE OF CONTENTS

PART I

GENERAL

PART II
GENERAL CONSTRUCTION

Explosive Actuated Fastening Tool

Welding and Cutting

Scaffolds and Work Platforms

Roofing

Hot Tar, Bitumen Roadtanker

Demolition and Damaged Structures

PART III
EXCAVATIONS

Interpretation

Application

PART IV
TUNNELS, SHAFTS, CAISSONS AND COFFERDAMS

PART V
WORK IN COMPRESSED AIR

Notes on Amendments to O. Reg. 213/91

O. Reg. 631/94 [effective November 15, 1994] amended the following:
s. 1 (1) [definitions of "full body harness" and "shaft"]; s. 84; s. 150 (1); s. 153; s. 158 (1); s. 181 (1); s. 235 (2); s. 237; s. 238 Table; s. 267; s. 281 (1); s. 286 (3); s. 359 (2) and (4).

O. Reg. 143/99 [Effective March 25, 1999] amended the following:
s. 183 (b).

O. Reg. 571/99 [Effective December 3, 1999] amended the following:
s. 359 (2).

O. Reg. 145/00 [Effective June 12, 2000] amended the following:
s. 1 (1) [definitions]; s. 1 (2) [Table]; s. 4; s. 5; s. 6 (2-7); s. 7; c. 8 (g); c. 9 (1) (g), (g.1); s. 9 (2); s. 12 (2); c. 13 (1) (c); s. 15-18; s. 26; s. 26.1-26.11; s. 29; s. 29.1-29.2; s. 52; s. 56; s. 57 (1); s. 57 (6-12); s. 59; s. 66; s. 67; s. 68; s. 69; s. 69.1; s. 85, 86; c. 93 (2) (c); s. 93 (3-4); s. 94; s. 96; s. 104; s. 105; s. 106 (1.1-1.5); s. 112 (1.1-1.2); s. 117; s. 119 (2), (4), (6), (7); s. 236 (8); s. 245 (1); c. 245 (2) (f); s. 265 (3); s. 265 (4); s. 280 (4); s. 316; s. 334 (2); s. 334 (3); c. 335 (1) (b); s. 338 (2); s. 365 (4); s. 397 (1); s. 397 (2).

O. Reg. 527/00 [Effective October 7, 2000] amended the following:
s. 29 (1) (2); s. 29.1 (0.1),(0.2); s. 29.1 (1); s. 29.1 (4); s. 29.1 (5); s. 29.1 (7); s. 29.2 (1); s. 135 (1)(c); s. 153 (2)(b)(v).

O. Reg. 85/04 [Effective April 17, 2004] amended the following:
s. 1 (1) [definitions]; s. 1.1, 1.2 [new]; s. 11 (1) 2.; s. 26 1.; s. 26.1 (2) 3.; s. 26.1 (3); s. 26.5; 26.6 (9) [new]; s. 26.7 (5) [new]; s. 26.8 (4); s. 26.10 & 26.11 revoked; s. 92 (1); s. 130 (2); s. 136.1 [new]; s. 139 (3); s. 142.1 [new]; s. 153 (5); s. 158 (2); s. 159 (4); s. 166 (6); s. 204 (5); s. 236 (3); s. 280 (4); s. 307 (7); s. 365 (4).

O. Reg. 627/05 [Effective January 1, 2006] amended the following: ss. 103 (4) [new]; s, 103.1 [new]; s. 183 / **[Effective April 1, 2006]** ss. 11 (1) 4.-11. [new]; ss. 181-195 [new]; ss. 195.1, 195.2 and 195.3 [new]; s. 274; s. 277 [revoked].

O. Reg. 628/05 [Effective September 30, 2006] amended the following: ss. 1 (1) [definition of "confined space" - revoked]; ss. 60 - 63 [revoked]; ss. 221.1 - 221.19 (Part II.1 Confined Spaces) [new]; ss. 247 (1) (b).

O. Reg. 443/09 [Effective January 1, 2010] amended the following: ss. 26.1 (3); ss. 26.3 (4) 3, 4; ss. 26.3 (6); ss. 26.3 (7); ss. 26.3 (7.1) [new]; ss. 26.3 (8); ss. 27 (1); ss. 27 (3) (a),(b); ss. 27 (6) [revoked]; s. 116; ss. 181 (1); s. 228; ss. 236 (8) [revoked]; ss. 280 (4) [revoked].

O. Reg. 96/11 [Effective July 1, 2011] amended the following: Part II.1 [revoked]; clause 247 (1) (b).

ALL of these amendments have been incorporated into the text that follows.

Occupational Health and Safety Act
Loi sur la santé et la sécurité au travail

ONTARIO REGULATION 213/91

CONSTRUCTION REGULATION

PART I: GENERAL

Interpretation and Application

Definitions

1.   (1)   In this Regulation,

"adequate", in relation to a procedure, material, device, object or thing, means,

  (a)   sufficient for both its intended and its actual use, and

  (b)   sufficient to protect a worker from occupational illness or occupational injury,

and "adequately" has a corresponding meaning;

"allowable unit stress", in relation to a material, means,

  (a)   the allowable unit stress assigned to a material by the standards required under the *Building Code*, or

  (b)   if no allowable unit stress is assigned under clause (a), the allowable unit stress for the material as determined by a professional engineer in accordance with good engineering practice;

"approved", in relation to a form, means approved by the Minister;

"blocker truck" means a truck that weighs at least 6,800 kilograms and has four-way flashers and a mounted flashing arrowboard sign;

"boom" means the projecting part of a backhoe, shovel, crane or similar lifting device from which a load is likely to be supported;

"Building Code" means Ontario Regulation 403/97 made under the Building Code Act, 1992;

"caisson" means,

(a) a casing below ground or water level whether or not it is designed to contain air at a pressure greater than atmospheric pressure,

(b) an excavation, including a waterwell but not a well within the meaning of the Petroleum Resources Act, drilled by an auger and into which a person may enter;

"cofferdam" means a structure constructed entirely or partially below water level or below the level of the groundwater table and intended to provide a work place that is free of water;

"competent worker", in relation to specific work, means a worker who,

(a) is qualified because of knowledge, training and experience to perform the work,

    (b)   is familiar with the Occupational Health and Safety Act and with the provisions of the regulations that apply to the work, and

    (c)   has knowledge of all potential or actual danger to health or safety in the work;

"conduit" means a sewer, a water main, a duct or cable for a telegraphic, telephonic, television or electrical service, a pipe or duct for the transportation of any solid, liquid or gas or any combination of these items and includes a service connection made or intended to be made thereto;

"crash truck" means a blocker truck that is equipped with a crash-attenuating device;

"excavation" means the hole that is left in the ground, as a result of removing material;

"excavation depth" means the vertical dimension from the highest point of the excavation wall to a point level with the lowest point of the excavation;

"excavation width" means the least horizontal dimension between the two opposite walls of the excavation;

"fall arrest system" means an assembly of components joined together so that when the assembly is connected to a fixed support, it is capable of arresting a worker's fall;

"fall restricting system" means a type of fall arrest system that has been designed to limit a worker's fall to a specified distance;

"falsework", in relation to a form or structure, means the structural supports and bracing used to support all or part of the form or structure;

"fixed support" means a permanent or temporary structure or a component of such a structure that can withstand all loads and forces the structure or component is intended to support or resist and is sufficient to protect a worker's health and safety, and includes equipment or devices that are securely fastened to the structure or component;

"flammable liquid" means a liquid with a flash point below 37.8 degrees celsius and a vapour pressure not exceeding 275 kilopascals absolute at 37.8 degrees celsius;

"form" means the mould into which concrete or another material is to be placed;

"formwork" means a system of forms connected together;

"freeway" means a controlled-access highway that has a continuous dividing median and a normal posted speed limit of 90 kilometres per hour or more;

"full body harness" means a device that can arrest an accidental vertical or near vertical fall of a worker and which can guide and distribute the impact forces of the fall by means of leg and shoulder strap supports and an upper dorsal suspension assembly which, after the arrest, will not by itself permit the release or further lowering of the worker;

"guardrail system" means an assembly of components joined together to provide a barrier to prevent a worker from falling from the edge of a surface;

"highway" means a common and public highway, street, avenue, parkway, driveway, square, place, bridge, viaduct or trestle, any part of which is intended for or used by the general public for the passage of vehicles;

"longitudinal buffer area" means the area of a project between the end of a lane closure taper and the start of a work area;

"magazine" means a place in which explosives are stored or kept, whether above or below ground;

"multi-point suspended scaffold" means a suspended scaffold or suspended work platform or a system of suspended scaffolds or suspended work platforms, each scaffold or platform being more than 750 millimetres in width, that is supported from an overhead support system by at least three primary load-carrying means of suspension to maintain the system's stability;

"professional engineer" means a person who is a professional engineer within the meaning of the Professional Engineers Act;

"public way" means a highway or other street, avenue, parkway, driveway, square, place, bridge, viaduct, or other open space to which the public has access, as of right or by expressed or implied invitation;

"roadway" means the travelled portion of a highway;

"safety belt" means a belt worn around the waist of a worker and all the fittings for the belt appropriate for the use being made of it;

"safety factor" means the ratio of the failure load to the specified load or rated load;

"safety net" means a safety net that complies with section 26.8, and is located and supported in such a way that it arrests the fall of a worker who may fall into it without endangering the worker;

"service shaft" means a shaft by which people or materials are passed into or out of a tunnel under construction;

"shaft" means an excavation with a longitudinal axis at an angle greater than 45 degrees from the horizontal that is used to pass people or materials into or out of a tunnel or that leads to a tunnel or that is used as an access to a boring or augering operation;

"sheathing" means the members of shoring that are placed up against the walls of an excavation to directly resist the pressure exerted from the walls of the excavation;

"sign truck" means a vehicle that has,

    (a)   four-way flashers and a mounted flashing arrowboard sign, or

    (b)   a portable trailer with a mounted flashing arrowboard sign;

"strut" means a transverse member of shoring that directly resists pressure from a wale;

"suitable", in relation to a procedure, material, device, object or thing, means sufficient to protect a worker from damage to the worker's body or health;

"tower crane" means a travelling, fixed or climbing mechanical device or structure that has,

    (a)   a boom, a jib or both,

    (b)   a power-driven drum and wire rope to raise, lower or move material, and

    (c)   a vertical mast;

"travel restraint system" means an assembly of components capable of restricting a worker's movement on a work surface and preventing the worker from reaching a location from which he or she could fall;

"traverse", when used in relation to a multi-point suspended scaffold, means to move the scaffold horizontally, in a controlled manner, along the building or structure to which it is attached;

"trench" means an excavation where the excavation depth exceeds the excavation width;

"tunnel" means a subterranean passage into which a person may enter that is made by excavating beneath the overburden;

"underground", in relation to work, means inside a shaft, tunnel or caisson;

"vehicle" means a vehicle propelled by mechanical power and includes a trailer, a traction engine and a road-building machine;

"wale" means a longitudinal member of the shoring that is placed against the sheathing to directly resist the pressure from the sheathing;

"work belt" means a belt that has a back support pad and a connecting hook at the front and that is capable of supporting a worker. O. Reg. 213/91, s. 1 (1); O. Reg. 631/94, s. 1; O. Reg. 145/00, s. 1 (1-13); O. Reg. 85/04, s. 1; O. Reg. 628/05, s. 1.

Table of Short Forms

(2)   In this Regulation, a short form listed in Column 1 of the Table to this subsection has the same meaning as the term set out opposite to it in Column 2.

TABLE

Column 1 Short forms	Column 2 Corresponding terms
ANSI	American National Standards Institute
CSA	Canadian Standards Association
CAN	National Standards of Canada
DIN	Deutsche Industrie Norm
Ga	Gauge

O. Reg. 213/91, s. 1 (2); O. Reg. 145/00, s. 1 (4).

1.1   In this Regulation, a requirement that something be done in accordance with good engineering practice includes a requirement that it be done in a manner that protects the health and safety of all workers. O. Reg. 85/04, s. 2.

1.2   In this Regulation, a requirement that a design, drawing, instruction, report, specification, opinion or other document be prepared by a professional engineer includes a requirement that he or she sign and seal it. O. Reg. 85/04, s. 2.

Application

2. This Part applies with respect to all projects. O. Reg. 213/91, s. 2.

Alternative Methods and Materials

3. An employer, owner or constructor may vary a procedure required by this Regulation or the composition, design, size or arrangement of a material, object, device or thing as required by this Regulation,

    (a) if the procedure, composition, design, size or arrangement as varied affords protection for the health and safety of workers that is at least equal to the protection that would otherwise be given; and

    (b) if the employer, owner or constructor gives written notice of the varied procedure, composition, design, size or arrangement to the joint health and safety committee or the health and safety representative, if any, for the work place. O. Reg. 213/91, s. 3.

Designation of a Project

4. A Director may designate in writing a part of a project as a project and the designated project is considered to be a project for the purposes of the Act and this Regulation. O. Reg. 213/91, s. 4; O. Reg. 145/00, s. 2.

Registration and Notices

Registration

5. (1) Before beginning work at a project, each constructor and employer engaged in construction shall complete an approved registration form. O. Reg. 145/00, s. 3.

(2)   The constructor shall ensure that,

    (a)   each employer at the project provides to the constructor a completed approved registration form; and

    (b)   a copy of the employer's completed form is kept at the project while the employer is working there. O. Reg. 145/00, s. 3.

Notification

6.   (1)   This section applies with respect to a project if,

    (a)   the total cost of labour and materials for the project is expected to exceed $50,000;

    (b)   the work is the erection or structural alteration of a building more than two storeys or more than 7.5 metres high;

    (c)   the work is the demolition of a building at least four metres high with a floor area of at least thirty square metres;

    (d)   the work is the erection, structural alteration or structural repair of a bridge, an earth-retaining structure or a water-retaining structure more than three metres high or of a silo, chimney or a similar structure more than 7.5 metres high;

    (e)   work in compressed air is to be done at the project;

    (f)   a tunnel, caisson, cofferdam or well into which a person may enter is to be constructed at the project;

    (g)   a trench into which a person may enter is to be excavated at the project and the trench is more than 300 metres long or more than 1.2 metres deep and over thirty metres long; or

(h)   a part of the permanent or temporary work is required by this Regulation to be designed by a professional engineer. O. Reg. 213/91, s. 6 (1).

Same

(2)   The constructor shall comply with subsection (3) or (4) before beginning work at the project. O. Reg. 145/00, s. 4.

(3)   The constructor shall complete an approved notification form and file it at the Ministry office located nearest to the project. O. Reg. 145/00, s. 4.

(4)   If the constructor believes that the work at the project will not take more than 14 days, the constructor may provide the relevant information to an inspector at the Ministry office located nearest to the project,

(a)   by faxing the completed form to the inspector; or

(b)   by providing the information that would be required to complete the form to the inspector by telephone. O. Reg. 145/00, s. 4.

(5)   Despite subsection (2), the constructor may begin work at a project before complying with subsection (3) or (4) if the following conditions are met:

1.   It is necessary to do the work immediately to prevent injury to people or damage to property.

2.   Before beginning the work, the constructor gives an inspector notice of the information required in the form by telephone or fax. O. Reg. 145/00, s. 4.

(6)   The constructor shall keep the completed notification form posted in a conspicuous place at the project or available at the project for review by an inspector. O. Reg. 145/00, s. 4.

(7)   **Revoked:** O. Reg. 145/00, s. 4.

Trench Work

7.   If section 6 does not apply to a project but the project includes work on a trench more than 1.2 metres deep into which a worker may enter, the constructor shall, before any work at the project is begun, give notice in person, by telephone or by fax to the Ministry office located nearest to the project. O. Reg. 145/00, s. 5.

Accident Notices and Reports under Sections 51-53 of the Act

8.   A written report under subsection 51 (1) of the Act respecting an occurrence in which a person is killed or critically injured shall set out,

(a)   the name and address of the constructor and the employer, if the person involved is a worker;

(b)   the nature and the circumstances of the occurrence and the bodily injury sustained by the person;

(c)   a description of the machinery or equipment involved;

(d)   the time and place of the occurrence;

(e)   the name and address of the person involved;

(f)   the names and addresses of all witnesses to the occurrence;

(g)   the name and address of the any legally qualified medical practitioner by whom the person was or is being attended for the injury; and

(h)   the steps taken to prevent a recurrence. O. Reg. 213/91, s. 8; O. Reg. 145/00, s. 6.

9. (1) A notice under subsection 52 (1) of the Act respecting an occurrence involving a worker shall set out,

   (a)   the name, address and type of business of the employer;

   (b)   the nature and the circumstances of the occurrence and the bodily injury or illness sustained by the worker;

   (c)   a description of the machinery or equipment involved;

   (d)   the time and place of the occurrence;

   (e)   the name and address of the worker involved;

   (f)   the names and addresses of all witnesses to the occurrence;

   (g)   the name and address of any legally qualified medical practitioner by whom the worker was or is being attended for the injury or illness;

   (g.1) the name and address of each medical facility, if any, where the worker was or is being attended for the injury or illness; and

   (h)   the steps taken to prevent a recurrence. O. Reg. 213/91, s. 9 (1); O. Reg. 145/00, s. 7 (1).

(2) A notice under subsection 52 (2) of the Act (information and particulars respecting a worker's occupational illness) shall contain the following information:

   1.   The employer's name, address and type of business.

2. The nature of the illness.

3. The worker's name and address.

4. The name and address of any legally qualified medical practitioner by whom the worker was or is being attended for the illness.

5. The name and address of each medical facility, if any, where the worker was or is being attended for the illness.

6. A description of the steps taken to prevent a recurrence. O. Reg. 145/00, s. 7 (2).

10. (1) An employer shall keep in the employer's permanent records a record of any accident, explosion or fire involving a worker that causes injury requiring medical attention but does not disable the worker from performing his or her usual work. O. Reg. 213/91, s. 10 (1).

(2) The record shall include particulars of,

(a) the nature and circumstances of the occurrence and the injury sustained by the worker;

(b) the time and place of the occurrence;

(c) the name and address of the injured worker; and

(d) the steps taken to prevent a recurrence. O. Reg. 213/91, s. 10 (2).

(3) An employer to whom subsection (1) applies shall make the record available to an inspector upon request. O. Reg. 213/91, s. 10 (3).

11 (1)   The following incidents are prescribed for the purpose of section 53 of the Act:

1.   A worker falling a vertical distance of three metres or more.

2.   A worker falling and having the fall arrested by a fall arrest system other than a fall restricting system.

3.   A worker becoming unconscious for any reason.

4.   Accidental contact by a worker or by a worker's tool or equipment with energized electrical equipment, installations or conductors.

5.   Accidental contact by a crane, similar hoisting device, backhoe, power shovel or other vehicle or equipment or its load with an energized electrical conductor rated at more than 750 volts.

6.   Structural failure of all or part of falsework designed by, or required by this Regulation to be designed by, a professional engineer.

7.   Structural failure of a principal supporting member, including a column, beam, wall or truss, of a structure.

8.   Failure of all or part of the structural supports of a scaffold.

9. Structural failure of all or part of an earth- or water-retaining structure, including a failure of the temporary or permanent supports for a shaft, tunnel, caisson, cofferdam or trench.

10. Failure of a wall of an excavation or of similar earthwork with respect to which a professional engineer has given a written opinion that the stability of the wall is such that no worker will be endangered by it.

11. Overturning or the structural failure of all or part of a crane or similar hoisting device. O. Reg. 213/91, s. 11 (1); O. Reg. 85/04, s. 3; O. Reg. 627/05, s. 1.

(2) A notice under section 53 of the Act shall set out the circumstances of the occurrence and the steps taken to prevent a recurrence. O. Reg. 213/91, s. 11 (2).

12. (1) This section applies with respect to an occurrence for which a report under subsection 51 (1) of the Act or a notice under section 52 or 53 of the Act is given, if the occurrence involves a failure of all or part of,

(a) temporary or permanent works;

(b) a structure;

(c) an excavation wall or similar earthwork for which a professional engineer has given a written opinion that the stability of the wall is such that no worker will be endangered by it; or

(d) a crane or similar hoisting device. O. Reg. 213/91, s. 12 (1).

(2)   A constructor or employer who submits a report under subsection 51 (1) of the Act (notice of death or injury) or gives a notice under section 52 or 53 of the Act (notice of accident, etc.) shall also provide, within 14 days after the occurrence, a professional engineer's written opinion stating the cause of the occurrence. O. Reg. 145/00, s. 8.

General Requirements

Notice

13   (1)   A constructor shall post in a conspicuous place at a project and keep posted while work is done at the project a notice setting out,

  (a)   the constructor's name and if the constructor carries on business in a different name, the business name;

  (b)   the address and telephone number of the constructor's head office or principal place of business in Ontario; and

  (c)   the address and telephone number of the nearest office of the Ministry. O. Reg. 213/91, s. 13 (1); O. Reg. 145/00, s. 9.

(2)   Within forty-eight hours after a health and safety representative or joint health and safety committee members are selected for a project, a constructor shall add to the notice the name, trade and employer of the health and safety representative or of each of the committee members. O. Reg. 213/91, s. 13 (2).

Constructor appointment of supervisor

14.   (1)   A constructor shall appoint a supervisor for every project at which five or more workers will work at the same time. O. Reg. 213/91, s. 14 (1).

(2) The supervisor shall supervise the work at all times either personally or by having an assistant, who is a competent person, do so personally. O. Reg. 213/91, s. 14 (2).

(3) A supervisor or a competent person appointed by the supervisor shall inspect all machinery and equipment, including fire extinguishing equipment, magazines, electrical installations, communication systems, sanitation and medical facilities, buildings and other structures, temporary supports and means of access and egress at the project to ensure that they do not endanger any worker. O. Reg. 213/91, s. 14 (3).

(4) An inspection shall be made at least once a week or more frequently as the supervisor determines is necessary in order to ensure that the machinery and equipment referred to in subsection (3) do not endanger any worker. O. Reg. 213/91, s. 14 (4).

(5) A competent person shall perform tests and observations necessary for the detection of hazardous conditions on a project. O. Reg. 213/91, s. 14 (5).

Employer appointment of supervisor
15. (1) An employer of five or more workers on a project shall appoint a supervisor for the workers. O. Reg. 213/91, s. 15.

(2) The supervisor shall supervise the work at all times either personally or by having an assistant, who is a competent person, do so personally. O. Reg. 145/00, s. 10.

Minimum age
16. At a project, no person younger than 16 years of age shall,

(a) be employed in or about the workplace; or

(b) be permitted to be present in or about the workplace while work is being performed. O. Reg. 145/00, s. 11.

Emergency procedures

17. (1) A constructor shall establish for a project written procedures to be followed in the event of an emergency and shall ensure that the procedures are followed at the project. O. Reg. 145/00, s. 11.

(2) The constructor shall review the emergency procedures with the joint health and safety committee or the health and safety representative for the project, if any. O. Reg. 145/00, s. 11.

(3) The constructor shall ensure that the emergency procedures are posted in a conspicuous place at the project. O. Reg. 145/00, s. 11.

Communication

18. The constructor shall ensure that every worker at the project has ready access to a telephone, two-way radio or other system of two-way communication in the event of an emergency. O. Reg. 145/00, s. 11.

Record Keeping

19. If, under this Regulation, a record is required to be kept available for inspection at a project, the constructor or employer, as the case may be, shall keep the record for at least one year after the project is finished. O. Reg. 213/91, s. 19.

PART II
GENERAL CONSTRUCTION

Application

20. This Part applies with respect to all projects. O. Reg. 213/91, s. 20.

Protective Clothing, Equipment and Devices

21. (1)   A worker shall wear such protective clothing and use such personal protective equipment or devices as are necessary to protect the worker against the hazards to which the worker may be exposed. O. Reg. 213/91, s. 21 (1).

(2)   A worker's employer shall require the worker to comply with subsection (1). O. Reg. 213/91, s. 21 (2).

Instruction, training

(3)   A worker required to wear protective clothing or use personal protective equipment or devices shall be adequately instructed and trained in the care and use of the clothing, equipment or device before wearing or using it. O. Reg. 213/91, s. 21 (3).

Headwear

22. (1)   Every worker shall wear protective headwear at all times when on a project. O. Reg. 213/91, s. 22 (1).

(2)   Protective headwear shall be a safety hat that,

(a)   consists of a shell and suspension that is adequate to protect a person's head against impact and against flying or falling small objects; and

(b)   has a shell which can withstand a dielectric strength test at 20,000 volts phase to ground. O. Reg. 213/91, s. 22 (2).

Footwear

23. (1)   Every worker shall wear protective footwear at all times when on a project. O. Reg. 213/91, s. 23 (1).

   (2)   Protective footwear shall be a safety shoe or safety boot,

        (a)   with a box toe that is adequate to protect the wearer's toes against injury due to impact and is capable of resisting at least 125 joules impact; and

        (b)   with a sole or insole that is adequate to protect the wearer's feet against injury due to puncture and is capable of resisting a penetration load of 1.2 kilonewtons when tested with a DIN standard pin. O. Reg. 213/91, s. 23 (2).

Eye protection

24. A worker shall use protection appropriate in the circumstances when there is a risk of eye injury to the worker. O. Reg. 213/91, s. 24.

Skin protection

25. A worker shall use protection appropriate in the circumstances when there is a risk of injury on a project from contact between the worker's skin and,

   (a)   a noxious gas, liquid, fume or dust;

   (b)   an object that may puncture, cut or abrade the skin;

   (c)   a hot object, hot liquid or molten metal; or

   (d)   radiant heat. O. Reg. 213/91, s. 25.

Fall protection: application

26. Sections 26.1 to 26.9 apply where a worker is exposed to any of the following hazards:

   1.   Falling more than 3 metres.

2. Falling more than 1.2 metres, if the work area is used as a path for a wheelbarrow or similar equipment.

3. Falling into operating machinery.

4. Falling into water or another liquid.

5. Falling into or onto a hazardous substance or object.

6. Falling through an opening on a work surface. O. Reg. 145/00, s. 12; O. Reg. 85/04, s. 4.

Fall protection: mandatory

26.1 (1) A worker shall be adequately protected by a guardrail system that meets the requirements of subsections 26.3 (2) to (8). O. Reg. 145/00, s. 12.

Same

(2) Despite subsection (1), if it is not reasonably possible to install a guardrail system as that subsection requires, a worker shall be adequately protected by at least one of the following methods of fall protection:

1. A travel restraint system that meets the requirements of section 26.4.

2. A fall restricting system that meets the requirements of section 26.5.

3. A fall arrest system, other than a fall restricting system designed for use in wood pole climbing, that meets the requirements of section 26.6.

4. A safety net that meets the requirements of section 26.8. O. Reg. 145/00, s. 12; O. Reg. 85/04, s. 5 (1).

System components

(3)   The components of any system listed in subsection (2) shall be designed by a professional engineer in accordance with good engineering practice, and shall meet the requirements of any of the following National Standards of Canada standards that are applicable:

1.   CAN/CSA-Z259.1-05: Body Belts and Saddles for Work Positioning and Travel Restraint.

2.   CAN/CSA-Z259.2.1-98 (R2008): Fall Arresters, Vertical Lifelines and Rails.

3.   CAN/CSA-Z259.2.2-98 (R2004): Self-Retracting Devices for Personal Fall-Arrest Systems.

4.   CAN/CSA-Z259.2.3-99 (R2004): Descent Control Devices.

5.   CAN/CSA-Z259.10-06: Full Body Harnesses.

6.   CAN/CSA-Z259.11-05: Energy Absorbers and Lanyards.

7.   CAN/CSA-Z259.12-01 (R2006): Connecting Components for Personal Fall Arrest Systems (PFAS).

8.   CAN/CSA-Z259.14-01 (R2007): Fall Restrict Equipment for Wood Pole Climbing. O. Reg. 85/04, s. 5 (2); O. Reg. 443/09, s. 1.

Rescue procedures

(4)   Before any use of a fall arrest system or a safety net by a worker at a project, the worker's employer shall develop written procedures for rescuing the worker after his or her fall has been arrested. O. Reg. 145/00, s. 12.

Worker training

26.2 (1) An employer shall ensure that a worker who may use a fall protection system is adequately trained in its use and given adequate oral and written instructions by a competent person. O. Reg. 145/00, s. 13.

Written record required

(2) The employer shall ensure that the person who provides the training and instruction referred to in subsection (1) prepares a written training and instruction record for each worker and signs the record. O. Reg. 145/00, s. 13.

(3) The training and instruction record shall include the worker's name and the dates on which training and instruction took place. O. Reg. 145/00, s. 13.

Record accessible

(4) The employer shall make the training and instruction record for each worker available to an inspector on request. O. Reg. 145/00, s. 13.

Guardrail systems

26.3 (1) Despite paragraph 1 of section 26, a guardrail system that meets the requirements of this section shall be used if a worker has access to the perimeter or an open side of any of the following work surfaces and is exposed to a fall of 2.4 metres or more:

1. A floor, including the floor of a mezzanine or balcony.

2. The surface of a bridge.

3. A roof while formwork is in place.

4. A scaffold platform or other work platform, runway or ramp. O. Reg. 145/00, s. 14.

Guardrail or protective clothing

(2)   One of the following precautions shall be used to prevent a worker from falling through an opening on a work surface:

1.   A guardrail system that meets the requirements of this section.

2.   A protective covering that,

   i.   completely covers the opening,

   ii.   is securely fastened,

   iii.   is adequately identified as covering an opening,

   iv.   is made from material adequate to support all loads to which the covering may be subjected, and

   v.   is capable of supporting a live load of at least 2.4 kilonewtons per square metre without exceeding the allowable unit stresses for the material used. O. Reg. 145/00, s. 14.

Where temporary removal allowed

(3)   The guardrail system or protective covering required under subsection (1) or (2) may be removed temporarily to perform work in or around the opening if a worker is adequately protected and signs are posted in accordance with subsections 44 (1) and (2). O. Reg. 145/00, s. 14.

Guardrail specifications

(4)   The following are the specifications for a guardrail system:

1.   It shall have a top rail, an intermediate rail and a toe board.

2. The intermediate rail may be replaced by material that can withstand a point load of 450 newtons applied in a lateral or vertical downward direction.

3. Subject to subsection 116 (8), the top of the guardrail system shall be located at least 0.9 metres but not more than 1.1 metres above the surface on which the system is installed.

4. The intermediate rail shall be located midway between the top rail and the toe board.

4.1 The toe board shall extend from the surface to which the guardrail system is attached to a height of at least 89 millimetres.

5. If the guardrail system is located at the perimeter of a work surface, the distance between the edge of the surface and the guardrail system shall not be greater than 300 millimetres. O. Reg. 145/00, s. 14; O. Reg. 443/09, s. 2 (1).

Loads

(5) A guardrail system shall be capable of resisting anywhere along the length of the system the following loads when applied separately, without exceeding the allowable unit stress for each material used:

1. A point load of 675 newtons applied in a lateral direction to the top rail.

2. A point load of 450 newtons applied in a vertical downward direction to the top rail.

3. A point load of 450 newtons applied in a lateral or vertical downward direction to the intermediate rail, or midway between the top rail and the toe board.

4. A point load of 225 newtons applied in a lateral direction to the toe board. O. Reg. 145/00, s. 14.

Same

(6) The distance between any two adjacent posts of the guardrail system may be greater than 2.4 metres only if the system is capable of resisting the loads specified in subsection (5) increased in proportion to the greater distance between the posts. O. Reg. 443/09, s. 2 (2).

Wooden guardrails

(7) The following additional requirements apply to a guardrail system that is made of wood:

1. The wood shall be spruce, pine or fir (S-P-F) timber of construction grade quality or better and shall not have any visible defect affecting its load-carrying capacity.

2. The wood shall be free of sharp objects such as splinters and protruding nails.

3. The system shall have posts that are at least 38 millimetres by 89 millimetres, are securely fastened to the surface and are spaced at intervals of not more than 2.4 metres.

4. The top rail and the intermediate rail shall each be at least 38 millimetres by 89 millimetres. O. Reg. 145/00, s. 14; O. Reg. 443/09, s. 2 (3).

Wooden guardrails

(7.1) If a guardrail system that is made of wood is constructed and installed so that it is capable of resisting all loads that it may be subjected to by a worker, the following do not apply:

1. The requirement in paragraph 2 of subsection (4) that the replacement material can withstand a point load of 450 newtons.

2. Subsections (5) and (6). O. Reg. 443/09, s. 2 (4).

Wire rope guardrails

(8) The following additional requirements apply to a guardrail system that is made of wire rope:

1. The top rail and intermediate rail shall be made of wire rope that is at least 10 millimetres in diameter, and the rope shall be kept taut by a turnbuckle or other device.

2. The outward deflection of the top rail and intermediate rail resulting from the loads specified in subsection (5) shall not extend beyond the edge of a work surface.

3. The system shall have vertical separators at intervals of not more than 2.4 metres and horizontal supports at intervals of not more than 9 metres.

4. **Revoked:** O. Reg. 443/09, s. 2 (6).
   O. Reg. 145/00, s. 14; O. Reg. 443/09, s. 2 (5, 6).

Travel restraint systems

26.4 (1) A travel restraint system shall consist of a full body harness with adequate attachment points or a safety belt. O. Reg. 145/00, s. 14.

(2)   The full body harness or safety belt shall be attached by a lifeline or lanyard to a fixed support that meets the requirements of section 26.7. O. Reg. 145/00, s. 14.

Inspection required

(3)   The travel restraint system shall be inspected by a competent worker before each use. O. Reg. 145/00, s. 14.

Defective components

(4)   If a component of the travel restraint system is found to be defective on inspection, the defective component shall immediately be taken out of service. O. Reg. 145/00, s. 14.

Fall restricting systems

26.5 (1)   A fall restricting system that is not designed for use in wood pole climbing shall consist of an assembly of components that is,

(a)   attached to an independent fixed support that meets the requirements of section 26.7; and

(b)   designed and arranged in accordance with the manufacturer's instructions and so that a worker's free fall distance does not exceed 0.6 metres. O. Reg. 85/04, s. 6.

(2)   A fall restricting system that is designed for use in wood pole climbing,

(a)   shall consist of an assembly of components that is designed and arranged in accordance with the manufacturer's instructions; and

(b)   shall not allow pole slippage in excess of the distances set out in the applicable National Standards of Canada standard referred to in subsection 26.1 (3). O. Reg. 85/04, s. 6.

Inspection required

(3)   A fall restricting system shall be inspected by a competent worker before each use. O. Reg. 85/04, s. 6.

(4)   If a component of the fall restricting system is found to be defective on inspection, the component shall be taken out of service immediately. O. Reg. 85/04, s. 6.

Defective systems

(5)   If a worker who is using the fall restricting system falls or slips more than the distance determined under clause (1) (b) or (2) (b), as the case may be, the system shall be taken out of service immediately and shall not be used again by a worker unless all components of the system have been certified by the manufacturer as being safe for reuse. O. Reg. 85/04, s. 6.

Fall arrest systems

26.6 (1)   A fall arrest system shall consist of a full body harness with adequate attachment points and a lanyard equipped with a shock absorber or similar device. O. Reg. 145/00, s. 14.

Arrangement

(2)   The fall arrest system shall be attached by a lifeline or by the lanyard to an independent fixed support that meets the requirements of section 26.7. O. Reg. 145/00, s. 14.

(3)   The fall arrest system shall be arranged so that a worker cannot hit the ground or an object or level below the work. O. Reg. 145/00, s. 14.

Exception

(4)   Despite subsection (1), the fall arrest system shall not include a shock absorber if wearing or using one could cause a worker to hit the ground or an object or level below the work. O. Reg. 145/00, s. 14.

Peak fall arrest force

(5) The fall arrest system shall not subject a worker who falls to a peak fall arrest force greater than 8 kilonewtons. O. Reg. 145/00, s. 14.

Inspection required

(6) The fall arrest system shall be inspected by a competent worker before each use. O. Reg. 145/00, s. 14.

Defective components

(7) If a component of the fall arrest system is found to be defective on inspection, the defective component shall immediately be taken out of service. O. Reg. 145/00, s. 14.

Same

(8) If a worker who is using the fall arrest system falls, the system shall be immediately removed from service and shall not be used again by a worker unless all components of the system have been certified by the manufacturer as being safe for re-use. O. Reg. 145/00, s. 14.

(9) Subsections (1) to (8) do not apply to fall restricting systems designed for use in wood pole climbing. O. Reg. 85/04, s. 7.

Fixed supports

26.7 (1) A permanent anchor system shall be used as the fixed support in a fall arrest system, fall restricting system or travel restraint system if the following conditions are met:

1. The anchor system has been installed according to the Building Code.

2. It is safe and practical to use the anchor system as the fixed support. O. Reg. 145/00, s. 14.

Temporary fixed supports

(2)   If the conditions set out in subsection (1) are not met, a temporary fixed support shall be used that meets the following requirements:

1.   Subject to paragraph 2, a support used in a fall arrest system shall be capable of supporting a static force of at least 8 kilonewtons without exceeding the allowable unit stress for each material used.

2.   If a shock absorber is also used in the fall arrest system, the support shall be capable of supporting a static force of at least 6 kilonewtons without exceeding the allowable unit stress for each material used.

3.   Subject to paragraph 4, a support used in a fall restricting system must be capable of supporting a static force of at least 6 kilonewtons without exceeding the allowable unit stress for each material used.

4.   Paragraph 3 does not apply to a support that is used in accordance with the manufacturer's written instructions and is adequate to protect a worker.

5.   A support used in a travel restraint system shall be capable of supporting a static force of at least 2 kilonewtons without exceeding the allowable unit stress for each material used. O. Reg. 145/00, s. 14.

Dynamic testing

(3)   Despite the requirements listed in subsection (2), the support capacity of a temporary fixed support used in a fall protection system may be determined by dynamic testing in accordance with good engineering practice to ensure that the temporary fixed support has adequate capacity to arrest a worker's fall. O. Reg. 145/00, s. 14.

Sharp edges prohibited

(4)   A fixed support shall not have any sharp edges that could cut, chafe or abrade the connection between it and another component of the system. O. Reg. 145/00, s. 14.

(5)   Subsections (1) to (4) do not apply to fall restricting systems designed for use in wood pole climbing. O. Reg. 85/04, s. 8.

Safety nets

26.8 (1)   A safety net shall be designed, tested and installed in accordance with ANSI Standard 10.11-1989, Personnel and Debris Nets for Construction and Demolition Operations. O. Reg. 145/00, s. 14.

Installation

(2)   The safety net shall be installed by a competent worker. O. Reg. 145/00, s. 14.

Inspection and testing required

(3)   A professional engineer or a competent person under the engineer's supervision shall inspect and test the installation of the safety net before it is put in service. O. Reg. 145/00, s. 14.

Documentation

(4)   The engineer shall document the inspection and testing of the safety net. O. Reg. 145/00, s. 14; O. Reg. 85/04, s. 9.

(5)   A copy of the document shall be kept at the project while the safety net is in service. O. Reg. 145/00, s. 14.

Lanyards and lifelines

26.9 (1)   This section applies to a lanyard or lifeline that is part of a travel restraint system or a fall arrest system. O. Reg. 145/00, s. 14.

Requirements

(2) The following requirements apply to a lanyard or a lifeline:

1. It shall not be used in such a way that it is likely to be cut, chafed or abraded.

2. It shall not be subjected to extreme temperature, flame, abrasive or corrosive materials or other hazards that may damage it.

3. The free end of the lanyard or lifeline shall be kept clear of equipment and machinery. O. Reg. 145/00, s. 14.

(3) Only one person at a time may use a lanyard. O. Reg. 145/00, s. 14.

(4) The connecting ends of a lanyard shall be wrapped around a protective thimble and securely fastened with a swaged fitting or eye splice supplied by the manufacturer of the lanyard. O. Reg. 145/00, s. 14.

(5) A horizontal or vertical lifeline shall be kept free from splices or knots, except knots used to connect it to a fixed support. O. Reg. 145/00, s. 14.

Vertical lifelines

(6) Only one person at a time may use a vertical lifeline. O. Reg. 145/00, s. 14.

(7) A vertical lifeline shall,

(a) extend to the ground; or

(b) have a positive stop that prevents the rope grab or other similar device from running off the end of the lifeline. O. Reg. 145/00, s. 14.

Horizontal lifeline system

(8)   The following requirements apply to a horizontal lifeline system:

1.   It shall be designed by a professional engineer in accordance with good engineering practice.

2.   The design may be a standard design or a custom design.

3.   The design shall,

    i.   show the arrangement of the system including the anchorage or fixed support system,

    ii.   indicate the components used,

    iii.   state the number of workers that can safely be attached to it,

    iv.   set out instructions for installation or erection, and

    v.   show the design loads for the system.

4.   The system shall be installed or erected, and maintained, in accordance with the professional engineer's design.

5.   Before each use, the system shall be inspected by a professional engineer or a competent worker designated by a supervisor.

6.   The constructor shall keep the design at the project while the system is in use. O. Reg. 145/00, s. 14.

26.10, 26.11 Revoked: O. Reg. 85/04, s. 10.

Drowning protection

27. (1) Despite subsections 26.1 (1) and (2), if the following conditions are met, a worker shall wear a lifejacket or other personal flotation device that is adequate:

1. The worker is exposed to a risk of drowning on a project.

2. It is not reasonably possible to install a guardrail system as subsection 26.1 (1) requires.

3. It is not reasonably possible to protect the worker adequately by means of a fall protection method as subsection 26.1 (2) requires. O. Reg. 443/09, s. 3 (1).

(2) If a worker may drown at a project,

(a) at least two workers trained to perform rescue operations shall be available to perform rescue operations;

(b) rescue equipment shall be provided in a suitable location on or near the project; and

(c) all workers on the project shall be advised of the rescue procedures to be followed and their role, if any, in carrying out a rescue. O. Reg. 213/91, s. 27 (2).

(3) The rescue equipment shall include,

(a) a seaworthy boat equipped with a lifebuoy attached to a buoyant heaving line not less than 15 metres in length and a boat hook; and

(b) **Revoked:** O. Reg. 443/09, s. 3 (2).

(c) an alarm system capable of warning a worker of the necessity of carrying out a rescue operation. O. Reg. 213/91, s. 27 (3); O. Reg. 443/09, s. 3 (2).

(4)   The boat shall be power-driven if the water is likely to be rough or swift. O. Reg. 213/91, s. 27 (4).

(5)   The alarm system shall be activated when a rescue operation is necessary. O. Reg. 213/91, s. 27 (5).

(6)   **Revoked:** O. Reg. 443/09, s. 3 (3).

Hygiene

Drinking water

28. (1)   A reasonable supply of potable drinking water shall be kept readily accessible at a project for the use of workers. O. Reg. 213/91, s. 28 (1).

(2)   Drinking water shall be supplied from a piping system or from a clean, covered container with a drain faucet. O. Reg. 213/91, s. 28 (2).

(3)   Workers shall be given a sanitary means of drinking the drinking water. O. Reg. 213/91, s. 28 (3).

(4)   Workers shall not be required to share a common drinking cup to drink water. O. Reg. 213/91, s. 28 (4).

Toilet, urinal and clean-up facilities

29. (1)   In this section,

"facilities" means toilet, urinal and clean-up facilities;

"service", when used as a verb, means to have waste pumped out and to have the facilities replenished where necessary. O. Reg. 527/00, s. 1.

(2)   **Revoked:** O. Reg. 527/00, s. 1.

Location of facilities

    (3)   The constructor shall ensure,

        (a)   that facilities are provided or arranged for workers before work has started at a project; and

        (b)   that workers at the project have reasonable access to these facilities. O. Reg. 145/00, s. 15.

(4)   Subject to subsections (5) and (6), the facilities shall be located within 180 metres horizontally of the work area of the project. O. Reg. 145/00, s. 15.

(5)   If work is being performed in a tunnel, the facilities shall be located within 180 metres horizontally from the entrance to the tunnel. O. Reg. 145/00, s. 15.

(6)   The facilities may be located within 3 kilometres of the work area if transportation to the facilities is provided for workers where reasonably required. O. Reg. 145/00, s. 15.

(7)   If the project is the construction of a building, then in addition to the requirement of subsection (4), the facilities must also be located within 9 metres vertically of the level at which work is being performed. O. Reg. 145/00, s. 15.

(8)   The location of the facilities under subsection (7) may be varied if the arrangement affords reasonable accessibility for workers. O. Reg. 145/00, s. 15.

(9)   If the location of the facilities is varied under subsection (8), the constructor shall document in writing the location and the reasons for the variance, and shall provide the document to,

        (a)   the joint health and safety committee or the health and safety representative, if any, for the workplace; or

      (b)   the workers, if there is no committee or representative for the workers. O. Reg. 145/00, s. 15.

(10) The constructor shall,

      (a)   inform workers of the location of the facilities; and

      (b)   post the location of the facilities in a conspicuous place at the project if it is practical to do so. O. Reg. 145/00, s. 15.

Service and maintenance

(11) The facilities shall be serviced, cleaned and sanitized as frequently as necessary to maintain them in a clean and sanitary condition. O. Reg. 145/00, s. 15.

(12) The constructor shall keep at the project for the duration of the project,

      (a)   a record of the servicing, cleaning and sanitizing of the facilities; and

      (b)   a copy of the document required under subsection (9), if any. O. Reg. 145/00, s. 15.

(13) Facilities that are not under the constructor's control satisfy the requirements of this section only if the constructor has received permission from the facilities' owner for workers to use the facilities. O. Reg. 145/00, s. 15.

29.1 (0.1) In this section,

      "non-sewered flush toilet facilities" means water flush toilets or chemical flush toilets that have the features listed in subsection (0.2);

"sewered toilet facilities" means water flush toilets that are connected to a sanitary sewer system and equipped with a trap in accordance with Part 7 of the *Building Code*. O. Reg. 527/00, s. 2 (1).

(0.2) The features referred to in the definition of "non-sewered flush toilet facilities" in subsection (0.1) are:

1. The toilets are not connected to a sanitary sewer system.

2. They are equipped with a trap or a positive seal separating stored waste from the bowl.

3. The waste is first flushed from the bowl with water or with water containing chemical additives. Then the waste is deposited into a container and chemically treated sufficiently for the container's maximum capacity. O. Reg. 527/00, s. 2 (1).

Toilet and urinal facilities

(1) Each toilet facility shall meet the following requirements:

1. There shall be a toilet with an open-front toilet seat.

2. There shall be a toilet paper holder and an adequate supply of toilet paper. If the facility is intended for use by female workers, there shall be a disposal receptacle for sanitary napkins.

3. The facility shall afford the user privacy and protection from weather and from falling objects. There shall be a self-closing door that can be locked from inside the facility.

4. The facility shall be,

   i. illuminated by natural or artificial light,

      ii.   adequately heated, if that is possible, and

      iii.   adequately ventilated.

5.   If the facility is intended for use by males only or by females only, it shall have a sign indicating that fact.

6.   The facility shall be kept in good repair at all times. O. Reg. 145/00, s. 15; O. Reg. 527/00, s. 2 (2, 3).

(2)   Separate toilet facilities shall be provided for male and female workers, unless the facilities are intended to be used by only one worker at a time. O. Reg. 145/00, s. 15.

(3)   Sewered toilet facilities or non-sewered flush toilet facilities shall be provided at a project, subject to subsection (4). O. Reg. 145/00, s. 15.

(4)   If a project is being carried out in a remote unpopulated area and it is not reasonably possible to provide the toilet facilities required under subsection (3), other types of toilet facilities that come as close as possible to having the features of non-sewered flush toilet facilities shall be provided instead. O. Reg. 527/00, s. 2 (4).

(5)   When water flush toilets or non-recirculating chemical flush toilets are provided, the minimum number of toilets required at the project is as follows:

TABLE 1

Minimum number of toilets	Number of workers regularly employed at the project
1	1-15
2	16-30
3	31-45
4	46-60
4, plus 1 additional toilet for each additional group of 15 or fewer workers	61 or more

O. Reg. 145/00, s. 15; O. Reg. 527/00, s. 2 (5).

(6)   If the toilets are located in a multiple water flush toilet facility and are intended to be used by male workers, water flush urinals may be substituted for a maximum of two-thirds of the number of toilets required by subsection (5). O. Reg. 145/00, s. 15.

(7)   When toilets other than water flush toilets or non-recirculating chemical flush toilets are provided, the minimum number of toilets required at the project is as follows:

TABLE 2

Minimum number of toilets	Number of workers regularly employed at the project
1	1-10
2	11-20
3	21-30
4	31-40
4, plus 1 additional toilet for each additional group of 15 or fewer workers	41 or more

O. Reg. 145/00, s. 15; O. Reg. 527/00, s. 2 (6).

(8)   If the toilets are located in a portable single-unit toilet facility intended for use by male workers, there shall be at least one urinal for each toilet. O. Reg. 145/00, s. 15.

(9)   Portable urinals equipped with clean-up facilities are permitted in addition to the requirements of this section. O. Reg. 145/00, s. 15.

Clean-up facilities

29.2 (1)   Each single-toilet facility shall be provided with its own clean-up facility. O. Reg. 527/00, s. 3.

(1.1) In a multiple-toilet facility at a project, one clean-up facility shall be provided for every two toilets. O. Reg. 527/00, s. 3.

(2)   Each clean-up facility shall meet the following requirements:

1.   Subject to subsection (3), the facility shall have a wash basin with running water. Both hot and cold running water shall be available if reasonably possible.

2.   Soap or hand cleanser shall be provided.

3.   Paper towels or a hand dryer shall be provided. If paper towels are provided, there shall be a waste disposal receptacle nearby. O. Reg. 145/00, s. 15.

(3)   If it is not reasonably possible to have a wash basin with running water at a clean-up facility, hand cleanser that can be used without water shall be provided instead. O. Reg. 145/00, s. 15.

30.   Workers who handle or use corrosive, poisonous or other substances likely to endanger their health shall be provided with washing facilities with clean water, soap and individual towels. O. Reg. 213/91, s. 30.

General Requirements

Strength

31. (1) Every part of a project, including a temporary structure,

    (a) shall be designed and constructed to support or resist all loads and forces to which it is likely to be subjected without exceeding the allowable unit stress for each material used; and

    (b) shall be adequately braced to prevent any movement that may affect its stability or cause its failure or collapse. O. Reg. 213/91, s. 31 (1).

Double connection

    (2) If two structural steel columns or structural steel beams are connected to a common column or common beam,

    (a) the connection shall be made using a clipped double connection; or

    (b) the first column or beam shall be secured in a seated connection. O. Reg. 213/91, s. 31 (2).

    (3) No part of a project, including a temporary structure, shall be subjected to a load in excess of the load it is designed and constructed to bear. O. Reg. 213/91, s. 31 (3).

Flooring

32. (1) During the construction of a building, temporary or permanent flooring shall be installed progressively as the building is erected. O. Reg. 213/91, s. 32 (1).

(2) Temporary flooring,

    (a)   shall consist of material that, without exceeding the allowable unit stress for the material used, is capable of supporting,

        (i)   any load to which it is likely to be subjected, and

        (ii)   a load of at least 2.4 kilonewtons per square metre;

    (b)   shall be securely fastened to and supported on girders, beams or other structural members that are capable of supporting any load likely to be applied to the flooring without exceeding the allowable unit stress for the structural members; and

    (c)   shall extend over the whole area of the surface on or above which work is being carried out. O. Reg. 213/91, s. 32 (2).

(3) Temporary flooring shall not be subjected to a load in excess of the load that it is designed and constructed to bear. O. Reg. 213/91, s. 32 (3).

33. (1) Subject to subsection (2), work on a building shall not be carried out at a distance higher than the higher of two storeys or the first column splice above the temporary or permanent flooring. O. Reg. 213/91, s. 33 (1).

(2) If the vertical distance between the tiers of column splices on a building exceeds two storeys, work shall not be carried out higher than three storeys above the temporary or permanent flooring. O. Reg. 213/91, s. 33 (2).

    (3)   This section does not apply to work carried out by a worker,

        (a)   who is working from a scaffold;

        (b)   whose fall would be arrested by means of a safety net without endangering the worker; or

        (c)   who is using a fall arrest system attached to the project. O. Reg. 213/91, s. 33 (3).

Overhead protection

34.   (1)   If material may fall on a worker, overhead protection shall be provided,

        (a)   at every means of access to and egress from a building or other structure under construction; and

        (b)   above every area where work is being carried out. O. Reg. 213/91, s. 34 (1).

(2)   Overhead protection shall consist of material capable of supporting 2.4 kilonewtons per square metre without exceeding the allowable unit stress for the material used. O. Reg. 213/91, s. 34 (2).

Housekeeping

Waste debris

35.   (1)   Waste material and debris shall be removed to a disposal area and reusable material shall be removed to a storage area as often as is necessary to prevent a hazardous condition arising and, in any event, at least once daily. O. Reg. 213/91, s. 35 (1).

(2)   Rubbish, debris and other materials shall not be permitted to fall freely from one level to another but shall be lowered by a chute, in a container or by a crane or hoist. O. Reg. 213/91, s. 35 (2).

(3) Despite subsection (2), rubbish, debris and other materials from demolition on a project may be permitted to fall or may be dropped into an enclosed designated area to which people do not have access. O. Reg. 213/91, s. 35 (3).

(4) A chute,

(a) shall be adequately constructed and rigidly fastened in place;

(b) if it has a slope exceeding a gradient of one in one, shall be enclosed on its four sides;

(c) shall have a gate at the bottom end if one is necessary to control the flow of material; and

(d) shall discharge into a container or an enclosed area surrounded by barriers. O. Reg. 213/91, s. 35 (4).

(5) The entrance to a chute,

(a) shall be constructed to prevent spilling over when rubbish, debris and other materials are being deposited into the chute;

(b) if it is at or below floor level, shall have a curb that is at least 100 millimetres high;

(c) shall not be more than 1.2 metres high;

(d) shall be kept closed when the chute is not in use; and

(e) shall be designed so that any person will be discouraged from entering it. O. Reg. 213/91, s. 35 (5).

Protruding hazards

36. If a formwork tie, reinforcing steel, a nail or another object protruding from concrete or another surface may endanger a worker, the protrusion shall be removed, cut off at the surface or otherwise protected as soon as practicable. O. Reg. 213/91, s. 36.

Material storage, movement

37. (1) Material or equipment at a project shall be stored and moved in a manner that does not endanger a worker. O. Reg. 213/91, s. 37 (1).

(2) No material or equipment to be moved by a crane or similar hoisting device shall be stored under or in close proximity to an energized outdoor overhead electrical conductor. O. Reg. 213/91, s. 37 (2).

Blocking

38. Blocking, support chains, metal bands, wire rope and rigging components shall be removed from material or equipment in a manner that does not endanger a worker. O. Reg. 213/91, s. 38.

Material/equipment piling, stacking, storing

39. Material and equipment at a project shall be piled or stacked in a manner that prevents it from tipping, collapsing or rolling. O. Reg. 213/91, s. 39.

40. (1) No material shall be stored, stacked or piled within 1.8 metres of,

   (a) an opening in a floor or roof;

   (b) the open edge of a floor, roof or balcony; or

   (c) an excavation. O. Reg. 213/91, s. 40 (1).

(2) Subsection (1) does not apply with respect to material in a building or a completely enclosed part of a building that is used solely for storing and distributing materials. O. Reg. 213/91, s. 40 (2).

(3) Subsection (1) does not apply with respect to small masonry units including bricks, blocks and similar objects,

(a) that can be handled by one worker;

(b) that are to be used at the edge of a floor, a roof, an excavation or an opening in a floor or roof; and

(c) that are stacked in a pile whose height is less than the distance from the face of the pile to the edge of the floor, roof, excavation or opening in a floor or roof. O. Reg. 213/91, s. 40 (3).

Substance storage

41. A combustible, corrosive or toxic substance shall be stored in a suitable container. O. Reg. 213/91, s. 41.

Cylinders

42. (1) A storage cylinder for compressed gas shall be secured in an upright position. O. Reg. 213/91, s. 42 (1).

(2) The control valve of a storage cylinder for compressed gas, other than a cylinder connected to a regulator, supply line or hose, shall be covered by a protective cap that is secured in its proper position. O. Reg. 213/91, s. 42 (2).

(3) A spent storage cylinder shall not be stored inside a building. O. Reg. 213/91, s. 42 (3).

(4) No storage cylinder for propane shall be placed closer than three metres to a source of ignition or fire. O. Reg. 213/91, s. 42 (4).

(5) Subsection (4) does not apply to a storage cylinder,

   (a) that forms part of hand-held propane equipment;

   (b) that forms part of a lead pot used in plumbing or electrical work;

   (c) that forms part of a propane-powered or propane-heated vehicle; or

   (d) that is protected from a source of ignition by a barrier, wall or other means of separation. O. Reg. 213/91, s. 42 (5).

Flammable liquid, gas

43. (1) A flammable liquid or gas shall be stored in a building or storage tank that is suitable for the purpose and, if practicable, not less than 100 metres from a magazine for explosives. O. Reg. 213/91, s. 43 (1).

(2) No more than one work day's normal supply of a flammable liquid shall be stored in a building or structure on a project unless it is stored,

   (a) in a container that is suitable for the particular hazards of the liquid; and

   (b) in a controlled access area or a room,

      (i) that has sufficient window area to provide explosion relief to the outside, and

        (ii)   that is remote from the means of egress from the building or structure. O. Reg. 213/91, s. 43 (2).

(3)   A portable container used to store or transport flammable liquids,

      (a)   shall be approved for use for that liquid by a recognized testing laboratory; and

      (b)   shall have a label stating the use for which the container is approved and the name of the testing laboratory which gave the approval required by clause (a). O. Reg. 213/91, s. 43 (3).

Signs

44.   (1)   Signs meeting the requirements of subsection (2) shall be posted in prominent locations and in sufficient numbers to warn workers of a hazard on a project. O. Reg. 213/91, s. 44 (1).

(2)   A sign shall contain the word "DANGER" written in legible letters that are at least 150 millimetres in height and shall state that entry by any unauthorized person to the area where the hazard exists is forbidden. O. Reg. 213/91, s. 44 (2).

(3)   Without limiting the generality of subsection (1), a sign shall be posted,

      (a)   adjacent to a hoisting area;

      (b)   under a boatswain's chair, a suspended scaffold or a suspended platform;

      (c)   at the outlet from a chute;

(d) at a means of access to a place where there may be a noxious gas, vapour dust or fume, noxious substance or a lack of oxygen; and

(e) where there is a potential hazard from an energized overhead electrical conductor at more than 750 volts. O. Reg. 213/91, s. 44 (3).

(4) No person shall enter an area in which a sign is posted other than a worker authorized to work in the area. O. Reg. 213/91, s. 44 (4).

Lighting

45. (1) The areas in which a worker is present and the means of access to and egress from those areas shall be adequately lit. O. Reg. 213/91, s. 45 (1).

(2) A light bulb used in a temporary lighting system shall be enclosed by a mechanical protection device. O. Reg. 213/91, s. 45 (2).

Ventilation

46. (1) A project shall be adequately ventilated by natural or mechanical means,

(a) if a worker may be injured by inhaling a noxious gas, vapour, dust or fume or from a lack of oxygen; or

(b) if a gas, vapour, dust or fume may be capable of forming an explosive mixture with air. O. Reg. 213/91, s. 46 (1).

(2) If it is not practicable to provide natural or mechanical ventilation in the circumstances described in clause (1) (a), respiratory protective equipment suitable for the hazard shall be provided to and used by the workers. O. Reg. 213/91, s. 46 (2).

47. No internal combustion engine shall be operated,

> (a) in an excavation unless provision is made to ensure that exhaust gases and fumes will not accumulate in the excavation; or

> (b) in a building or other enclosed structure,

>> (i) unless the exhaust gases and fumes from the engine are discharged directly outside the building or structure to a point sufficiently remote to prevent the return of the gases and fumes, or

>> (ii) unless there is an adequate supply of air for combustion and adequate natural or mechanical ventilation to ensure exhaust gases and fumes will not accumulate. O. Reg. 213/91, s. 47.

Drum, tank repair

48. (1) When a drum, tank, pipeline or other container is to be repaired or altered,

> (a) its internal pressures shall be adjusted to atmospheric pressure before any fastening is removed;

> (b) it shall be drained, cleaned and ventilated or otherwise rendered free from any explosive, flammable or harmful substance; and

> (c) it shall not be refilled during repair or alteration if the substance which is to be placed in it may vaporize or ignite. O. Reg. 213/91, s. 48 (1).

(2) Clauses (1) (a) and (b) do not apply with respect to a pipeline if hot-tapping and boxing-in are carried out by a competent worker

under controlled conditions that provide for the protection of all persons. O. Reg. 213/91, s. 48 (2).

Temporary Heat

Fire protection

49. (1)   A fuel-fired heating device shall be located, protected and used in such a way that there is no risk of igniting a tarpaulin or similar temporary enclosure or combustible materials adjacent to it. O. Reg. 213/91, s. 49 (1).

(2)   No fuel-fired heating device shall be used in a confined or enclosed space unless there is an adequate supply of air for combustion and adequate general ventilation. O. Reg. 213/91, s. 49 (2).

(3)   A fuel-fired heating device shall be protected from damage and from overturning. O. Reg. 213/91, s. 49 (3).

(4)   No fuel-fired heating device shall be located so as to restrict any means of egress. O. Reg. 213/91, s. 49 (4).

(5)   A fuel-fired heating device that generates noxious products of combustion shall discharge the products of combustion outside the building or structure in which it is located. O. Reg. 213/91, s. 49 (5).

Fuel supply lines

50.   All fuel supply lines shall be constructed, guarded or placed in such a way as to be protected from damage. O. Reg. 213/91, s. 50.

Steam-piping

51. (1)   Temporary steam-piping shall be installed and supported so as not to endanger a worker. O. Reg. 213/91, s. 51 (1).

(2)   Temporary steam-piping shall be insulated or otherwise protected if a worker is likely to come into contact with it. O. Reg. 213/91, s. 51 (2).

Fire Safety

Locations

52. (1)   Fire extinguishing equipment shall be provided at readily accessible and adequately marked locations at a project. O. Reg. 213/91, s. 52 (1).

(1.1) Every worker who may be required to use fire extinguishing equipment shall be trained in its use. O. Reg. 145/00, s. 16.

(2)   Without limiting subsection (1), at least one fire extinguisher shall be provided,

     (a)   where flammable liquids or combustible materials are stored, handled or used;

     (b)   where oil-fired or gas-fired equipment, other than permanent furnace equipment in a building, is used;

     (c)   where welding or open-flame operations are carried on; and

     (d)   on each storey of an enclosed building being constructed or altered. O. Reg. 213/91, s. 52 (2).

(3)   At least one fire extinguisher shall be provided in a workshop for each 300 or fewer square metres of floor area. O. Reg. 213/91, s. 52 (3).

(4)   Clause (2) (d) and subsection (3) do not apply to a building,

    (a)   that is to be used as a detached or semi-detached single-family dwelling;

    (b)   that has two storeys or less and is to be used as a multiple family dwelling; or

    (c)   that has one storey with no basement or cellar. O. Reg. 213/91, s. 52 (4).

Type, size

53. (1)   Fire extinguishing equipment shall be of a suitable type and size to permit the evacuation of workers during a fire. O. Reg. 213/91, s. 53 (1).

(2)   Every fire extinguisher,

    (a)   shall be a type whose contents are discharged under pressure; and

    (b)   shall have an Underwriters' Laboratories of Canada 4A40BC rating. O. Reg. 213/91, s. 53 (2).

Protection

54. (1)   Fire extinguishing equipment shall be protected from physical damage and from freezing. O. Reg. 213/91, s. 54 (1).

Refill, replacement

(2)   After a fire extinguisher is used, it shall be refilled or replaced immediately. O. Reg. 213/91, s. 54 (2).

Inspection

55.   Every fire extinguisher shall be inspected for defects or deterioration at least once a month by a competent worker who shall record the date of the inspection on a tag attached to it. O. Reg. 213/91, s. 55.

Fire pumps

56. No work shall be carried out at a height of 84 metres or more in a building unless the building has temporary or permanent fire pumps that provide a minimum water flow of 1,890 litres per minute at a discharge pressure of at least 450 kilopascals at and above the 84-metre height. O. Reg. 145/00, s. 17.

Standpipe

57. (1)   As construction proceeds in a building with two or more storeys, a permanent or temporary standpipe shall be installed to within two storeys of the uppermost work level. O. Reg. 145/00, s. 18 (1).

(2)   Subsection (1) does not apply to work carried out in a building which is not required by the *Building Code* to have a permanent standpipe. O. Reg. 213/91, s. 57 (2).

(3)   A permanent standpipe,

   (a)   shall have sufficient hose outlets to permit every part of the building to be protected by a hose not longer than twenty-three metres;

   (b)   shall have a connection for the use of the local fire department located on the street side of the building not more than 900 millimetres and not less than 300 millimetres above ground level and to which there is clear access at all times; and

   (c)   shall be maintained so as to be readily operable if required to be used. O. Reg. 213/91, s. 57 (3).

(4)   Every hose outlet in a permanent standpipe shall have a valve. O. Reg. 213/91, s. 57 (4).

(5)   Every hose used with a permanent standpipe,

    (a)   shall be at least thirty-eight millimetres in diameter;

    (b)   shall have a combination straight stream and fog nozzle; and

    (c)   shall be stored on a rack in such a way as to protect it from damage and keep it available for immediate use. O. Reg. 213/91, s. 57 (5).

Temporary standpipe

(6)   If a temporary standpipe has been installed, it shall not be disconnected until the permanent standpipe is connected, so that there is always a standpipe in service. O. Reg. 145/00, s. 18 (2).

(7)   A temporary standpipe shall be maintained so that it is readily operable. O. Reg. 145/00, s. 18 (2).

(8)   A temporary standpipe shall have at least one hose outlet per floor, with a valve and a hose attached to each hose outlet and a nozzle attached to each hose. O. Reg. 145/00, s. 18 (2).

(9)   In addition to the requirements of subsection (8), there shall be a connection to which there is clear access at all times, located between 30 and 90 centimetres above ground level on a side of the building that faces the street. O. Reg. 145/00, s. 18 (2).

(10) A hose outlet on a temporary standpipe,

    (a)   shall have a valve; and

    (b)   shall be capable of accepting a hose that is 38 millimetres in diameter. O. Reg. 145/00, s. 18 (2).

(11) If a temporary standpipe is installed in a building under construction, the constructor shall post at the project, or have available for review, a floor plan of the building indicating,

    (a)   the location of the hose outlets on each floor;

    (b)   the location of the point on the perimeter of each floor that is furthest from the hose outlet on that floor; and

    (c)   the location of each exit on each floor. O. Reg. 145/00, s. 18 (2).

(12) The constructor shall give a copy of the floor plan to the fire department located nearest to the project. O. Reg. 145/00, s. 18 (2).

58. No flammable liquid shall be transferred from one container to another by the direct application of air under pressure. O. Reg. 213/91, s. 58.

Dust Control

59. If the dissemination of dust is a hazard to a worker, the dust shall be adequately controlled or each worker who may be exposed to the hazard shall be provided with adequate personal protective equipment. O. Reg. 145/00, s. 19.

60.-63. Revoked: O. Reg. 628/05, s. 2.

Public Way Protection

Covered way
64. (1)   No work shall be carried out on a building or structure located within 4.5 metres of a public way unless a covered way is constructed over the part of the public way that is adjacent to the project. O. Reg. 213/91, s. 64 (1).

(2)   Subsection (1) does not apply with respect to a building or structure if the work being done is enclosed. O. Reg. 213/91, s. 64 (2).

(3)   A covered way,

   (a)   shall have an unobstructed height of not less than 2.4 metres;

   (b)   shall have an unobstructed width of not less than 1.1 metres or, if it is over a sidewalk that is less than 1.1 metres wide, have a width equal to the width of the sidewalk;

   (c)   shall be capable of supporting any load likely to be applied to it and capable of supporting a load of at least 2.4 kilonewtons per square metre;

   (d)   shall have a weather-tight roof;

   (e)   shall have the side adjacent to the project covered with a partition that has a smooth surface on the public way side;

   (f)   shall have a railing one metre high from ground level on the street side; and

   (g)   shall have adequate lighting within the public way. Reg. 213/91, s. 64 (3).

Fence

65.   If work on a project may endanger a person using a public way, a sturdy fence at least 1.8 metres in height shall be constructed between the public way and the project. O. Reg. 213/91, s. 65.

Hazard marking

66. Machinery, equipment and material that is being used, left or stored
where it may be a hazard to traffic on a public way shall be marked
by flashing devices. O. Reg. 213/91, s. 66; O. Reg. 145/00, s. 20.

Traffic Control

Definitions

67. (1) In this section,

"barricade" means a device that provides a visual indicator of
the path a motorist is supposed to take;

"barrier" means a device that provides a physical limitation
through which a vehicle would not normally pass, and includes
a concrete barrier;

"mobile operation" means work, including a paving operation,
that is done on a highway or the shoulder of a highway and
moves along at speeds of less than 30 kilometres per hour.
O. Reg. 145/00, s. 21.

Protective measures: general

(2) If a worker at a project on a highway may be endangered by
vehicular traffic unrelated to the project, the project shall make use
of as many of the following measures as is necessary to adequately
protect the worker:

1. Barriers.

2. Barricades.

3. Delineators.

4. Lane control devices.

5. Warning signs.

6. Flashing lights.

7. Flares.

8. Traffic control devices.

9. Blocker trucks.

10. Crash trucks.

11. Sign trucks.

12. Speed control devices.

13. Longitudinal buffer areas. O. Reg. 145/00, s. 21.

Same

(3) In addition to the measures listed in subsection (2) but subject to section 68, a worker may be used to direct traffic. O. Reg. 145/00, s. 21.

Traffic protection plan

(4) Every employer shall develop in writing and implement a traffic protection plan for the employers' workers at a project if any of them may be exposed to a hazard from vehicular traffic. O. Reg. 145/00, s. 21.

(5) The traffic protection plan,

(a) shall specify the vehicular traffic hazards and the measures described in subsection (2) to be used to protect workers; and

(b) shall be kept at the project and made available to an inspector or a worker on request. O. Reg. 145/00, s. 21.

Traffic control measures: set up and removal

(6)   A worker who is required to set up or remove measures described in subsection (2) on a roadway or a shoulder of a roadway,

   (a)   shall be a competent worker;

   (b)   shall not perform any other work while setting up or removing the measures; and

   (c)   shall be given adequate written and oral instructions, in a language that he or she understands, with respect to setting up or removing the measures. O. Reg. 145/00, s. 21.

Non-mobile operations on freeways

(7)   Subject to subsection (8), adequate barriers shall be installed to protect workers at a project from vehicular traffic if the project,

   (a)   is on a freeway;

   (b)   is not a mobile operation; and

   (c)   is expected to require more than five days to complete. O. Reg. 145/00, s. 21.

Alternative protections

(8)   Until January 1, 2003, if a project to which subsection (7) would otherwise apply is expected to require five days or less to complete, or if it is not practical to install barriers as that subsection requires, the following measures shall be taken to protect workers at the project:

   1.   An adequate longitudinal buffer area shall be provided if physically possible.

2. If information about the annual average daily travel rate of vehicular traffic on the freeway is available and the rate is less than 25,000, blocker trucks shall be adequately positioned between vehicular traffic and workers.

3. If the annual average daily travel rate of vehicular traffic on the freeway is 25,000 or more or if information about the rate is unavailable, crash trucks shall be adequately positioned between vehicular traffic and workers. O. Reg. 145/00, s. 21.

Record accessible

(9) If subsection (8) applies and information about the annual average daily travel rate of vehicular traffic on the freeway is available, a record of the rate shall be maintained at the project and be made available to an inspector upon request. O. Reg. 145/00, s. 21.

Crash trucks

(10) On and after January 1, 2003, if it is not practical to install barriers as subsection (7) requires, or if the project is expected to require five days or less to complete, crash trucks shall be adequately positioned to protect workers. O. Reg. 145/00, s. 21.

Work on freeway shoulders

(11) If work on a shoulder of a freeway is expected to take less than 30 minutes to complete, a vehicle with four-way flashers and a 360-degree beacon light shall be provided. O. Reg. 145/00, s. 21.

Mobile operations on freeways

(12) The following measures shall be taken to protect a worker at a project if the project is on a freeway and involves a mobile operation:

1. Until January 1, 2003, an adequate number of blocker trucks shall be adequately positioned between vehicular traffic and the worker.

2. On and after January 1, 2003, an adequate number of crash trucks shall be adequately positioned between vehicular traffic and the worker.

3. If the operation involves intermittent stops averaging 30 minutes or less, an adequate number of barricades or delineators shall be adequately positioned between vehicular traffic and the worker.

4. If the operation involves intermittent stops averaging more than 30 minutes,

   i. an adequate longitudinal buffer area shall be provided if physically possible,

   ii. the lane on which work is being done shall be adequately identified with lane closure signs and a lane closure taper, and

   iii. an adequate number of barricades or delineators shall be adequately positioned between vehicular traffic and the work area. O. Reg. 145/00, s. 21.

Traffic signs

68. The following requirements apply with respect to a sign used by a worker to direct vehicular traffic:

1. It shall be octagonal in shape, measure 450 millimetres between opposite sides, and be mounted on a pole that is 1.2 metres long.

2. It shall be made of material with at least the rigidity of plywood that is six millimetres thick.

3. On one side it shall be high-intensity retro-reflective grade red in colour, with the word "STOP" written in legible high-intensity retro-reflective grade white letters 150 millimetres high in a central position on the sign.

4. On the other side it shall be high retro-reflective micro-prismatic fluorescent chartreuse in colour, with a black diamond-shaped border that is at least 317 millimetres by 317 millimetres, and with the word "SLOW" written in legible black letters 120 millimetres high in a central position on the sign.

5. It shall be maintained in a clean and legible condition. O. Reg. 145/00, s. 22.

Traffic control persons

69. (1) This section applies with respect to directing vehicular traffic that may be a hazard to workers on a public way. O. Reg. 145/00, s. 23.

(2) A worker shall not direct vehicular traffic for more than one lane in the same direction. O. Reg. 145/00, s. 23.

(3) A worker shall not direct vehicular traffic if the normal posted speed limit of the public way is more than 90 kilometres per hour. O. Reg. 145/00, s. 23.

(4) A worker who is required to direct vehicular traffic,

    (a) shall be a competent worker;

    (b) shall not perform any other work while directing vehicular traffic;

    (c)   shall be positioned in such a way that he or she is endangered as little as possible by vehicular traffic; and

    (d)   shall be given adequate written and oral instructions, in a language that he or she understands, with respect to directing vehicular traffic, and those instructions shall include a description of the signals that are to be used. O. Reg. 145/00, s. 23.

(5)   The written instructions referred to in clause (4) (d) shall be kept at the project. O. Reg. 145/00, s. 23.

Protective clothing

69.1 (1)   A worker who may be endangered by vehicular traffic shall wear a garment that covers at least his or her upper body and has the following features:

1. The garment shall be fluorescent blaze or international orange in colour.

2. On the front and the back, there shall be two yellow stripes that are 5 centimetres wide. The yellow area shall total at least 500 square centimetres on the front and at least 570 square centimetres on the back.

3. On the front, the stripes shall be arranged vertically and centred and shall be approximately 225 millimetres apart, measured from the centre of each stripe. On the back, they shall be arranged in a diagonal "X" pattern.

4. The stripes shall be retro-reflective and fluorescent. O. Reg. 145/00, s. 23.

(2)   If the garment is a vest, it shall have adjustable fit. O. Reg. 145/00, s. 23.

(3)   On and after January 1, 2001, a nylon vest to which this section applies shall also have a side and front tear-away feature. O. Reg. 145/00, s. 23.

Night work

(4)   In addition, a worker who may be endangered by vehicular traffic during night-time hours shall wear retro-reflective silver stripes encircling each arm and leg, or equivalent side visibility-enhancing stripes with a minimum area of 50 square centimetres per side. O. Reg. 145/00, s. 23.

Access To and Egress From Work Areas

Access, egress, means

70. (1)   Access to and egress from a work area located above or below ground level shall be by stairs, runway, ramp or ladder. O. Reg. 213/91, s. 70 (1).

(2)   Subsection (1) does not apply to a work area that is a suspended scaffold able to be moved to give access to a floor, roof or platform or to ground level. O. Reg. 213/91, s. 70 (2).

Emergency egress

71. Adequate means of egress shall be provided from a work area to permit the evacuation of workers during an emergency. O. Reg. 213/91, s. 71.

Maintenance

72. A work area, a route to and from a work area and a scaffold platform on which work is being performed shall be maintained at all times in a condition that does not endanger workers and, without limiting the generality of the foregoing,

(a)   shall be kept clear of obstructions;

(b) shall be kept clear of snow, ice or other slippery material; and

(c) shall be treated with sand or similar material when necessary to ensure a firm footing. O. Reg. 213/91, s. 72.

Platforms, Runways and Ramps

Design, construction, maintenance

73. (1) Runways, ramps and platforms other than scaffold platforms shall meet the requirements of this section. O. Reg. 213/91, s. 73 (1).

(2) A runway, ramp or platform shall be designed, constructed and maintained to support or resist, without exceeding the allowable unit stresses for the materials of which it is made,

(a) all loads and forces to which it is likely to be subjected; and

(b) at least 2.4 kilonewtons per square metre. O. Reg. 213/91, s. 73 (2).

(3) No runway, ramp or platform shall be loaded in excess of the load that it is designed and constructed to bear. O. Reg. 213/91, s. 73 (3).

(4) A runway, ramp or platform shall be at least 460 millimetres wide and shall be securely fastened in place. O. Reg. 213/91, s. 73 (4).

74. (1) A ramp shall have,

(a) a slope not exceeding a gradient of 1 in 3; and

(b)   if its slope exceeds a gradient of 1 in 8, cross cleats made from nineteen millimetres by thirty-eight millimetres boards that are securely nailed to the ramp and spaced at regular intervals not exceeding 500 millimetres. O. Reg. 213/91, s. 74 (1).

(2)   Subsection (1) does not apply to a ramp installed in the stairwell of a building not exceeding two storeys in height if the ramp,

(a)   has a slope not exceeding a gradient of 1 in 1; and

(b)   has cross cleats made from thirty-eight millimetres by thirty-eight millimetres boards that are securely nailed to the ramp and spaced at regular intervals not exceeding 300 millimetres. O. Reg. 213/91, s. 74 (2).

Stairs and Landings

75.   (1)   No work shall be performed in a building or structure that will be at least two storeys high when it is finished unless stairs are installed in accordance with this section. O. Reg. 213/91, s. 75 (1).

(2)   As the construction of a building or structure progresses, permanent or temporary stairs shall be installed up to,

(a)   the uppermost work level; or

(b)   if stairs would interfere with work on the uppermost work level, to within the lesser of two storeys or nine metres below the uppermost work level. O. Reg. 213/91, s. 75 (2).

(3)   Subsection (2) does not apply with respect to,

(a)   a part of a building or structure in which only the structural steel beams or columns are erected; or

      (b)   a structure to which a permanent ladder is attached before the structure is raised into position. O. Reg. 213/91, s. 75 (3).

Temporary stairs, landings

76. (1)   Temporary stairs and landings shall be designed, constructed and maintained to support a live load of 4.8 kilonewtons per square metre without exceeding the allowable unit stresses for each material used. O. Reg. 213/91, s. 76 (1).

(2)   No temporary stair or landing shall be loaded in excess of the load it is designed and constructed to bear. O. Reg. 213/91, s. 76 (2).

77. (1)   No work shall be performed in a building or structure with stairs unless the stairs meet the requirements of this section. O. Reg. 213/91, s. 77 (1).

(2)   Stairs shall have,

      (a)   a clear width of at least 500 millimetres;

      (b)   treads and risers of uniform width, length and height;

      (c)   subject to subsection (3), stringers with a maximum slope of 50 degrees from the horizontal;

      (d)   landings that are less than 4.5 metres apart measured vertically;

      (e)   a securely fastened and supported wooden handrail on the open sides of each flight; and

      (f)   a guardrail on the open side of each landing. O. Reg. 213/91, s. 77 (2).

Stringers

(3)   The stringers of prefabricated stairs erected inside a tower formed by scaffold frame sections shall have a maximum slope of 60 degrees from the horizontal. O. Reg. 213/91, s. 77 (3).

Handrail

(4)   A wooden handrail shall measure thirty-eight millimetres by eighty-nine millimetres and shall be free of loose knots, sharp edges, splinters and shakes. O. Reg. 213/91, s. 77 (4).

(5)   Skeleton steel stairs shall have temporary wooden treads securely fastened in place that are made of suitable planking extending the full width and breadth of the stairs and landings. O. Reg. 213/91, s. 77 (5).

Ladders

Strength

78. (1)   A ladder shall be designed, constructed and maintained so as not to endanger a worker and shall be capable of withstanding all loads to which it may be subjected. O. Reg. 213/91, s. 78 (1).

(2)   A ladder,

   (a)   shall be free from defective or loose rungs;

   (b)   shall have rungs spaced at 300 millimetres on centres;

   (c)   shall have side rails at least 300 millimetres apart;

   (d)   shall be placed on a firm footing; and

   (e)   shall be situated so that its base is not less than one-quarter, and not more than one-third, of the length of the ladder from a point directly below the top of the ladder and at the same level as the base of the ladder, if the ladder is not securely fastened. O. Reg. 213/91, s. 78 (2).

Length

(3) The maximum length of a ladder measured along its side rail shall not be more than,

(a) five metres for a trestle ladder or for each of the base and extension sections of an extension trestle ladder;

(b) six metres for a step-ladder;

(c) nine metres for a single ladder or an individual section of a ladder;

(d) fifteen metres for an extension ladder with two sections; and

(e) twenty metres for an extension ladder with more than two sections. O. Reg. 213/91, s. 78 (3).

Lashing

(4) No ladder shall be lashed to another ladder to increase its length. O. Reg. 213/91, s. 78 (4).

(5) In this section,

"extension trestle ladder" means a combination of a trestle ladder and a vertically-adjustable single ladder with a suitable means of securely locking the ladders together. O. Reg. 213/91, s. 78 (5).

Hazardous area

79. No ladder shall be present in an elevator shaft or a similar hoisting area when the shaft or area is being used for hoisting. O. Reg. 213/91, s. 79.

80. A ladder used as a regular means of access between levels of a structure,

    (a) shall extend at the upper level at least 900 millimetres above the landing or floor;

    (b) shall have a clear space of at least 150 millimetres behind every rung;

    (c) shall be located so that an adequate landing surface that is clear of obstructions is available at the top and bottom of the ladder; and

    (d) shall be secured at the top and bottom to prevent movement. O. Reg. 213/91, s. 80.

Wooden ladder

81. (1) A wooden ladder,

    (a) shall be made of wood that is straight-grained and free of loose knots, sharp edges, splinters and shakes; and

    (b) shall not be painted or coated with an opaque material. O. Reg. 213/91, s. 81 (1).

(2) The side rails of a wooden ladder of the cleat type,

    (a) shall be not less than 400 millimetres and not more than 610 millimetres apart; and

    (b) shall measure not less than,

        (i) thirty-eight millimetres by eighty-nine millimetres if the ladder is 5.8 metres or less long, or

           (ii)   thirty-eight millimetres by 140 millimetres if the ladder is more than 5.8 metres long. O. Reg. 213/91, s. 81 (2).

  (3) The rungs of a wooden ladder of the cleat type,

      (a)   shall measure not less than,

           (i)   nineteen millimetres by sixty-four millimetres if the side rails are 400 millimetres apart, or

           (ii)   nineteen millimetres by eighty-nine millimetres if the side rails are more than 400 millimetres and not more than 610 millimetres apart; and

      (b)   shall be braced by filler blocks that are nineteen millimetres thick and are located between the rungs. O. Reg. 213/91, s. 81 (3).

Double-width ladder

82. A double-width wooden ladder,

      (a)   shall have three evenly-spaced rails that measure at least thirty-eight millimetres by 140 millimetres;

      (b)   shall have rungs that,

           (i)   measure at least thirty-eight millimetres by eighty-nine millimetres,

           (ii)   extend the full width of the ladder, and

           (iii)   are braced by filler blocks that are at least 19 millimetres thick; and

      (c)   shall not be less than 1.5 metres wide and not more than two metres wide. O. Reg. 213/91, s. 82.

Step-ladder

83. (1)   When a step-ladder is being used as a self-supporting unit, its legs shall be fully-spread and its spreader shall be locked. O. Reg. 213/91, s. 83 (1).

(2)   No worker shall stand on the top of or the pail shelf of a step-ladder. O. Reg. 213/91, s. 83 (2).

Vertical access ladder

84. (1)   Subject to subsection (2), an access ladder fixed in position,

  (a)   shall be vertical;

  (b)   shall have rest platforms at not more than nine metre intervals;

  (c)   shall be offset at each rest platform;

  (d)   where the ladder extends over three metres above grade, floor or landing, shall have a safety cage commencing not more than 2.2 metres above grade, floor or landing and continuing at least 90 centimetres above the top landing with openings to permit access by a worker to rest platforms or to the top landing;

  (e)   shall have side rails that extend 90 centimetres above the landing; and

  (f)   shall have rungs that are at least 15 centimetres from the wall and spaced at regular intervals. O. Reg. 631/94, s. 2.

(2)   Subsection (1) does not apply to an access ladder on a tower, water tank, chimney or similar structure that has a safety device that will provide protection should a worker using the ladder fall. O. Reg. 631/94, s. 2.

85., 86. Revoked: O. Reg. 145/00, s. 24.

Forms, Formwork, Falsework and Re-shoring

Strength

87. (1)   Formwork, falsework and re-shoring shall be designed, constructed, supported and braced so that they are capable of withstanding all loads and forces likely to be applied to them,

> (a)   without exceeding the allowable working loads established for any component of the structure; and

> (b)   without causing uplift, sliding, overturning or lateral displacement of the system. O. Reg. 213/91, s. 87 (1).

(2)   No formwork, falsework or re-shoring shall be loaded in excess of the load that it is designed and constructed to bear. O. Reg. 213/91, s. 87 (2).

(3)   The allowable working load of the formwork, falsework or re-shoring shall be established,

> (a)   by a professional engineer in accordance with good engineering practice; or

> (b)   by testing the principal components to their ultimate strength in a manner that simulates the actual loading conditions to which the formwork, falsework or re-shoring is likely to be subjected and by applying a reduction factor, in accordance with good engineering practice, to the values of ultimate strength. O. Reg. 213/91, s. 87 (3).

(4)   The results of the testing in clause (3) (b) shall be verified and certified by a professional engineer and made available to an inspector upon request. O. Reg. 213/91, s. 87 (4).

(5)   If single post shores are placed more than one tier high, the junction of each tier shall be braced against a fixed support in at least two directions in order to prevent any lateral movement. O. Reg. 213/91, s. 87 (5).

Removal

88.   Formwork and falsework shall not be removed unless,

(a)   the concrete is strong enough to support itself and any loads that may be applied to the structure; or

(b)   the concrete and the structure are adequately re-shored. O. Reg. 213/91, s. 88.

89.   (1)   This section applies with respect to formwork, falsework and re-shoring that includes,

(a)   a tubular metal frame;

(b)   a column whose effective length is dependent upon lateral restraints between the ends of the column;

(c)   shores placed one upon another to form a supporting system that is more than one tier in height;

(d)   shores which are three metres or more in height;

(e)   a truss;

(f)   members so connected to one another that a load applied to one member may alter or induce stress in another member; or

(g)   a unitized modular formwork or falsework structure intended to be moved as a unit. O. Reg. 213/91, s. 89 (1).

Design, installation, erection

(2)   Formwork and falsework shall be designed by a professional engineer in accordance with good engineering practice and be installed or erected in accordance with the design drawings. O. Reg. 213/91, s. 89 (2).

(3)   Formwork and falsework shall, before the placement of concrete, be inspected by a professional engineer or by a competent worker designated in writing by the professional engineer. O. Reg. 213/91, s. 89 (3).

(4)   The person carrying out the inspection shall state in writing whether the formwork and falsework is installed or erected in accordance with the design drawings for it. O. Reg. 213/91, s. 89 (4).

(5)   The constructor shall keep the design drawings and the statements on the project while the formwork or the falsework is in use. O. Reg. 213/91, s. 89 (5).

Re-shoring

90.   Re-shoring shall be designed by a professional engineer in accordance with good engineering practice and be erected in accordance with the design drawings. O. Reg. 213/91, s. 90.

91.   Falsework and re-shoring,

(a)   shall have sound and rigid footings capable of carrying the maximum load to which the footings may be subjected without settlement or deformation of the soil or structure below the footings; and

(b)   shall be adequately protected to prevent deformation caused by frost heave. O. Reg. 213/91, s. 91.

Design drawings

92. (1)   Design drawings by a professional engineer for the formwork, falsework or re-shoring,

(a)   if a manufactured system is used, shall identify the components;

(b)   if non-manufactured system components are used, shall show the size, grade and specifications of the non-manufactured system components;

(c)   shall show the design loads for the structure and shall detail the bracing and external ties required to adequately support the design loads;

(d)   if the structure is a unitized modular formwork or falsework structure intended to be lifted or moved as a unit, shall show the attachment points for rigging and hoisting; and

(e)   shall set out the erection instructions that are specified by the manufacturer or by the professional engineer.

(f)   **Revoked:** O. Reg. 213/91, s. 92 (1); O. Reg. 85/04, s. 11.

(2)   The constructor shall keep the design drawings on the project while the formwork, falsework or re-shoring is in use. O. Reg. 213/91, s. 92 (2).

Equipment, General

Maintenance

93. (1)   All vehicles, machinery, tools and equipment shall be maintained in a condition that does not endanger a worker. O. Reg. 213/91, s. 93 (1).

General restrictions on use

    (2)   No vehicle, machine, tool or equipment shall be used,

        (a)   while it is defective or hazardous;

        (b)   when the weather or other conditions are such that its use is likely to endanger a worker; or

        (c)   while it is being repaired or serviced, unless the repair or servicing requires that it be operated. O. Reg. 213/91, s. 93 (2); O. Reg. 145/00, s. 25 (1).

Operating manual

    (3)   All vehicles, machines, tools and equipment shall be used in accordance with any operating manuals issued by the manufacturers. O. Reg. 145/00, s. 25 (2).

Same

    (4)   For vehicles, machines, tools and equipment rated at greater than 10 horsepower, copies of any operating manuals issued by the manufacturers shall be kept readily available at the project. O. Reg. 145/00, s. 25 (2).

Inspection of equipment

94.   (1)   All mechanically-powered vehicles, machines, tools and equipment rated at greater than 10 horsepower shall be inspected by a competent worker to determine whether they can handle their rated capacity and to identify any defects or hazardous conditions. O. Reg. 145/00, s. 26.

    (2)   The inspections shall be performed before the vehicles, machines, tools or equipment are first used at the project and thereafter at least once a year or more frequently as recommended by the manufacturer. O. Reg. 145/00, s. 26.

Safety factor

95. (1)   Every replacement part for a vehicle, machine, tool or equipment shall have at least the same safety factor as the part it is replacing. O. Reg. 213/91, s. 95 (1).

(2)   No modification to, extension to, repair to or replacement of a part of a vehicle, machine, tool or equipment shall result in a reduction of the safety factor of the vehicle, machine, tool or equipment. O. Reg. 213/91, s. 95 (2).

Worker qualifications

96. (1)   No worker shall operate a vehicle at a project unless he or she is competent to do so. O. Reg. 145/00, s. 26.

(2)   However, a worker being trained in the operation of a vehicle may operate it while being instructed and supervised by a competent person. O. Reg. 145/00, s. 26.

Brakes, seat

97. (1)   Every vehicle other than a trailer shall be equipped with brakes and a seat or other place for the vehicle operator. O. Reg. 213/91, s. 97 (1).

(2)   No person other than the operator shall ride on a vehicle unless a seat is provided for the use of, and is used by, the person. O. Reg. 213/91, s. 97 (2).

Means of access

98.   The means of access to any operator's station in a vehicle, machine or equipment shall not endanger the operator and shall have skid-resistant walking, climbing and work surfaces. O. Reg. 213/91, s. 98.

Overhead protection

99. A cab or screen shall be provided to protect a worker who is exposed to an overhead hazard while operating a vehicle. O. Reg. 213/91, s. 99.

Drawing, towing

100. (1) No vehicle, machine or equipment shall be drawn or towed by another vehicle on a project unless there are two separate means of attachment to the vehicle drawing or towing it. O. Reg. 213/91, s. 100 (1).

(2) Subsection (1) does not apply with respect to a vehicle being drawn or towed in which there is an operator and that has brakes that are able to stop the vehicle with its load, if any. O. Reg. 213/91, s. 100 (2).

(3) Each means of attachment referred to in subsection (1) shall be constructed and attached in such a way that the failure of one means of attachment does not permit the vehicle, machine or equipment being drawn or towed to become detached from the other vehicle. O. Reg. 213/91, s. 100 (3).

Loading, unloading

101. (1) No worker shall remain on or in a vehicle, machine or equipment while it is being loaded or unloaded if the worker might be endangered by remaining there. O. Reg. 213/91, s. 101 (1).

Unattended equipment

(2) Such action as may be necessary to prevent an unattended vehicle, machine or equipment from being started or set in motion by an unauthorized person shall be taken. O. Reg. 213/91, s. 101 (2).

(3) An unattended vehicle, machine or equipment shall have its brakes applied and its wheels blocked to prevent movement when

the vehicle, machine or equipment is on sloping ground or is adjacent to an excavation. O. Reg. 213/91, s. 101 (3).

Control attendance

102. No operator shall leave unattended the controls of,

(a) a front-end loader, backhoe or other excavating machine with its bucket raised;

(b) a bulldozer with its blade raised;

(c) a fork-lift truck with its forks raised; or

(d) a crane or other similar hoisting device with its load raised. O. Reg. 213/91, s. 102.

Overhead loads

103. (1) No worker shall operate a shovel, backhoe or similar excavating machine in such a way that it or part of its load passes over a worker. O. Reg. 213/91, s. 103 (1).

(2) No worker shall operate a crane or similar hoisting device in such a way that part of its load passes over another worker unless the other worker is receiving the load or is engaged in sinking a shaft. O. Reg. 213/91, s. 103 (2).

(3) If practicable, a worker who is receiving a load or is engaged in sinking a shaft shall be positioned so that no load or part of a load carried by a crane or similar hoisting device passes over the worker. O. Reg. 213/91, s. 103 (3).

(4) Subsections (2) and (3) do not apply in respect of a multi-tiered load as defined in section 103.1 if written procedures have been developed and implemented for the particular project in accordance with that section. O. Reg. 627/05, s. 2.

103.1(1)   In this section,

"move" includes raise and lower;

"multi-tiered load" means two or three individually rigged structural steel pieces that are,

(a)   suspended so that they remain horizontal,

(b)   aligned vertically, and

(c)   moved simultaneously by a crane;

"multi-tiered load hoisting operation" means the moving of one or more multi-tiered loads by one crane at a project;

"procedures" means the procedures prepared under subsection (7). O. Reg. 627/05, s. 3.

(2)   A multi-tiered load,

(a)   shall not contain structural steel pieces that are bundled together;

(b)   shall not contain more than three structural steel pieces;

(c)   shall not use one structural steel piece to support another;

(d)   shall have each structural steel piece independently slung back to the main load hook or master link;

(e)   shall be lowered only by a crane using power-controlled lowering. O. Reg. 627/05, s. 3.

(3)   A crane shall be used to move only one multi-tiered load at a time. O. Reg. 627/05, s. 3.

(4)   A crane shall not be used for a multi-tiered load if it is contrary to the crane manufacturer's specifications or limitations to do so. O. Reg. 627/05, s. 3.

(5)   No worker shall be in an area where a multi-tiered load hoisting operation is taking place unless he or she is directly engaged in the operation. O. Reg. 627/05, s. 3.

(6)   Before a multi-tiered load hoisting operation is begun at a project, written procedures to ensure the safety of workers engaged in the operation shall be developed and implemented. O. Reg. 627/05, s. 3.

(7)   The procedures shall be prepared by a professional engineer in accordance with good engineering practice and shall,

(a)   include design drawings that illustrate the arrangement and dimensions of the structural steel pieces, the assembly of rigging components and devices, and all attachment points;

(b)   identify the crane and its rated load-carrying capacity, and identify and specify its limitations and restrictions, if any;

(c)   describe the method of determining the weight of the structural steel pieces;

(d)   specify the maximum load per lift and the maximum reach of the crane per lift;

(e)   identify all factors that could affect the safety of the multi-tiered load hoisting operation, such as wind speed, weather conditions, potential overlapping of cranes and other restrictions;

(f)   state the measures to be taken to control and secure multi-tiered loads while they are being moved;

(g)   specify any circumstances that would require additional work, including inspections, to be performed by a professional engineer to ensure the safety of any worker engaged in the multi-tiered load hoisting operation; and

(h)   identify all critical parts of the rigging and the rigged structural steel pieces that are to be inspected before each lift, and set out the inspection criteria to be followed. O. Reg. 627/05, s. 3.

(8)   The employer responsible for a multi-tiered load hoisting operation shall,

(a)   create a document that identifies the workers engaged in the multi-tiered load hoisting operation by name and job title and states their respective duties;

(b)   ensure that, before the multi-tiered load hoisting operation is begun, a copy of the procedures is provided to and reviewed with each worker engaged in the operation;

(c)   ensure that the procedures are implemented, and are followed throughout the multi-tiered load hoisting operation;

(d)   ensure that any deviations from the procedures are approved by a professional engineer, in writing, before any multi-tiered load is moved; and

(e)   unless the professional engineer who prepared the procedures specifies otherwise, appoint a competent worker to ensure that the procedures, including the inspections described in clause (7) (h), are followed before any multi-tiered load is moved. O. Reg. 627/05, s. 3.

(9)   The employer responsible for a multi-tiered load hoisting operation shall keep a copy of the following available for inspection at the project until the operation is completed:

1.   The procedures.

2.   The document described in clause (8) (a).

3.   Any approvals given under clause (8) (d). O. Reg. 627/05, s. 3.

(10) Before the first multi-tiered load hoisting operation is started at a project, the constructor shall give notice to the Ministry office located nearest the project, in person, by telephone, by fax or by electronic means. O. Reg. 627/05, s. 3.

Reversing

104. (1)   Every project shall be planned and organized so that vehicles, machines and equipment are not operated in reverse or are operated in reverse as little as possible. O. Reg. 145/00, s. 27.

(2)   Vehicles, machines and equipment at a project shall not be operated in reverse unless there is no practical alternative to doing so. O. Reg. 145/00, s. 27.

Signaller

(3)   Operators of vehicles, machines and equipment shall be assisted by signallers if either of the following applies:

1.   The operator's view of the intended path of travel is obstructed.

2. A person could be endangered by the vehicle, machine or equipment or by its load. O. Reg. 145/00, s. 27.

(4) Subsection (3) also applies to shovels, backhoes and similar excavating machines and to cranes and similar hoisting devices. O. Reg. 145/00, s. 27.

(5) The operator and the signaller shall,

(a) jointly establish the procedures by which the signaller assists the operator; and

(b) follow those procedures. O. Reg. 145/00, s. 27.

Signs

(6) If subsection (3) applies to the project and it is not possible to carry out the project without some operation of vehicles and equipment in reverse, signs shall be posted at the project in conspicuous places warning workers of the danger. O. Reg. 145/00, s. 27.

Dump truck alarm

105. A dump truck shall be equipped with an automatic audible alarm that signals when the truck is being operated in reverse. O. Reg. 145/00, s. 27.

106. (1) A signaller shall be a competent worker and shall not perform other work while acting as a signaller. O. Reg. 213/91, s. 106 (1).

Protective clothing

(1.1) The signaller shall wear a garment that covers at least his or her upper body and has the following features:

1. The garment shall be fluorescent blaze or international orange in colour.

2. On the front and the back, there shall be two yellow stripes that are 5 centimetres wide. The yellow area shall total at least 500 square centimetres on the front and at least 570 square centimetres on the back.

3. On the front, the stripes shall be arranged vertically and centred and shall be approximately 225 millimetres apart, measured from the centre of each stripe. On the back, they shall be arranged in a diagonal "X" pattern.

4. The stripes shall be retro-reflective and fluorescent. O. Reg. 145/00, s. 28.

(1.2) If the garment is a vest, it shall have adjustable fit. O. Reg. 145/00, s. 28.

(1.3) On and after January 1, 2001, a nylon vest to which this section applies shall also have a side and front tear-away feature. O. Reg. 145/00, s. 28.

(1.4) In addition, a signaller who may be endangered during night-time hours shall wear retro-reflective silver stripes encircling each arm and leg, or equivalent side visibility-enhancing stripes with a minimum area of 50 square centimetres per side. O. Reg. 145/00, s. 28.

Training

(1.5) The employer shall,

(a) ensure that the signaller has received adequate oral training in his or her duties and has received adequate oral and written instructions in a language that he or she understands; and

(b) keep the written instructions at the project. O. Reg. 145/00, s. 28.

(2)   A signaller,

   (a)   shall be clear of the intended path of travel of the vehicle, machine or equipment, crane or similar hoisting device, shovel, backhoe or similar excavating machine or its load;

   (b)   shall be in full view of the operator of the vehicle, machine or equipment, crane or similar hoisting device, shovel, backhoe or similar excavating machine;

   (c)   shall have a clear view of the intended path of travel of the vehicle, machine or equipment, crane or similar hoisting device, shovel, backhoe or similar excavating machine or its load; and

   (d)   shall watch the part of the vehicle, machine or equipment or crane or similar hoisting device, shovel, backhoe or similar excavating machine or its load whose path of travel the operator cannot see. O. Reg. 213/91, s. 106 (2).

(3)   The signaller shall communicate with the operator by means of a telecommunication system or, where visual signals are clearly visible to the operator, by means of prearranged visual signals. O. Reg. 213/91, s. 106 (3).

Platform, etc., as workplace
107. No worker shall use as a work place a platform, bucket, basket, load, hook or sling that is capable of moving and that is supported by a fork-lift truck, front-end loader or similar machine. O. Reg. 213/91, s. 107.

Blocking

108. Blocking shall be installed to prevent the collapse or movement of part or all of a piece of equipment that is being dismantled, altered or repaired if its collapse or movement may endanger a worker. O. Reg. 213/91, s. 108.

Guarding

109. Every gear, pulley, belt, chain, shaft, flywheel, saw and other mechanically-operated part of a machine to which a worker has access shall be guarded or fenced so that it will not endanger a worker. O. Reg. 213/91, s. 109.

Chains, cages

110. (1) Safety chains, cages or other protection against blown-off side or lock rings shall be used when inflating a tire mounted on a rim. O. Reg. 213/91, s. 110 (1).

(2) If a cage is used, the tire shall be inflated by remote means. O. Reg. 213/91, s. 110 (2).

Lifting jack

111. (1) A lifting jack shall have its rated capacity legibly cast or stamped on it in a place where it can be readily seen. O. Reg. 213/91, s. 111 (1).

(2) A lifting jack shall be equipped with a positive stop to prevent overtravel or, if a positive stop is not practicable, with an overtravel indicator. O. Reg. 213/91, s. 111 (2).

Chain-saw

112. (1) Every chain-saw shall have a chain that minimizes kickback and a device to stop the chain in the event of a kickback. O. Reg. 213/91, s. 112 (1).

Chain-saw training and protection

(1.1) No worker shall use a chain-saw unless he or she has been adequately trained in its use. O. Reg. 145/00, s. 29.

(1.2) No worker shall use a chain-saw unless he or she is wearing,

    (a)   adequate personal protective equipment and clothing, including gloves; and

    (b)   adequate eye protection and hearing protection. O. Reg. 145/00, s. 29.

(2)   A worker shall hold a chain-saw firmly when starting it and firmly in both hands when using it. O. Reg. 213/91, s. 112 (2).

(3)   The chain of a chain-saw shall be stopped when not cutting. O. Reg. 213/91, s. 112 (3).

Miscellaneous object hazard

113. No object or material shall be placed, left or stored in a location or manner that may endanger a worker. O. Reg. 213/91, s. 113.

Hose

114. A hose that may whip shall be attached to a rope or chain in order to prevent whipping. O. Reg. 213/91, s. 114.

Barrel, etc., as workplace

115. No barrel, box or other loose object shall be used as a work place or as a support for a ladder, scaffold or work platform. O. Reg. 213/91, s. 115.

Stilts

116. (1)   No stilts shall be present at or used on a project except in accordance with this section. O. Reg. 443/09, s. 4.

(2)   No leg extensions, other than stilts, shall be present at or used on a project. O. Reg. 443/09, s. 4.

(3)   Subject to subsection (4), stilts may be used on a project for work in residential units and residential common areas only if they are used for the following purposes:

    1.   Drywall finishing work.

    2.   Installation of insulation.

    3.   Installation of vapour barriers. O. Reg. 443/09, s. 4.

(4)   Stilts shall not be used on a scaffold or to climb up or down stairs. O. Reg. 443/09, s. 4.

(5)   Stilts used in accordance with this section shall,

    (a)   be commercially manufactured;

    (b)   be made of unpainted metal;

    (c)   have a non-slip surface on the bottom of each base plate;

    (d)   be in good working condition; and

    (e)   be suitable for their intended use. O. Reg. 443/09, s. 4.

(6)   Stilts may be used to a maximum height of 76 centimetres as measured from the work surface that the user of the stilts would otherwise stand on to the top of the foot plate. O. Reg. 443/09, s. 4.

(7)   Stilts may be used on a work surface only if the work surface satisfies the following conditions:

    1.   It is made of rigid material.

2. It is either level or does not have a slope of more than three per cent.

3. All openings on the work surface are adequately covered or guarded.

4. All open sides of the work surface are adequately guarded.

5. It is free of debris or anything else that may be a hazard to a worker on stilts.

6. All obstructions that cannot be removed are adequately guarded, placed or secured to prevent a worker on stilts from being injured. O. Reg. 443/09, s. 4.

(8) If stilts are used in a work area for which sections 26.1 and 26.3 require a guardrail system, the guardrail system shall be modified by adding,

(a) an additional top rail,

(i) 76 centimetres above the existing top rail, or

(ii) at a height above the existing top rail equal to the height of the stilts being used in the work area; and

(b) an intermediate rail that is located midway between the additional top rail and the existing top rail. O. Reg. 443/09, s. 4.

(9) A modified guardrail system described in subsection (8) shall be capable of resisting any load it could be subjected to by a worker on stilts. O. Reg. 443/09, s. 4.

(10) An employer shall ensure that a worker who uses stilts is trained in their use by completing an adequate training program that,

(a) enables the worker to demonstrate proficiency in the safe and proper use of stilts; and

(b) provides instruction on the relevant requirements of this Regulation; and

(c) provides instruction on,

(i) mounting and dismounting,

(ii) adjusting stilts to suit the individual worker and the work,

(iii) walking on and working with stilts while maintaining balance and stability,

(iv) inspecting stilts for damage and defects,

(v) maintaining, servicing and storing stilts,

(vi) conducting an inspection of the work area before commencing work to identify hazards for stilts use,

(vii) correcting any hazardous conditions identified under subclause (vi), and

(viii) setting up tools and materials to ensure they are adequately accessible when using stilts. O. Reg. 443/09, s. 4.

(11) No worker shall use stilts at a project unless he or she has successfully completed a program described in subsection (10) and

carries proof of completing the program at all times when using the stilts. O. Reg. 443/09, s. 4.

(12) A worker using stilts at a project shall inspect the stilts for damage, wear, corrosion and other defects the first time each day that the worker uses the stilts. O. Reg. 443/09, s. 4.

(13) An employer shall ensure that a worker does not use stilts that are damaged, worn, corroded or defective and no worker shall use such stilts. O. Reg. 443/09, s. 4.

(14) Stilts shall be stored, serviced and maintained in accordance with the manufacturer's instructions. O. Reg. 443/09, s. 4.

Explosive Actuated Fastening Tool

Training

117. (1)   No worker shall use an explosive actuated fastening tool unless he or she has been adequately trained in its use. O. Reg. 145/00, s. 30.

(2)   When using an explosive actuated fastening tool, the worker shall carry proof of his or her training in its use. O. Reg. 145/00, s. 30.

Protection

(3)   No worker shall use an explosive actuated fastening tool unless he or she is wearing,

(a)   adequate personal protective equipment; and

(b)   adequate eye protection. O. Reg. 145/00, s. 30.

Inspection

118. A worker using an explosive actuated fastening tool shall inspect it before using it to ensure,

    (a)   that it is clean;

    (b)   that all moving parts operate freely;

    (c)   that its barrel is free from obstruction; and

    (d)   that it is not defective. O. Reg. 213/91, s. 118.

Guard

119. (1)   No worker shall use an explosive actuated fastening tool unless it has a suitable protective guard,

    (a)   that is at least seventy-five millimetres in diameter;

    (b)   that is mounted at right angles to the barrel of the tool; and

    (c)   that is centred on the muzzle end of the tool, if practicable. O. Reg. 213/91, s. 119 (1).

(2)   An explosive actuated fastening tool shall be inoperable unless,

    (a)   its muzzle end is held against a surface using a force at least 22 newtons greater than the force equivalent of the weight of the tool measured in newtons; and

    (b)   when a protective guard is centred on the muzzle end of the tool, the bearing surface of the guard is not tilted more than eight degrees from the work surface. O. Reg. 145/00, s. 31.

(3)   Subsection (1) and clause (2) (b) do not apply with respect to an explosive actuated fastening tool if the velocity of a fastener fired from it does not exceed 90 metres per second measured at a distance of two metres from its muzzle end when propelled by the

maximum commercially-available explosive load it is chambered to accept. O. Reg. 213/91, s. 119 (3).

(4)   An explosive actuated fastening tool that is designed to require dismantling into separate parts for loading shall be inoperable unless the separate parts are locked together. O. Reg. 145/00, s. 31.

(5)   An explosive actuated fastening tool shall have a firing mechanism that prevents the tool from being fired if it is dropped or while it is being loaded and prepared for firing. O. Reg. 213/91, s. 119 (5).

(6)   The firing movement for an explosive actuated fastening tool shall be a separate action from the operation of bringing the tool into firing position. O. Reg. 145/00, s. 31.

(7)   An explosive actuated fastening tool shall not be capable of being fired until the operator performs the two separate actions described in subsection (6). O. Reg. 145/00, s. 31.

Storage
120. (1)   Every explosive actuated fastening tool shall be stored in a locked container when not in use. O. Reg. 213/91, s. 120 (1).

(2)   No explosive actuated fastening tool shall be left unattended when out of its container. O. Reg. 213/91, s. 120 (2).

(3)   No explosive actuated fastening tool shall be loaded unless it is being prepared for immediate use. O. Reg. 213/91, s. 120 (3).

(4)   No explosive actuated fastening tool, whether or not it is loaded, shall be pointed at a person. O. Reg. 213/91, s. 120 (4).

Load

121. (1) Every explosive load for an explosive actuated fastening tool,

    (a) shall be marked or labelled so that a worker can easily identify its strength; and

    (b) shall be stored in a locked container unless it is required for immediate use. O. Reg. 213/91, s. 121 (1).

(2) No explosive load for an explosive actuated fastening tool,

    (a) shall be stored in a container with explosive loads of other strengths; or

    (b) shall be left unattended where it may be available to a worker who is not qualified to operate an explosive actuated fastening tool. O. Reg. 213/91, s. 121 (2).

(3) A misfired explosive load removed from an explosive actuated fastening tool shall be placed in a water-filled container on the project until the misfired explosive load is removed from the project. O. Reg. 213/91, s. 121 (3).

Welding and Cutting

122. (1) Cylinders, piping and fittings used in welding and cutting shall be protected against damage. O. Reg. 213/91, s. 122 (1).

(2) No cylinder of compressed gas used in welding and cutting shall be dropped, hoisted by slings or magnets or transported or stored in a horizontal position. O. Reg. 213/91, s. 122 (2).

(3) The valve of a cylinder shall be closed when the cylinder is spent or is not being used. O. Reg. 213/91, s. 122 (3).

123. Precautions to prevent a fire shall be taken when using a blow torch or welding or cutting equipment or a similar piece of equipment. O. Reg. 213/91, s. 123.

124. (1)   No arc welding electrode or ground lead shall be hung over a compressed gas cylinder. O. Reg. 213/91, s. 124 (1).

(2)   An area where electric welding is carried on shall be kept free of electrode stubs and metal scrap. O. Reg. 213/91, s. 124 (2).

(3)   Receptacles for electrode stubs shall be provided and used. O. Reg. 213/91, s. 124 (3).

Scaffolds and Work Platforms

125. (1)   A scaffold which meets the requirements of sections 126, 128, 129, 130, 134, 135, 137, 138, 139, 140, 141 and 142 shall be provided for workers where work cannot be done on or from the ground or from a building or other permanent structure without hazard to the workers. O. Reg. 213/91, s. 125 (1).

(2)   A worker who is on or under a scaffold while it is being erected, altered or dismantled shall be on a part of the scaffold or scaffold platform that meets the requirements of sections 126, 128, 129, 130, 134, 135, 137, 138, 139, 140, 141 and 142. O. Reg. 213/91, s. 125 (2).

Strength

126. (1)   Every scaffold shall be designed and constructed to support or resist,

(a)   two times the maximum load or force to which it is likely to be subjected, without exceeding the allowable unit stresses for the materials of which it is made; and

(b)   four times the maximum load or force to which it is likely to be subjected without overturning. O. Reg. 213/91, s. 126 (1).

(2)   Despite clause (1) (a), a scaffold with structural components whose capacity can only be determined by testing shall be designed and constructed to support or resist three times the maximum load or force to which it is likely to be subjected without causing the failure of any component. O. Reg. 213/91, s. 126 (2).

(3)   No scaffold shall be loaded in excess of the load that it is designed and constructed to bear. O. Reg. 213/91, s. 126 (3).

Failure load

127. (1)   The failure load of a scaffold which consists of structural components whose capacity cannot be determined by testing shall be established by testing the components in a manner that simulates the actual loading conditions for which each of the components is fabricated. O. Reg. 213/91, s. 127 (1).

(2)   A professional engineer shall verify and certify the results of a test and the corresponding rated load of the scaffold. O. Reg. 213/91, s. 127 (2).

(3)   The constructor shall make available to an inspector upon request a copy of the certification by the professional engineer. O. Reg. 213/91, s. 127 (3).

Construction

128. (1)   Every scaffold,

(a)   shall have uprights braced diagonally in the horizontal and vertical planes to prevent lateral movement;

(b)   shall have horizontal members that are adequately secured to prevent lateral movement and that do not have splices between the points of support;

(c)   shall have footings, sills or supports that are sound, rigid and capable of supporting at least two times the maximum load to which the scaffold may be subjected without settlement or deformation that may affect the stability of the scaffold;

(d)   shall have all fittings and gear, including base plates or wheels, installed in accordance with the manufacturer's instructions;

(e)   shall have connecting devices between frames that provide positive engagement in tension and compression;

(f)   shall have safety catches on all hooks; and

(g)   shall be adequately secured at vertical intervals not exceeding three times the least lateral dimension of the scaffold, measured at the base, to prevent lateral movement. O. Reg. 213/91, s. 128 (1).

(2)   A scaffold shall be constructed of suitable structural materials and, if lumber is used, it shall be construction grade or Number 1 Grade spruce. O. Reg. 213/91, s. 128 (2).

(3)   A scaffold mounted on pneumatic tires shall not be supported by the pneumatic tires while the scaffold is being erected, used or dismantled. O. Reg. 213/91, s. 128 (3).

Tubular metal frames

(4)   If tubular metal frames are used to support masonry units on a scaffold platform, each frame leg shall have a minimum working load of,

(a)   twenty-two kilonewtons for standard frames; and

(b)   16.7 kilonewtons for walk-through frames. O. Reg. 213/91, s. 128 (4).

Castors, wheels

129. (1)   A scaffold mounted on castors or wheels,

(a)   shall be equipped with a suitable braking device on each castor or wheel; and

(b)   shall have the brakes applied when a worker is on the scaffold. O. Reg. 213/91, s. 129 (1).

(2)   A scaffold mounted on castors or wheels shall be equipped with guy wires or outriggers to prevent its overturning if the height of the scaffold platform exceeds three times the least lateral dimension of the scaffold,

(a)   measured at the base of the scaffold; or

(b)   if outriggers are used, measured between the outriggers. O. Reg. 213/91, s. 129 (2).

(3)   No scaffold mounted on castors or wheels that has a scaffold platform more than 2.4 metres above the base shall be moved when a worker is on it unless,

(a)   the worker is wearing a full body harness as part of a fall arrest system attached to a fixed support; and

(b) the scaffold is being moved on a firm level surface.
O. Reg. 213/91, s. 129 (3).

Design, installation

130. (1) A scaffold shall be designed by a professional engineer and shall be erected in accordance with the design if the scaffold exceeds,

(a) fifteen metres in height above its base support; or

(b) ten metres in height above its base support if the scaffold is constructed of a tube and clamp system. O. Reg. 213/91, s. 130 (1).

(2) Design drawings for a scaffold shall set out erection instructions and the rated loads for the scaffold. O. Reg. 85/04, s. 12.

Inspection

(3) A professional engineer or a competent worker designated by the supervisor of the project shall inspect the scaffold before it is used to ensure that it is erected in accordance with the design drawings. O. Reg. 213/91, s. 130 (3).

(4) The person carrying out an inspection shall state in writing whether the scaffold is erected in accordance with the design drawings. O. Reg. 213/91, s. 130 (4).

(5) The constructor shall keep at a project the design drawings and the written statement for a scaffold while the scaffold is erected. O. Reg. 213/91, s. 130 (5).

Competent worker

131. Only a competent worker shall supervise the erection, alteration and dismantling of a scaffold. O. Reg. 213/91, s. 131.

Centre pole

132. (1) A professional engineer shall inspect and give a written opinion as to the structural adequacy of a centre pole scaffold used in silo construction when required by subsection (2). O. Reg. 213/91, s. 132 (1).

(2) An inspection shall be performed on the earlier of,

(a) the twenty-fourth time the scaffold is erected following the most recent inspection; or

(b) for a scaffold used in the construction of,

(i) a monolithic silo, two years after the scaffold is erected or after the most recent inspection, and

(ii) a stave silo, one year after the scaffold is erected or after the most recent inspection. O. Reg. 213/91, s. 132 (2).

(3) The employer responsible for constructing the silo shall keep with a scaffold every written opinion by a professional engineer concerning the scaffold while it is in use on a project. O. Reg. 213/91, s. 132 (3).

(4) The employer responsible for constructing the silo shall record information about the frequency of use of the scaffold in a log book which shall be kept with the scaffold while it is in use on a project. O. Reg. 213/91, s. 132 (4).

Re-bar installation

133. (1) This section applies with respect to a worker who is installing reinforcing steel on a vertical surface consisting of horizontal reinforcing steel bars. O. Reg. 213/91, s. 133 (1).

(2)   A scaffold shall be provided for a worker who is working more than 3.7 metres above the ground or a floor. O. Reg. 213/91, s. 133 (2).

Work belts

(3)   If a scaffold cannot be erected, a worker shall use and wear a work belt. O. Reg. 213/91, s. 133 (3).

(4)   No worker who is climbing the vertical surface shall carry reinforcing steel bars. O. Reg. 213/91, s. 133 (4).

Strength

134. (1)   Every scaffold platform and other work platform shall be designed, constructed and maintained to support or resist, without exceeding the allowable unit stresses for the materials of which it is constructed,

   (a)   all loads and forces to which it is likely to be subjected; and

   (b)   at least 2.4 kilonewtons per square metre. O. Reg. 213/91, s. 134 (1).

(2)   Each component of a scaffold platform or other work platform shall be capable of supporting a load of at least 2.2 kilonewtons without exceeding the allowable unit stress for each material used. O. Reg. 213/91, s. 134 (2).

(3)   No scaffold platform or other work platform shall be loaded in excess of the load that it is designed and constructed to bear. O. Reg. 213/91, s. 134 (3).

135. (1)   A scaffold platform or other work platform,

   (a)   shall be at least 460 millimetres wide;

    (b)   if it is 2.4 metres or more above a floor, roof or other surface, consist of planks laid tightly side by side for the full width of the scaffold;

    (c)   shall be provided with a guardrail as required by section 26.3;

    (d)   shall be provided with a means of access as required by section 70;

    (e)   shall not have any unguarded openings; and

    (f)   shall have each component secured against slipping from its supports. O. Reg. 213/91, s. 135 (1); O. Reg. 527/00, s. 4.

(2)   A scaffold platform or other work platform made of sawn lumber planks shall have planks of number 1 grade spruce that do not have any defect affecting their load-carrying capacity and,

    (a)   that bear a legible grade identification stamp or are permanently identified as being number 1 grade spruce;

    (b)   that are at least forty-eight millimetres thick by 248 millimetres wide;

    (c)   that are arranged so that their span does not exceed 2.1 metres;

    (d)   that overhang their supports by not less than 150 millimetres and not more than 300 millimetres; and

    (e)   that are cleated or otherwise secured against slipping. O. Reg. 213/91, s. 135 (2).

Masonry

136. (1) Cubes of masonry units on a scaffold platform shall be placed directly over the scaffold frame. O. Reg. 213/91, s. 136 (1).

(2) If it is not practicable to comply with subsection (1), the masonry units shall be placed on the scaffold platform in a manner that conforms with the load capability provisions of the scaffold platform as set out in section 134. O. Reg. 213/91, s. 136 (2).

(3) The surface of an outrigger bracket platform used by a masonry worker shall be not more than one metre below the associated material storage platform. O. Reg. 213/91, s. 136 (3).

(4) Masonry units to be installed in a building or structure shall be distributed along the scaffold platform before being used. O. Reg. 213/91, s. 136 (4).

Suspended Platforms and Scaffolds and Boatswain's Chairs

136.1 Sections 137 to 142 do not apply to multi-point suspended scaffolds. O. Reg. 85/04, s. 13.

Platform, scaffold, boatswain's chair

137. (1) Every suspended platform, suspended scaffold and boatswain's chair shall meet the requirements of this section. O. Reg. 213/91, s. 137 (1).

(2) A suspended platform, suspended scaffold or boatswain's chair shall be attached to a fixed support or outrigger beam in accordance with the manufacturer's instructions. O. Reg. 213/91, s. 137 (2).

(3) A fixed support or outrigger beam shall be capable of supporting at least four times the maximum load to which it may be subjected without exceeding the allowable unit stresses for the

materials of which it is constructed and without overturning. O. Reg. 213/91, s. 137 (3).

(4)   An outrigger beam shall be tied back to a fixed support with a secondary line, each of which is capable of supporting the weight of the suspended load and the supporting system. O. Reg. 213/91, s. 137 (4).

(5)   An outrigger beam shall be secured against horizontal and vertical movement. O. Reg. 213/91, s. 137 (5).

(6)   An outrigger beam shall have securely attached counterweights that are designed and manufactured for the purpose. O. Reg. 213/91, s. 137 (6).

(7)   Adequate legible instructions for the use of the counterweights shall be affixed to the outrigger beam. O. Reg. 213/91, s. 137 (7).

(8)   Every part of the hoisting and rigging system for a suspended platform, suspended scaffold or boatswain's chair shall be capable of supporting at least ten times the maximum load to which the part is likely to be subjected. O. Reg. 213/91, s. 137 (8).

(9)   A suspended platform, suspended scaffold or boatswain's chair that is capable of moving either horizontally or vertically shall have,

    (a)   supporting cables,

        (i)   that are vertical from the fixed support or outrigger beam,

        (ii)   that are parallel if there is more than one supporting cable, and

        (iii)   that extend to the ground or have a positive stop that prevents the suspended platform, suspended scaffold or boatswain's chair from running off the end of the supporting cables; and

Rope falls

(b) rope falls equipped with suitable pulley blocks or a mechanical hoisting device that,

(i) has legible operating and safety instructions affixed to it in a conspicuous location, and

(ii) is equipped with a positive device to prevent the platform, scaffold or boatswain's chair from falling freely. O. Reg. 213/91, s. 137 (9).

(10) A suspended platform, suspended scaffold or boatswain's chair shall have steel wire rope support cables,

(a) if the distance between the platform, scaffold or boatswain's chair and the fixed support exceeds 90 metres;

(b) if a corrosive substance is in the vicinity of the support rope; or

(c) if mechanical grinding or flame-cutting equipment is used in the vicinity of the support rope. O. Reg. 213/91, s. 137 (10).

Inspection

(11) A competent worker shall inspect a suspended platform, suspended scaffold or boatswain's chair before each day's use if it is operated by mechanical power. O. Reg. 213/91, s. 137 (11).

138. (1) Every suspended platform and suspended scaffold shall meet the requirements of this section. O. Reg. 213/91, s. 138 (1).

(2)   A suspended platform or suspended scaffold shall have hangers located at least 150 millimetres but not more than 450 millimetres from the ends of the platform or scaffold that are securely attached to it. O. Reg. 213/91, s. 138 (2).

(3)   A suspended platform or suspended scaffold shall be firmly anchored to the building or structure if practicable unless the platform or scaffold is being raised or lowered. O. Reg. 213/91, s. 138 (3).

(4)   Wire mesh at least 1.6 millimetres in diameter and capable of rejecting a ball thirty-eight millimetres in diameter shall be securely fastened in place from the toe-board to the top rail of the guardrails of a suspended platform or suspended scaffold. O. Reg. 213/91, s. 138 (4).

Tiering, stacking

139. (1)   Every suspended scaffold that consists of more than one platform and every suspended platform that, together with its components, weighs more than 525 kilograms shall meet the requirements of this section. O. Reg. 213/91, s. 139 (1).

(2)   A professional engineer shall design a suspended scaffold or suspended platform in accordance with good engineering practice. O. Reg. 213/91, s. 139 (2).

Design drawings

(3)   There shall be design drawings for a suspended scaffold or suspended platform that,

(a)   set out the size and specification of all components of the scaffold or platform including the type and grade of all materials to be used;

(b)   state the maximum live load of the scaffold or platform; and

(c)   state that, in the opinion of the professional engineer who designed the scaffold or platform, the design meets the requirements of this section.

(d)   **Revoked:** O. Reg. 213/91, s. 139 (3); O. Reg. 85/04, s. 14.

(4)   A suspended scaffold or suspended platform shall be erected in accordance with the design drawings. O. Reg. 213/91, s. 139 (4).

(5)   Before a suspended scaffold or suspended platform is used, a professional engineer shall inspect it and state in writing that it has been erected in accordance with the design drawings. O. Reg. 213/91, s. 139 (5).

(6)   No person shall use a suspended scaffold or suspended platform until the statement required by subsection (5) has been given. O. Reg. 213/91, s. 139 (6).

(7)   The constructor shall keep a copy of the design drawings and the statement required by subsection (5) on a project while the suspended scaffold or suspended platform is on the project. O. Reg. 213/91, s. 139 (7).

(8)   If it is stacked or tiered a suspended platform or suspended scaffold shall have at least two independent means of support which shall be so arranged that the failure of one support will not result in the failure of the suspended platform or suspended scaffold. O. Reg. 213/91, s. 139 (8).

Boatswain's chair

140. (1)   A boatswain's chair shall be at least 600 millimetres long and 250 millimetres wide. O. Reg. 213/91, s. 140 (1).

(2)   A boatswain's chair which is or is to be used by a worker who is using a corrosive substance or mechanical-grinding or flame-

cutting equipment shall be supported by a sling consisting of wire rope at least nine millimetres in diameter. O. Reg. 213/91, s. 140 (2).

Fall protection

141. (1)   A worker who is on or is getting on or off a suspended platform, suspended scaffold or boatswain's chair shall wear a full body harness connected to a fall arrest system. O. Reg. 213/91, s. 141 (1).

(2)   Every lifeline used with a suspended platform, suspended scaffold or boatswain's chair,

    (a)   shall be suspended independently from the platform, scaffold or boatswain's chair; and

    (b)   shall be securely attached to a fixed support so that the failure of the platform, scaffold or boatswain's chair or its supporting system will not cause the lifeline to fail. O. Reg. 213/91, s. 141 (2).

(3)   Despite clause (2) (a), the fall arrest system shall be securely fastened to the suspended platform or suspended scaffold if,

    (a)   all or part of the platform or scaffold has more than one means of support or suspension; and

    (b)   the platform or scaffold is so designed, constructed and maintained that the failure of one means of support or suspension will not cause the collapse of all or part of the platform or scaffold. O. Reg. 213/91, s. 141 (3).

142. (1)   The distance between the platform of an outrigger scaffold and the wall beyond which the scaffold extends shall not exceed 75 millimetres. O. Reg. 213/91, s. 142 (1).

(2)   The outrigger beams of an outrigger scaffold shall be secured against horizontal and vertical movement. O. Reg. 213/91, s. 142 (2).

Multi-Point Suspended Scaffolds

142.1 Sections 142.2 to 142.8 apply to every multi-point suspended scaffold. O. Reg. 85/04, s. 15.

142.2 (1) A multi-point suspended scaffold and all its components shall be designed by a professional engineer in accordance with good engineering practice and with this section. O. Reg. 85/04, s. 15.

(2)   A multi-point suspended scaffold shall be designed to support, in addition to its dead load, live loads uniformly distributed over the platform surface of at least,

(a)   2.4 kilonewtons per square metre if the platform is to be used for masonry work;

(b)   3.6 kilonewtons per square metre if the platform is to be used for demolition work or for storage of masonry units or other related material or equipment; or

(c)   1.2 kilonewtons per square metre in any other case. O. Reg. 85/04, s. 15.

(3)   In addition to the loads specified in subsection (2), a multi-point suspended scaffold shall be able to support or resist,

(a)   1.1 kilonewtons concentrated on an area measuring 0.3 metres by 0.3 metres that is located on the platform at the position having the most adverse effect on the component under consideration;

    (b)   the wind load determined in accordance with Table 2.5.1.1. (Design Data for Selected Locations in Ontario) of the Building Code, assuming a probability factor of at least one in ten; and

    (c)   any other loads likely to be applied to it. O. Reg. 85/04, s. 15.

(4)   The wind load referred to in clause (3) (b) may be reduced by 30 per cent if the professional engineer who designs the scaffold determines that it is appropriate to do so and indicates in writing that he or she has made the determination. O. Reg. 85/04, s. 15.

(5)   Subject to clause (2) (c) and subsections (3) and (4), the professional engineer who designs the scaffold shall determine the minimum specified loads for erecting, dismantling, traversing, or otherwise moving multi-point suspended scaffolds. O. Reg. 85/04, s. 15.

(6)   If a multi-point suspended scaffold is to be used for abrasive blasting operations, there shall be an additional load allowance for the accumulation of grit on the platform to a depth of at least 25 millimetres. O. Reg. 85/04, s. 15.

(7)   Subject to subsection (8), in designing a multi-point suspended scaffold and its structural members, the following values of load factors, as described in Section 4.1.3. (Limit States Design) of the Building Code, shall be applied to the load requirements referred to in subsections (2) to (6):

    1.   Live load factor $\alpha_L = 3.0$.

    2.   Dead load factor $\alpha_D = 1.5$.

    3.   Wind load factor $\alpha_W = 1.5$. O. Reg. 85/04, s. 15.

(8)   In designing the suspension and anchorage system of a multi-point suspended scaffold,

    (a)   the value of the live load factor α_L shall be 4.0;

    (b)   the value of the dead load factor α_D shall be 2.0; and

    (c)   the value of the wind load factor α_W shall be 2.0. O. Reg. 85/04, s. 15.

(9)   Despite subsections (7) and (8), a multi-point suspended scaffold and its components may be designed by working stress design if the safety factors for the scaffold and the structural members are at least equal to what would otherwise be provided under those subsections. O. Reg. 85/04, s. 15.

(10) Despite subsections (7) and (8), if the failure load of a component has been determined by testing, the minimum safety factors shall be,

    (a)   3.0 for components of the multi-point suspended scaffold;

    (b)   4.0 for components of the suspension and anchorage system; and

    (c)   10.0 for wire ropes, cables or chains used for hoisting, traversing or otherwise moving the multi-point suspended scaffold. O. Reg. 85/04, s. 15.

(11) The failure load of a component referred to in subsection (10) shall be verified in writing by a professional engineer. O. Reg. 85/04, s. 15.

(12) A multi-point suspended scaffold shall be designed, constructed and maintained in such a way that,

    (a)   the failure of one means of support or suspension will not cause any part of the scaffold to collapse or fail, under the most adverse loading condition as determined by the professional engineer who designs the scaffold; and

    (b)   compliance with subsections (7), (8), (9) and (10) is maintained in all fixed and moving conditions. O. Reg. 85/04, s. 15.

(13) The design of a multi-point suspended scaffold shall include adequate movement-limiting devices to be used when traversing or otherwise moving it. O. Reg. 85/04, s. 15.

(14) Before a multi-point suspended scaffold is erected, the constructor shall ensure that the professional engineer responsible for the structural integrity of the permanent building or structure from which the scaffold is suspended provides a written report approving the design loads imposed on the building or structure by the scaffold. O. Reg. 85/04, s. 15.

(15) Design drawings for a multi-point suspended scaffold shall include,

    (a)   a statement by the professional engineer that the design meets the requirements of this Regulation;

    (b)   the size and specifications of all components, including the type and grade of all materials to be used;

    (c)   the load factors and safety factors for the scaffold and all its components;

    (d)   all the specified loads, including the loads during erection, dismantling, traversing and otherwise moving; and

    (e)   the procedures for erection, dismantling, traversing and otherwise moving. O. Reg. 85/04, s. 15.

(16) The design drawings shall be followed, subject to subsection (17). O. Reg. 85/04, s. 15.

(17) A deviation from the design drawings is permitted if the deviation,

    (a)   is approved, in advance and in writing, by a professional engineer; and

    (b)   complies with this Regulation. O. Reg. 85/04, s. 15.

142.3 (1) Before erecting or dismantling a multi-point suspended scaffold, the constructor shall give notice, in person, by telephone, by fax or by electronic means, to the Ministry office located nearest the project. O. Reg. 85/04, s. 15.

(2) A multi-point suspended scaffold shall be inspected by a professional engineer to determine whether it complies with the design drawings, or the design drawings subject to any deviations approved under subsection 142.2 (17), as the case may be,

    (a)   after it is erected but before it is first used; and

    (b)   if the scaffold is moved to another anchorage position, before it is used there. O. Reg. 85/04, s. 15.

(3) The inspection under subsection (2) shall include a determination of whether all components are in adequate condition. O. Reg. 85/04, s. 15.

(4) The professional engineer who conducts the inspection under subsection (2) shall prepare a written report of the inspection. O. Reg. 85/04, s. 15.

    (5)   The written report is a positive report if it indicates that,

        (a)   the multi-point suspended scaffold complies with the design drawings, or the design drawings subject to any deviations approved under subsection 142.2 (17), as the case may be; and

        (b)   all components are in adequate condition. O. Reg. 85/04, s. 15.

(6)   Subsections (1), (2), (3), (4) and (5) do not apply to a multi-point suspended scaffold whose platform area is six square metres or less. O. Reg. 85/04, s. 15.

(7)   A competent worker shall inspect a multi-point suspended scaffold each day before it is used. O. Reg. 85/04, s. 15.

142.4 The constructor shall keep at the project a copy of,

    (a)   the written report under subsection 142.2 (14);

    (b)   the design drawings under subsection 142.2 (15);

    (c)   any written approvals under subsection 142.2 (17); and

    (d)   the written reports under subsection 142.3 (4). O. Reg. 85/04, s. 15.

142.5 (1) A multi-point suspended scaffold shall be erected, dismantled, traversed or otherwise moved only by a competent worker under the supervision of a competent person and in accordance with the design drawings, or the design drawings subject to any deviations approved under subsection 142.2 (17), as the case may be. O. Reg. 85/04, s. 15.

(2)   Before a worker is on a multi-point suspended scaffold for the first time, the employer shall provide the worker with adequate oral and written instructions for using the scaffold, including,

(a)   the manufacturer's instructions or a professional engineer's instructions;

(b)   instructions on the load limitations;

(c)   instructions in, and a hands-on demonstration of, the proper operation of the scaffold. O. Reg. 85/04, s. 15.

(3)   A worker who is to erect, dismantle, traverse or otherwise move a multi-point suspended scaffold shall, in addition to the instructions set out in subsection (2), be given instructions in the procedures described in clause 142.2 (15) (e). O. Reg. 85/04, s. 15.

(4)   No person shall use a multi-point suspended scaffold until the design drawings described in subsection 142.2 (15) have been given to the constructor and the following documents have been prepared and given to the constructor:

1.   The report described in subsection 142.2 (14).

2.   A positive report described in subsections 142.3 (4) and (5), if applicable.

3.   Any approval described in subsection 142.2 (17), if applicable. O. Reg. 85/04, s. 15.

142.6 (1) A multi-point suspended scaffold shall not be loaded in excess of the specified loads indicated on the design drawings for the scaffold. O. Reg. 85/04, s. 15.

(2)   Signs indicating the specified live loads shall be posted in conspicuous places on the scaffold. O. Reg. 85/04, s. 15.

142.7 (1)   A worker who is on a multi-point suspended scaffold while it is being erected, dismantled, traversed or otherwise moved shall use a fall arrest system that is,

(a)   connected to a fixed support independent from the scaffold; and

(b)   designed, constructed and maintained in accordance with this Regulation. O. Reg. 85/04, s. 15.

(2)   Despite subsection (1), a worker is not required to use a fall arrest system while the scaffold is stationary if guardrails are installed in accordance with section 26.3. O. Reg. 85/04, s. 15.

142.8 (1)   The constructor of a project where a multi-point suspended scaffold is used shall keep a written record of all inspections, tests, repairs, modifications and maintenance performed on the scaffold and make copies of the record available to an inspector upon request. O. Reg. 85/04, s. 15.

(2)   The record referred to in subsection (1) shall,

(a)   be kept up to date;

(b)   include the signature, name and business address of each person who performs an inspection, test, repair, modification or maintenance; and

(c)   be kept at the project while the scaffold is there. O. Reg. 85/04, s. 15.

Elevating Work Platforms

Elevating work platforms

143. (1) Subject to subsection (2), every elevating work platform, including elevating rolling work platforms, self-propelled elevating work platforms, boom-type elevating work platforms and vehicle-mounted aerial devices shall comply with section 144. O. Reg. 213/91, s. 143 (1).

(2) Subsection (1) does not apply to,

(a) suspended scaffolds or suspended work platforms; and

(b) buckets or baskets suspended from or attached to the boom of a crane. O. Reg. 213/91, s. 143 (2).

Design

144. (1) An elevating work platform shall be designed by a professional engineer in accordance with good engineering practice,

(a) to meet the requirements of the applicable National Standards of Canada standard, set out in the Table to subsection (6); and

Strength

(b) to support a minimum of 1.3 kilonewtons rated working load as determined in accordance with the applicable National Standards of Canada standard set out in the Table to subsection (6). O. Reg. 213/91, s. 144 (1).

Manufacture

(2) An elevating work platform shall be manufactured in accordance with the design referred to in subsection (1). O. Reg. 213/91, s. 144 (2).

(3) An elevating work platform,

Testing

    (a)   shall be tested in accordance with the National Standards of Canada standard set out in the Table to subsection (6); and

Inspection

    (b)   shall be inspected each day before use, in accordance with the manufacturer's instructions by a worker trained in accordance with section 147. O. Reg. 213/91, s. 144 (3).

Certification

(4)   An elevating work platform shall only be used if a professional engineer has certified in writing that it complies with the National Standards of Canada standard set out in the Table to subsection (6). O. Reg. 213/91, s. 144 (4).

(5)   The certification required by subsection (4) shall include the details of testing. O. Reg. 213/91, s. 144 (5).

(6)   The National Standards of Canada standard applicable to the type of elevating work platform listed in Column 1 of the Table to this subsection are the standards set out opposite it in Column 2:

TABLE

Column 1	Column 2
Elevating Work Platform	National Standards of Canada standard
Elevating Rolling Work Platform	CAN3-B354.1-M82
Self-Propelled Elevating Work Platform	CAN3-B354.2-M82 and CAN3-B354.3-M82
Boom-Type Elevating Work Platform	CAN3-B354.4-M82
Vehicle-Mounted Aerial Device	CAN-CSA-C225-M88

O. Reg. 213/91, s. 144 (6).

Guardrails

(7)   An elevating work platform shall be equipped with guardrails.
O. Reg. 213/91, s. 144 (7).

Signs

(8)   An elevating work platform shall have signs that are clearly visible to an operator at its controls indicating,

(a)   the rated working load;

(b)   all limiting operating conditions including the use of outriggers, stabilizers and extendable axles;

(c)   the specific firm level surface conditions required for use in the elevated position;

(d)   such warnings as may be specified by the manufacturer;

(e)   other than for a boom-type elevating work platform, the direction of machine movement for each operating control;

(f) the name and number of the National Standards of Canada standard to which it was designed; and

(g) the name and address of the owner. O. Reg. 213/91, s. 144 (8).

Safety factors

145. (1) The owner of an elevating work platform shall maintain it such that the safety factors of the original design are maintained. O. Reg. 213/91, s. 145 (1).

Records

(2) The owner of an elevating work platform shall keep a permanent record of all inspections, tests, repairs, modifications and maintenance performed on it. O. Reg. 213/91, s. 145 (2).

(3) The permanent record required by subsection (2),

(a) shall be kept up-to-date;

(b) shall include complete records from the more recent of,

(i) the date of purchase, or

(ii) the date this Regulation is filed; and

(c) shall include the signature and name of the person who performed the inspection, test, repair, modification or maintenance. O. Reg. 213/91, s. 145 (3).

Maintenance, inspection, tag

146. A maintenance and inspection record tag,

(a) shall be provided and attached to the elevating work platform near the operator's station; and

(b) shall include,

      (i)   the date of the last maintenance and inspection,

      (ii)   the signature and name of the person who performed the maintenance and inspection, and

      (iii) an indication that the maintenance has been carried out in accordance with the manufacturer's recommendations. O. Reg. 213/91, s. 146.

Instruction, training

147. (1)   A worker who operates an elevating work platform shall, before using it for the first time, be given oral and written instruction on the operation and be trained to operate that class of elevating work platform. O. Reg. 213/91, s. 147 (1).

(2)   The instruction and training required by subsection (1) shall include,

     (a)   the manufacturer's instruction;

     (b)   instruction in the load limitations;

     (c)   instruction in and a hands-on demonstration of the proper use of all controls; and

     (d)   instruction in the limitations on the kinds of surfaces on which it is designed to be used. O. Reg. 213/91, s. 147 (2).

Operating criteria

148. An elevating work platform,

     (a)   shall not be loaded in excess of its rated working load;

     (b)   shall be used only on a firm level surface;

(c) shall be used only in accordance with the written instructions of the manufacturer;

(d) shall not be loaded and used in such a manner as to affect its stability or endanger a worker; and

(e) shall not be moved unless all workers on it are protected against falling by a safety belt attached to the platform. O. Reg. 213/91, s. 148.

Operator's manual

149. An operator's manual for an elevating work platform shall be kept with it while it is on a project. O. Reg. 213/91, s. 149.

Cranes, Hoisting and Rigging

Certification

150. (1) Subject to subsection (2), no worker shall operate a crane or similar hoisting device unless the worker holds a certificate of qualification issued under the Ontario College of Trades and Apprenticeship Act, 2009, that is not suspended, or the worker is an apprentice and is working pursuant to a training agreement registered under that Act, that is not suspended, in the trade of,

(a) hoisting engineer — mobile crane operator 1, if the worker is operating a crane or similar hoisting device capable of raising, lowering or moving any material that weighs more than 30,000 pounds;

(b) hoisting engineer — mobile crane operator 1 or hoisting engineer — mobile crane operator 2, if the worker is operating a crane or similar hoisting device capable of raising, lowering or moving only material that weighs more than 16,000 pounds but no more than 30,000 pounds; or

(c)   hoisting engineer — tower crane operator, if the worker is operating a tower crane. O. Reg. 88/13, s. 1.

(1.1) Subsection (1) does not apply when a worker is using excavation equipment to place pipes into a trench. O. Reg. 631/94, s. 3.

(2)   No worker shall operate a crane or similar hoisting device, other than one described in subsection (1), unless,

(a)   the worker has written proof of training indicating that he or she is trained in the safe operation of the crane or similar hoisting device; or

(b)   the worker is being instructed in the operation of the crane or similar hoisting device and is accompanied by a person who meets the requirements of clause (a). O. Reg. 213/91, s. 150 (2).

(3)   A worker shall carry his or her proof of training while operating a crane or similar hoisting device. O. Reg. 213/91, s. 150 (3).

Capacity
151. (1)   No crane or similar hoisting device shall be subjected to a load greater than its rated load-carrying capacity. O. Reg. 213/91, s. 151 (1).

(2)   The manufacturer of a crane or similar hoisting device or a professional engineer shall determine its rated load-carrying capacity in accordance with,

(a)   for a mobile crane, Canadian Standards Association Standard Z150-1974 Safety Code for Mobile Cranes; and

(b)   for a tower crane, Canadian Standards Association Standard Z248-1976 Code for Tower Cranes. O. Reg. 213/91, s. 151 (2).

Load rating plate

(3)   Every crane or similar hoisting device shall have affixed to it a load rating plate,

(a)   that the operator can read while at the controls; and

(b)   that contains enough information for the operator to determine the load that can be lifted for each configuration of the crane. O. Reg. 213/91, s. 151 (3).

Boom angle indicator

(4)   A luffing boom crane, other than a tower crane, shall have affixed to it a boom angle indicator that the operator can read while at the controls. O. Reg. 213/91, s. 151 (4).

Inspection, records

152. (1)   The owner of a crane or similar hoisting device shall keep a permanent record of all inspections of, tests of, repairs to, modifications to and maintenance of the crane or similar hoisting device. O. Reg. 213/91, s. 152 (1).

Log book

(2)   The owner of a crane or similar hoisting device shall prepare a log book for it for use at a project that shall include the record referred to in subsection (1) covering the period that is the greater of,

(a)   the immediately preceding twelve months; and

(b)   the period the crane or similar hoisting device is on the project. O. Reg. 213/91, s. 152 (2).

(3)   The log book shall be kept with the crane or similar hoisting device. O. Reg. 213/91, s. 152 (3).

(4)   The owner of a crane or similar hoisting device shall retain and make available to the constructor on request copies of all log books and records for the crane or similar hoisting device. O. Reg. 213/91, s. 152 (4).

Platforms, etc., as workplace

153. (1)   No worker shall use as a workplace a platform, bucket, basket, load, hook, sling or similar device that is capable of moving and is supported by a cable attached to the boom of a crane or similar hoisting device, except in accordance with this section. O. Reg. 631/94, s. 4.

(2)   A crane may be used to raise, support or lower a worker only if,

    (a)   conventional access equipment cannot be used;

    (b)   the platform that the worker is on,

        (i)   is designed by a professional engineer in accordance with good engineering practice,

        (ii)   is constructed in accordance with the design drawings,

        (iii)   is equipped with more than one means of suspension or support,

        (iv)   is equipped with anchor points for the attachment of the worker's fall arrest systems,

        (v)   is equipped with a guardrail in accordance with section 26.3,

    (vi) is suspended from, or supported by, a direct attachment to the boom of the crane,

    (vii) is designed, constructed and maintained so that the failure of one means of support or suspension will not cause the collapse of all or part of the platform, and

    (viii) has its maximum rated load capacity legibly and permanently marked in a conspicuous place on it; and

(c) the crane,

Fail-safe mechanisms

    (i) is equipped with fail-safe mechanisms that will prevent the boom and the suspended platform from free falling in the event of a power source or system failure or the inadvertent release of any operating controls,

    (ii) is not used to hoist material while the platform is being used to support a worker,

    (iii) is not loaded in excess of 25 per cent of its maximum rated load,

Load rating chart

    (iv) has a revised load rating chart prepared by a professional engineer in accordance with good engineering practice and affixed in a conspicuous place on the crane,

    (v) has, on its hoist line, hooks equipped with self-closing safety catches at the point where the platform is suspended, and

Limit switch

(vi) is equipped with an automatic limit switch that prevents the platform and load from reaching beyond the highest permissible position specified by the crane manufacturer. O. Reg. 631/94, s. 4; O. Reg. 527/00, s. 5.

(3) Any modifications or repairs to the boom of the crane shall be made in accordance with the instructions of the crane manufacturer or a professional engineer. O. Reg. 631/94, s. 4.

Full body harness

(4) Every worker on the platform shall wear a full body harness connected independently to anchor points on the platform and used in conjunction with a lanyard fitted with a shock absorber. O. Reg. 631/94, s. 4.

(5) The design drawings of the platform shall,

(a) set out the size and specifications of all components of the platform, including the type and grade of materials used for it;

(b) state the maximum live load of the platform;

(c) specify the model and type of crane to be used in conjunction with the platform; and

(d) include a statement that, in the opinion of the professional engineer who designed the platform, the design meets the requirements of clauses (a), (b) and (c).

(e) **Revoked:** O. Reg. 631/94, s. 4; O. Reg. 85/04, s. 16.

(6)   Before the platform is used, a competent worker shall inspect it and verify in writing that it has been constructed in accordance with the design drawings. O. Reg. 631/94, s. 4.

(7)   No person shall use the platform until the verification required under subsection (6) is given. O. Reg. 631/94, s. 4.

Structural integrity inspection

(8)   A professional engineer or a competent worker designated by the professional engineer shall inspect the crane to ensure its structural integrity using non-destructive testing methods approved by the Canadian General Standards Board before the crane is used to lift persons and then at least once every 12 months after that. O. Reg. 631/94, s. 4.

(9)   A competent worker shall visually inspect the crane's structural elements and the rigging equipment for defects before each use of the crane. O. Reg. 631/94, s. 4.

(10) The employer shall ensure that an adequate means of communication between the worker on the platform and the crane operator is established, maintained and used. O. Reg. 631/94, s. 4.

(11) Before beginning any hoisting operation under this section, the constructor shall notify by telephone an inspector in the office of the Ministry of Labour nearest to the project. O. Reg. 631/94, s. 4.

Instructions

(12) The employer shall ensure that every worker involved with the hoisting operation receives adequate instructions about the requirements, restrictions and hazards associated with the hoisting operation. O. Reg. 631/94, s. 4.

Emergency rescue procedures

(13) The employer shall develop adequate emergency rescue procedures and communicate these in writing to all workers involved with the hoisting operation. O. Reg. 631/94, s. 4.

(14) The constructor shall keep all design drawings, test reports, written statements and certification documents required under this section with the crane at all times during the hoisting operation. O. Reg. 631/94, s. 4.

(15) On request, the constructor shall provide an inspector with copies of any document described in subsection (14). O. Reg. 631/94, s. 4.

Set-up, assembly, etc.
154. (1)   A crane or similar hoisting device shall be set up, assembled, extended and dismantled only by a competent worker acting in accordance with the written instructions of the manufacturer and in such a manner as to not endanger any person or property. O. Reg. 213/91, s. 154 (1).

Sections

(2)   No crane or similar hoisting device shall include sections that are not designed for it or that are damaged. O. Reg. 213/91, s. 154 (2).

Nuts, bolts, etc.

(3)   No crane or similar hoisting device shall include nuts, bolts, pins or fastenings that are not the size and quality specified by the manufacturer. O. Reg. 213/91, s. 154 (3).

155. Unless otherwise specified by its manufacturer, a crane or similar hoisting device,

Level indicator

    (a)   shall be equipped with a device to indicate whether its turntable is level; and

Turntable

    (b)   shall be operated with its turntable level. O. Reg. 213/91, s. 155.

Outriggers

156. An outrigger or stabilizing device used on a crane or similar hoisting device,

    (a)   shall be extended to meet load capacity chart requirements; and

    (b)   shall rest on blocking able to support the crane or similar hoisting device and its maximum load without failure or without deformation or settlement which affects its stability. O. Reg. 213/91, s. 156.

Tower Cranes

157. (1)   No tower crane shall be erected at a project except in accordance with this section. O. Reg. 213/91, s. 157 (1).

Foundations

(2)   The foundations supporting a tower crane shall be designed by a professional engineer in accordance with the crane manufacturer's specifications and shall be constructed in accordance with the design. O. Reg. 213/91, s. 157 (2).

Shoring, bracing

(3)   The shoring and bracing that support a tower crane or tie it in place shall be designed by a professional engineer in accordance with the crane manufacturer's specifications and shall be installed in accordance with the design. O. Reg. 213/91, s. 157 (3).

Integrity review

(4) The structural engineer responsible for the structural integrity of the building or structure shall review the design drawings for the foundation, shoring and bracing for a tower crane before the crane is erected at a project to ensure the structural integrity of the building or structure. O. Reg. 213/91, s. 157 (4).

(5) The structural engineer who reviews the design drawings shall sign the drawings upon approving them. O. Reg. 213/91, s. 157 (5).

(6) The constructor shall keep at the project while a tower crane is erected a copy of the signed design drawings for its foundation, shoring and bracing and any written opinion about the drawings by a structural engineer. O. Reg. 213/91, s. 157 (6).

Non-destructive testing

158. (1) Before a tower crane is erected at a project, a professional engineer or a competent worker designated by a professional engineer shall inspect its structural elements and components using methods of non-destructive testing approved by the Canadian General Standards Board to determine their structural integrity. O. Reg. 213/91, s. 158 (1); O. Reg. 631/94, s. 5.

(2) The professional engineer conducting an inspection or under whose direction an inspection is done shall prepare a written report of the test results. O. Reg. 213/91, s. 158 (2); O. Reg. 85/04, s. 17.

(3) The constructor shall keep the report at the project while the crane is erected. O. Reg. 213/91, s. 158 (3).

Inspection

159. (1) A professional engineer or a competent worker designated by a professional engineer shall visually inspect for defects the structural elements and components of a tower crane,

    (a)   after the crane is erected and before it is used; and

    (b)   after the inspection under clause (a), at intervals not greater than twelve months. O. Reg. 213/91, s. 159 (1).

(2)   No tower crane shall be used until any defects found during an inspection are repaired in accordance with the instructions of the crane's manufacturer or a professional engineer. O. Reg. 213/91, s. 159 (2).

Inspection of repairs

3)   A professional engineer or a competent worker designated by a professional engineer shall inspect a tower crane that has been repaired to ensure that the defects are corrected. O. Reg. 213/91, s. 159 (3).

(4)   The professional engineer conducting an inspection or under whose direction the inspection is done shall prepare a written report of the test results. O. Reg. 213/91, s. 159 (4); O. Reg. 85/04, s. 18.

(5)   The constructor shall keep the report at a project while the crane is erected. O. Reg. 213/91, s. 159 (5).

Switches, devices

160. (1)   A tower crane shall have automatic limit switches and automatic overload limit devices that prevent,

    (a)   overloading at relative radii;

    (b)   a load on the crane from reaching beyond the highest permissible position specified by the manufacturer; and

    (c)   the trolley from reaching beyond the permissible travel limit specified by the manufacturer. O. Reg. 213/91, s. 160 (1).

(2)   In addition to automatic limit switches and overload limit devices, a tower crane shall have such other switches and devices as the manufacturer specifies. O. Reg. 213/91, s. 160 (2).

Operational tests

161. (1)   A competent worker shall perform operational tests on a tower crane to ensure that its automatic limit switches and overload limit devices are installed and functioning in accordance with the manufacturer's specifications, if any. O. Reg. 213/91, s. 161 (1).

(2)   Operational tests shall be done,

(a)   after the tower crane is erected on the project and before it is used; and

(b)   at one-week intervals after the test under clause (a) while the crane is erected on the project. O. Reg. 213/91, s. 161 (2).

Test blocks

(3)   Overload limit devices for a tower crane shall be tested using test blocks designed for the purpose that have their weight clearly marked on them. O. Reg. 213/91, s. 161 (3).

(4)   The test blocks shall be kept on the project while the crane is erected. O. Reg. 213/91, s. 161 (4).

Slewing

162. (1)   A tower crane boom shall be able to slew freely when the crane is unattended except when,

(a)   the boom may collide with another crane, a structure or another object; or

(b)   to slew freely would be contrary to the written procedures of the crane's manufacturer. O. Reg. 213/91, s. 162 (1).

(2)   When a tower crane boom is not permitted to slew freely it shall be secured in accordance with the written procedures of the crane's manufacturer. O. Reg. 213/91, s. 162 (2).

Operator's cabin

163. (1)   Subject to subsection (2), the operator's cabin of a tower crane shall be located on and attached to or positioned on the crane in accordance with the instructions of the crane's manufacturer for the specific model and configuration of the crane and in such a manner that in the event of a failure of the boom, the cabin will not be crushed against the mast. O. Reg. 213/91, s. 163 (1).

(2)   The operator's cabin shall not be located on or attached to the boom unless,

(a)   the cabin and its attachments have been specifically designed and fabricated for that purpose by the original manufacturer of the crane in accordance with good engineering practice;

(b)   the boom of the crane cannot affect or be affected by the operation of another crane or make contact with a structure or equipment;

(c)   the crane is not overlapped by any part of another crane;

(d)   because of specific site conditions, the location of the cabin on the boom provides greater visibility for the operator than does the manufacturer's standard cabin location;

(e)   the means of access to the cabin or other locations on the boom is by a catwalk constructed of skid resistant expanded metal or similar material and fitted with solidly constructed guardrails and devices which provide fall protection for the operator;

(f)   the structural, environmental and ergonomic design of the cabin is equal to or greater than that of the crane's manufacturer's standard cabin design; and

(g)   the proposed location and attachment method provide a structural and mechanical safety factor equal to or greater than that of a cabin located on the crane mast or attached to the slewing ring. O. Reg. 213/91, s. 163 (2).

(3)   If the crane manufacturer specifies the location of the operator's cabin to be on the boom of a tower crane, the crane manufacturer shall provide to the owner of the crane a report for the specific model and specific configuration of crane on a project. O. Reg. 213/91, s. 163 (3).

(4)   The crane manufacturer's report shall include,

(a)   the crane load restrictions, reductions or modifications resulting from the effect of the cabin weight and its offset from the boom centreline;

(b)   the crane configuration and operating restrictions resulting from the effect of the cabin location and attachment method; and

(c)   engineering design drawings that include,

(i)   the structural and ergonomic design of the cabin,

(ii)   the location of the cabin on the boom,

(iii)   the attachment method including all fittings and hardware, and

(iv)   all means of access. O. Reg. 213/91, s. 163 (4).

Load block

164. A load block of an unattended tower crane shall be left empty, at the top position and located at minimum radius. O. Reg. 213/91, s. 164.

Track bed

165. (1)   The track bed of a rail-mounted tower crane shall have a sound and rigid base capable of carrying all loads to which it is likely to be subjected without deformation or settlement which affects the stability of the crane. O. Reg. 213/91, s. 165 (1).

Rail clamps

(2)   The undercarriage of a rail-mounted tower crane shall be fitted with rail clamps that can be firmly attached to the rails to lock the crane in position. O. Reg. 213/91, s. 165 (2).

(3)   A rail-mounted tower crane shall be locked in position on the rails when not in use. O. Reg. 213/91, s. 165 (3).

Rail stops

(4)   A rail-mounted tower crane shall have rail stops or bumpers that extend at least as high as the centre of the undercarriage wheels and that are securely attached to the rail at both ends. O. Reg. 213/91, s. 165 (4).

Derricks, Stiff-Leg Derricks and Similar Hoisting Devices

166. (1)   No derrick, stiff-leg derrick or similar hoisting device shall be attached to a building or structure unless this section is complied with. O. Reg. 213/91, s. 166 (1).

Drawings

(2)   A professional engineer shall prepare design drawings and specifications for the attachment of a derrick, stiff-leg derrick or similar hoisting device to a building or structure. O. Reg. 213/91, s. 166 (2).

(3)   The design drawings and specifications shall include,

    (a)   the location of the derrick, stiff-leg derrick or similar hoisting device on the building or structure;

    (b)   the location of anchor bolts, guy wires, supports and shoring for it;

    (c)   particulars of the weight of the loads and the radius at which the loads are to be lifted; and

    (d)   particulars of the loads and forces on the building or structure imposed by the derrick, stiff-leg derrick or similar hoisting device. O. Reg. 213/91, s. 166 (3).

Integrity review

(4)   The constructor shall ensure that the structural engineer responsible for the structural integrity of a building or structure reviews and approves in writing the design drawings and specifications for a derrick, stiff-leg derrick or similar hoisting device before it is installed. O. Reg. 213/91, s. 166 (4).

Inspection of installation

(5)   A professional engineer shall inspect a derrick, stiff-leg derrick or similar hoisting device before it is first used on a building or structure to ensure that it is installed in accordance with the design drawings and specifications. O. Reg. 213/91, s. 166 (5).

(6)   The professional engineer conducting the inspection shall prepare a written report of the inspection. O. Reg. 213/91, s. 166 (6); O. Reg. 85/04, s. 19.

(7)   The constructor shall keep a copy of the design drawings and specifications for a derrick, stiff-leg derrick or similar hoisting device and the report prepared under subsection (6) at a project while the

derrick, stiff-leg derrick or similar hoisting device is on the project. O. Reg. 213/91, s. 166 (7).

Helicopters

167. (1)   The pilot of a helicopter that is hoisting materials shall be competent to fly an externally-loaded helicopter. O. Reg. 213/91, s. 167 (1).

(2)   The pilot shall be in charge of the hoisting operation and shall determine the size and weight of loads to be hoisted and the method by which they are attached to the helicopter. O. Reg. 213/91, s. 167 (2).

(3)   Ground personnel including signallers for a helicopter being used to hoist materials shall be competent workers. O. Reg. 213/91, s. 167 (3).

(4)   The constructor shall take precautions against hazards caused by helicopter rotor downwash. O. Reg. 213/91, s. 167 (4).

Cables, Slings, Rigging

Construction

168. (1)   A cable used by a crane or similar hoisting device,

(a)   shall be steel wire rope of the type, size, grade and construction recommended by the manufacturer of the crane or similar hoisting device;

(b)   shall be compatible with the sheaves and the drum of the crane or similar hoisting device;

(c)   shall be lubricated to prevent corrosion and wear;

(d)   shall not be spliced; and

  (e) shall have its end connections securely fastened and shall be kept with at least three full turns on the drum. O. Reg. 213/91, s. 168 (1).

(2) No cable used by a crane or similar hoisting device,

  (a) subject to subsection (3), shall contain six randomly-distributed wires that are broken in one rope lay or three or more wires that are broken in one strand in a rope lay;

  (b) shall be smaller than its nominal rope diameter by more than,

    (i) one millimetre for a diameter up to and including nineteen millimetres,

    (ii) two millimetres for a diameter greater than nineteen millimetres up to and including twenty-nine millimetres, and

    (iii) three millimetres for a diameter greater than twenty-nine millimetres;

  (c) shall be worn by more than one-third of the original diameter of its outside individual wires;

  (d) shall show evidence of kinking, bird-caging, corrosion or other damage resulting in distortion of the rope structure; or

  (e) shall show evidence of possible rope failure including rope damage caused by contact with electricity. O. Reg. 213/91, s. 168 (2).

(3) No cable that is static or is used for pendants,

    (a) shall contain three or more broken wires in one lay or in a section between end connectors; or

    (b) shall have more than one broken wire at an end connector. O. Reg. 213/91, s. 168 (3).

Rotation-resistant

(4) Rotation-resistant wire rope shall not be used for a cable for boom hoist reeving and pendants. O. Reg. 213/91, s. 168 (4).

(5) Rotation-resistant wire rope shall not be used where an inner wire or strand for a cable is damaged or broken. O. Reg. 213/91, s. 168 (5).

Strength

169. A cable used by a crane or similar hoisting device shall be capable of supporting at least,

    (a) three and one-half times the maximum load to which it is likely to be subjected if it is used on a device other than a tower crane and it winds on a drum or passes over a sheave;

    (b) five times the maximum load to which it is likely to be subjected if it is used on a tower crane and it winds on a drum or passes over a sheave;

    (c) three times the maximum load to which it is likely to be subjected if it is a pendant or is not subject to winding or bending; and

    (d) ten times the maximum load to which it is likely to be subjected if the crane or similar hoisting device is used for supporting persons. O. Reg. 213/91, s. 169.

Inspection

170. (1) All cable used by a crane or similar hoisting device shall be visually inspected by a competent worker at least once a week when the crane or similar hoisting device is being used. O. Reg. 213/91, s. 170 (1).

(2) The worker performing an inspection shall record the condition of the rope or cable inspected in the log book for the crane or similar hoisting device. O. Reg. 213/91, s. 170 (2).

Fastening

171. (1) A cable used by a crane or similar hoisting device shall be securely attached,

    (a) by binding and fastening the cable around an oval thimble in a way that is strong enough to prevent the cable thimble from separating; or

    (b) by fastening the cable within either a tapered socket by means of virgin zinc or a wedge-type socket fitted with a wire rope clip at the dead end to prevent the accidental release or loosening of the wedge. O. Reg. 213/91, s. 171 (1).

(2) The dead end cable of a wedge socket assembly on a hoisting line shall extend between 100 millimetres and 300 millimetres out of the socket. O. Reg. 213/91, s. 171 (2).

Sling, etc.

172. (1) A container, sling or similar device for rigging or hoisting an object, including its fittings and attachments,

    (a) shall be suitable for its intended use;

    (b) shall be suitable for and capable of supporting the object being rigged or hoisted;

(c) shall be so arranged as to prevent the object or any part of the object from slipping or falling;

(d) shall be capable of supporting at least five times the maximum load to which it may be subjected; and

(e) shall be capable of supporting at least ten times the load to which it may be subjected if it is to be used to support a person. O. Reg. 213/91, s. 172 (1).

(2) A sling or similar device made of web-type fabric or nylon shall be labelled to indicate its load rating capacity. O. Reg. 213/91, s. 172 (2).

(3) No sling or similar device for rigging or hoisting made of web-type fabric or nylon shall be used if it may be cut. O. Reg. 213/91, s. 172 (3).

Safety catch

173. (1) Every hoisting hook shall be equipped with a safety catch. O. Reg. 213/91, s. 173 (1).

(2) No safety catch is required on a hoisting hook used in placing structural members if the method of placing protects workers to the same standard as a safety catch does. O. Reg. 213/91, s. 173 (2).

(3) A hoisting hook shall have its load rating legibly cast or stamped on it in a location where the person using the hook can readily see it. O. Reg. 213/91, s. 173 (3).

(4) A hoisting hook shall not be used if it is cracked, has a throat opening that is greater than as manufactured or is twisted from the plane of the unbent hook. O. Reg. 213/91, s. 173 (4).

Hook block

174. A hook block shall have its load rating and weight legibly cast or stamped on it in a conspicuous location. O. Reg. 213/91, s. 174.

Overhauling weight

175. (1) An overhauling weight used on the cable of a crane or similar hoisting device,

    (a) shall be prevented from sliding up or down the cable; and

    (b) shall be securely attached to the load hook and the cable. O. Reg. 213/91, s. 175 (1).

(2) No overhauling weight used on the cable of a crane or similar hoisting device shall be split. O. Reg. 213/91, s. 175 (2).

Chain

176. Only an alloy steel chain or a chain manufactured for the purpose shall be used for hoisting. O. Reg. 213/91, s. 176.

177. (1) No alloy chain shall be annealed or welded. O. Reg. 213/91, s. 177 (1).

(2) A chain used for hoisting shall be selected, annealed, normalized and repaired in accordance with the specifications of its manufacturer. O. Reg. 213/91, s. 177 (2).

Clamp

178. A friction-type clamp used in hoisting materials shall be constructed so that an accidental slackening of the hoisting cable does not release the clamp. O. Reg. 213/91, s. 178.

Guide ropes

179. (1) If a worker may be endangered by the rotation or uncontrolled motion of a load being hoisted by a crane or similar hoisting device, one or more guide ropes or tag lines shall be used to prevent the rotation or uncontrolled motion. O. Reg. 213/91, s. 179 (1).

(2)   No guide rope or tag line shall be removed from a load referred to in subsection (1) until the load is landed and there is no danger of it tipping, collapsing or rolling. O. Reg. 213/91, s. 179 (2).

Piles

180. (1)   Piles and sheet-piling shall be adequately supported to prevent their uncontrolled movement while they are being hoisted, placed, removed or withdrawn. O. Reg. 213/91, s. 180 (1).

(2)   No worker shall be in an area where piles or sheet-piling are being hoisted, placed, removed or withdrawn unless the worker is directly engaged in the operation. O. Reg. 213/91, s. 180 (2).

Electrical Hazards

Rule book

181. (1)   Except where otherwise required by this Regulation, electrical work performed on or near electrical transmission or distribution systems shall be performed in accordance with the document entitled "Electrical Utility Safety Rules" published by the Electrical and Utilities Safety Association of Ontario Incorporated and revised January, 2009. O. Reg. 627/05, s. 4; O. Reg. 443/09, s. 5.

(2)   Sections 182, 187, 188, 189, 190, 191 and 193 do not apply to electrical work that is performed on or near electrical transmission or distribution systems if the work is performed in accordance with the document referred to in subsection (1). O. Reg. 627/05, s. 4.

Qualification

182. (1)   No worker shall connect, maintain or modify electrical equipment or installations unless,

    (a)   the worker holds a certificate of qualification issued under the Ontario College of Trades and Apprenticeship Act, 2009, that is not suspended, in the trade of,

        (i)   electrician — construction and maintenance, or

        (ii)   electrician — domestic and rural, if the worker is performing work that is limited to the scope of practice for that trade; or

    (b)   the worker is otherwise permitted to connect, maintain or modify electrical equipment or installations under the Ontario College of Trades and Apprenticeship Act, 2009 or the Technical Standards and Safety Act, 2000. O. Reg. 627/05, s. 4; O. Reg. 88/13, s. 2.

(2)   A worker who does not meet the requirements of clause (1) (a) or (b) may insert an attachment plug cap on the cord of electrical equipment or an electrical tool into, or remove it from, a convenience receptacle. O. Reg. 627/05, s. 4.

183. Every reasonable precaution shall be taken to prevent hazards to workers from energized electrical equipment, installations and conductors. O. Reg. 627/05, s. 6.

Entry

184. (1)   No person, other than a person authorized to do so by the supervisor in charge of the project, shall enter or be permitted to enter a room or other enclosure containing exposed energized electrical parts. O. Reg. 627/05, s. 7.

(2)   The entrance to a room or other enclosure containing exposed energized electrical parts shall be marked by conspicuous warning signs stating that entry by unauthorized persons is prohibited. O. Reg. 627/05, s. 7.

Suitability

185. (1)   Electrical equipment, installations, conductors and insulating materials shall be suitable for their intended use and shall be installed, maintained, modified and operated so as not to pose a hazard to a worker. O. Reg. 627/05, s. 7.

(2)   For greater certainty, the regulations made under section 113 of the Electricity Act, 1998 apply to electrical equipment, installations, conductors and insulating materials and to temporary wiring installations on projects. O. Reg. 627/05, s. 7.

Remove or lock-out

186. Electrical equipment, installations and conductors that are not to be used for the purpose for which they were designed shall be,

(a)   removed; or

(b)   left in an electrically non-hazardous condition by being disconnected, de-energized, tagged and,

(i)   grounded, in the case of power lines,

(ii)   locked out, in the case of electrical equipment. O. Reg. 627/05, s. 7.

Proximity

187. Tools, ladders, scaffolding and other equipment or materials capable of conducting electricity shall not be stored or used so close to energized electrical equipment, installations or conductors that they can make electrical contact. O. Reg. 627/05, s. 7.

Same

188. (1)   This section applies unless the conditions set out in clauses 189 (a) and (b) are satisfied. O. Reg. 627/05, s. 7.

(2)   No object shall be brought closer to an energized overhead electrical conductor with a nominal phase-to-phase voltage rating set out in Column 1 of the Table to this subsection than the distance specified opposite to it in Column 2.

TABLE

Column 1	Column 2
Nominal phase-to-phase voltage rating	**Minimum distance**
750 or more volts, but no more than 150,000 volts	3 metres
more than 150,000 volts, but no more than 250,000 volts	4.5 metres
more than 250,000 volts	6 metres

O. Reg. 627/05, s. 7.

(3)   Subsections (4) to (9) apply if a crane, similar hoisting device, backhoe, power shovel or other vehicle or equipment is operated near an energized overhead electrical conductor and it is possible for a part of the vehicle or equipment or its load to encroach on the minimum distance permitted under subsection (2). O. Reg. 627/05, s. 7.

(4)   A constructor shall,

     (a)   establish and implement written measures and procedures adequate to ensure that no part of a vehicle or equipment or its load encroaches on the minimum distance permitted by subsection (2); and

     (b)   make a copy of the written measures and procedures available to every employer on the project. O. Reg. 627/05, s. 7.

(5)   The written measures and procedures shall include taking the following precautions to protect workers:

1.   Adequate warning devices, visible to the operator and warning of the electrical hazard, shall be positioned in the vicinity of the hazard.

2.   The operator shall be provided with written notification of the electrical hazard before beginning the work.

3.   A legible sign, visible to the operator and warning of the potential electrical hazard, shall be posted at the operator's station. O. Reg. 627/05, s. 7.

(6)   Before a worker begins work that includes an activity described in subsection (3), the employer shall provide a copy of the written measures and procedures to the worker and explain them to him or her. O. Reg. 627/05, s. 7.

(7)   The worker shall follow the written measures and procedures. O. Reg. 627/05, s. 7.

(8)   A competent worker, designated as a signaller, shall be stationed so that he or she is in full view of the operator and has a clear view of the electrical conductor and of the vehicle or equipment, and shall warn the operator each time any part of the vehicle or equipment or its load may approach the minimum distance. O. Reg. 627/05, s. 7.

(9)   Section 106 also applies with respect to the signaller designated under subsection (8). O. Reg. 627/05, s. 7.

189. Section 188 does not apply if,

(a)   under the authority of the owner of the electrical conductor, protective devices and equipment are installed, and written measures and procedures are established and implemented, that are adequate to protect workers from electrical shock and burn; and

(b) the workers involved in the work use protective devices and equipment, including personal protective equipment, and follow written measures and procedures that are adequate to protect workers from electrical shock and burn. O. Reg. 627/05, s. 7.

190. (1) This section applies if work is to be done on or near energized exposed parts of electrical equipment or of an electrical installation or conductor. O. Reg. 627/05, s. 7.

(2) An employer shall,

(a) establish and implement written measures and procedures for complying with this section to ensure that workers are adequately protected from electrical shock and burn; and

(b) make a copy of the written measures and procedures available to every worker on the project. O. Reg. 627/05, s. 7.

(3) The worker shall follow the written measures and procedures. O. Reg. 627/05, s. 7.

(4) Subject to subsection (9), the power supply to the electrical equipment, installation or conductor shall be disconnected, locked out of service and tagged in accordance with subsection (6) before the work begins, and kept disconnected, locked out of service and tagged while the work continues. O. Reg. 627/05, s. 7.

(5) Hazardous stored electrical energy shall be adequately discharged or contained before the work begins and shall be kept

discharged or contained while the work continues. O. Reg. 627/05, s. 7.

(6)   The following rules apply to the tagging of the power supply under subsection (4):

1.   The tag shall be made of non-conducting material and shall be installed so as not to become energized.

2.   The tag shall be placed in a conspicuous location and shall be secured to prevent its inadvertent removal.

3.   The tag shall indicate,

   i.   why the equipment, installation or conductor is disconnected,

   ii.   the name of the person who disconnected the equipment, installation or conductor,

   iii.   the name of the person's employer, and

   iv.   the date on which the equipment, installation or conductor was disconnected.

4.   The tag shall not be removed unless it is safe to do so. O. Reg. 627/05, s. 7.

(7)   A worker, before beginning work to which this section applies, shall verify that subsections (4) and (5) have been complied with. O. Reg. 627/05, s. 7.

(8)   If more than one worker is involved in work to which this section applies, a means shall be provided to communicate the purpose and status of,

(a)   the disconnecting, locking out and tagging of the electrical equipment, installation or conductor; and

(b)   the discharging and containment of any hazardous stored electrical energy. O. Reg. 627/05, s. 7.

(9)   Locking out is not required under subsection (4) if,

(a)   in the case of a conductor, it is adequately grounded with a visible grounding mechanism;

(b)   in the case of equipment or an installation,

(i)   the power supply is less than 300 volts, the equipment or installation was not manufactured with provision for a locking device for the circuit breakers or fuses, and a written procedure has been implemented that is adequate to ensure that the circuit is not inadvertently energized, or

(ii)   the power supply is 300 or more volts but not more than 600 volts, the equipment or installation was not manufactured with provision for a locking device for the circuit breakers or fuses, a written procedure as to how work is to be done has been implemented and the work is supervised by a competent worker to ensure that the circuit is not inadvertently energized. O. Reg. 627/05, s. 7.

Live line work

191. (1)   This section applies instead of section 190 if work is to be done on or near energized exposed parts of electrical equipment or of an electrical installation or conductor and,

    (a)   it is not reasonably possible to disconnect the equipment, installation or conductor from the power supply before working on or near the energized exposed parts;

    (b)   the equipment, installation or conductor is rated at a nominal voltage of 600 volts or less, and disconnecting the equipment, installation or conductor would create a greater hazard to a worker than proceeding without disconnecting it; or

    (c)   the work consists only of diagnostic testing of the equipment, installation or conductor. O. Reg. 627/05, s. 7.

(2)   Subsection (10) applies, in addition to subsections (3) to (9), if the equipment, installation or conductor is nominally rated at,

    (a)   greater than 400 amperes and greater than 200 volts; or

    (b)   greater than 200 amperes and greater than 300 volts. O. Reg. 627/05, s. 7.

(3)   Only a worker who meets the requirements of clause 182 (1) (a) or (b) shall perform the work. O. Reg. 627/05, s. 7.

(4)   The constructor shall,

    (a)   ensure that written measures and procedures for complying with this section are established and implemented, so that workers are adequately protected from electrical shock and burn; and

    (b)   make a copy of the written measures and procedures available to every employer on the project. O. Reg. 627/05, s. 7.

(5)   Before a worker begins work to which this section applies, the employer shall provide a copy of the written measures and procedures to the worker and explain them to him or her. O. Reg. 627/05, s. 7.

(6)   The worker shall follow the written procedures. O. Reg. 627/05, s. 7.

(7)   A worker shall use mats, shields or other protective devices or equipment, including personal protective equipment, adequate to protect the worker from electrical shock and burn. O. Reg. 627/05, s. 7.

(8)   If the electrical equipment, installation or conductor is rated at a nominal voltage of 300 volts or more, an adequately equipped competent worker who can perform rescue operations, including cardiopulmonary resuscitation, shall be stationed so that he or she can see the worker who is performing the work. O. Reg. 627/05, s. 7.

(9)   Subsection (8) does not apply if the work consists only of diagnostic testing of the equipment, installation or conductors. O. Reg. 627/05, s. 7.

(10) In the case of equipment or of an installation or conductor described in subsection (2), a worker shall not perform the work unless the following additional conditions are satisfied:

1.   The owner of the equipment, installation or conductor has provided the employer and the constructor with a record showing that it has been maintained according to the manufacturer's specifications.

2.   A copy of the maintenance record is readily available at the project.

3.   The employer has determined from the maintenance record that the work on the equipment, installation or conductor can be performed safely without disconnecting it.

4.   Before beginning the work, the worker has verified that paragraphs 1, 2 and 3 have been complied with. O. Reg. 627/05, s. 7.

192. All tools, devices and equipment, including personal protective equipment, that are used for working on or near energized exposed parts of electrical equipment, installations or conductors shall be designed, tested, maintained and used so as to provide adequate protection to workers. O. Reg. 627/05, s. 7.

193. (1)   A worker who may be exposed to the hazard of electrical shock or burn while performing work shall use rubber gloves,

(a)   that are adequate to protect him or her against electrical shock and burn;

(b)   that have been tested and certified in accordance with subsection (2), if applicable; and

(c)   that have been air tested and visually inspected for damage and adequacy immediately before each use. O. Reg. 627/05, s. 7.

(2)   Rubber gloves rated for use with voltages above 5,000 volts AC shall be tested and certified to ensure that they can withstand the voltages for which they are rated,

(a)   at least once every three months, if they are in service;

(b)   at least once every six months, if they are not in service. O. Reg. 627/05, s. 7.

(3)   Rubber gloves shall be worn with adequate leather protectors and shall not be worn inside out. O. Reg. 627/05, s. 7.

(4)   Leather protectors shall be visually inspected for damage and adequacy immediately before each use. O. Reg. 627/05, s. 7.

(5)   Rubber gloves or leather protectors that are damaged or not adequate to protect workers from electrical shock and burn shall not be used. O. Reg. 627/05, s. 7.

(6)   Workers shall be trained in the proper use, care and storage of rubber gloves and leather protectors. O. Reg. 627/05, s. 7.

Switch, panel board

194. (1)   A switch and panel board controlling a service entrance, service feeder or branch circuit shall meet the requirements of this section. O. Reg. 627/05, s. 7.

(2)   A switch and panel board shall be securely mounted on a soundly constructed vertical surface and shall have a cover over uninsulated parts carrying current. O. Reg. 627/05, s. 7.

(3)   A switch and panel board shall be located,

    (a)   in an area where water will not accumulate; and

    (b)   within easy reach of workers and readily accessible to them. O. Reg. 627/05, s. 7.

(4)   The area in front of a panel board shall be kept clear of obstructions. O. Reg. 627/05, s. 7.

(5)   A switch that controls a service entrance, service feeder or branch circuit providing temporary power,

    (a)   shall not be locked in the energized position; and

    (b)   shall be housed in an enclosure that can be locked and is provided with a locking device. O. Reg. 627/05, s. 7.

195. All electrical extension cords used at a project shall have a grounding conductor and at least two other conductors. O. Reg. 627/05, s. 7.

Grounding

195.1 (1) Cord-connected electrical equipment or tools shall have a casing that is adequately grounded. O. Reg. 627/05, s. 7.

(2) All cord connections to electrical equipment or tools shall be polarized. O. Reg. 627/05, s. 7.

(3) Subsections (1) and (2) do not apply to cord-connected electrical equipment or tools that are adequately double-insulated and whose insulated casing shows no evidence of cracks or defects. O. Reg. 627/05, s. 7.

(4) Subsection (1) does not apply to a portable electrical generator in which the electrical equipment or tools are not exposed to an external electric power source if the casing of portable electrical equipment or tools connected to the generator is bonded to a non-current-carrying part of the generator. O. Reg. 627/05, s. 7.

Ground fault circuit interrupter

195.2 When a portable electrical tool is used outdoors or in a wet location,

    (a)   if the source of power is an ungrounded portable generator having a maximum output of 1.8 kilowatts or less, a ground fault circuit interrupter of the Class A type shall be located in the cord feeding the tool, as close to the tool as possible;

(b)   in all other cases, the tool shall be plugged into a receptacle protected by a ground fault circuit interrupter of the Class A type. O. Reg. 627/05, s. 7.

195.3 (1)   Defective electrical equipment and tools that may pose a hazard shall be immediately disconnected, removed from service and tagged as being defective. O. Reg. 627/05, s. 7.

(2)   The cause of a ground fault or the tripping of a ground fault circuit interrupter shall be immediately investigated to determine the hazard and corrective action shall be taken immediately. O. Reg. 627/05, s. 7.

Explosives

Competent worker in charge
196. (1)   If explosives are to be used on a project, the employer responsible for blasting shall designate a competent worker to be in charge of blasting operations. O. Reg. 213/91, s. 196 (1).

(2)   The employer shall post the name of the worker in charge of blasting operations for a project in a conspicuous place on the project and in every magazine. O. Reg. 213/91, s. 196 (2).

Supervision
(3)   The worker in charge of blasting operations for a project shall personally supervise blasting operations at the project, including the loading, priming and initiating of all charges. O. Reg. 213/91, s. 196 (3).

Duties
(4)   The worker in charge of blasting operations for a project,

(a)   shall inspect for hazardous conditions explosives and the magazines in which they are stored,

      (i)   at least once a month, and

      (ii)   on the day they are to be used;

  (b)   shall promptly report the results of inspections under clause (a) to the supervisor in charge of the project;

  (c)   shall take immediate steps to correct any hazardous condition; and

  (d)   shall dispose of all deteriorated explosives. O. Reg. 213/91, s. 196 (4).

(5) If an act of careless placing or handling of explosives on the project is discovered by, or reported to the worker in charge of blasting operations, the worker shall promptly investigate the circumstances and report the results of the investigation to the supervisor in charge of the project. O. Reg. 213/91, s. 196 (5).

Handle, transport
197. Only a competent worker or a worker who is working under the direct personal supervision of a competent worker shall handle, transport, prepare and use explosives on a project. O. Reg. 213/91, s. 197.

Magazine
198. (1) A magazine containing an explosive shall be securely locked at all times when the competent worker described in section 197 is not present. O. Reg. 213/91, s. 198 (1).

(2) No explosive shall be outside a magazine unless the explosive is required for immediate use. O. Reg. 213/91, s. 198 (2).

(3) An explosive outside a magazine shall be attended at all times. O. Reg. 213/91, s. 198 (3).

Wrapping

199. An explosive shall remain in its original wrapper unless it is manufactured and intended for use other than in its original wrapper. O. Reg. 213/91, s. 199.

Fire, flame

200. (1) No fire or other naked flame shall be located in a magazine or within eight metres of any explosive. O. Reg. 213/91, s. 200 (1).

(2) No person shall smoke in a magazine or within eight metres of any explosive. O. Reg. 213/91, s. 200 (2).

Mats

201. Blasting mats shall be used to prevent flying objects caused by blasting operations from endangering persons and property located on or adjacent to a project. O. Reg. 213/91, s. 201.

Electric blasting caps

202. (1) This section applies if electric blasting caps are used on a project. O. Reg. 213/91, s. 202 (1).

(2) The protective shunt shall not be removed from the leg wire until connections are made. O. Reg. 213/91, s. 202 (2).

(3) The firing circuit shall be short-circuited while the leads from the blasting caps are being connected to each other and to the firing cables. O. Reg. 213/91, s. 202 (3).

(4) The short circuit shall not be removed until immediately before blasting and until all workers have left the area affected by the blasting operations. O. Reg. 213/91, s. 202 (4).

(5) The source of energy for a blasting operation shall be disconnected from the firing circuit immediately after firing. O. Reg. 213/91, s. 202 (5).

Worker posting

203. (1) Before blasting begins, the worker in charge of blasting operations shall post workers at the approaches to the affected area in order to prevent access to it. O. Reg. 213/91, s. 203 (1).

(2) Before blasting begins, the worker in charge of blasting operations shall ensure,

    (a) that only workers required to carry out the blasting are located in the affected area;

    (b) that no workers remain in an area whose means of egress passes the affected area; and

    (c) that a warning that is clearly audible within a radius of one kilometre of the blast is given by siren. O. Reg. 213/91, s. 203 (2).

Examination

204. (1) Before a drill hole for loading explosives is drilled, the exposed surface shall be examined for drill holes or remnants of drill holes that may contain explosives and any explosive found shall be removed if practicable. O. Reg. 213/91, s. 204 (1).

(2) No drill hole shall be drilled,

Specification

    (a) within 7.5 metres of another hole that is being loaded with or contains explosives; and

    (b) within 150 millimetres of another hole or remnant of a hole that has been charged or blasted unless adequate precautions have been taken to ensure that the other hole is free from explosives. O. Reg. 213/91, s. 204 (2).

(3)   Clause (2) (a) does not apply to a hole being drilled adjacent to another hole that is being loaded with explosives,

    (a)   if a professional engineer prepares a specification showing the location of the drill hole and the adjacent hole and describing the precautions to be taken to prevent the accidental detonation by the drilling operation of the explosives in the adjacent hole; and

    (b)   if the drilling is done as described in the specification referred to in clause (a). O. Reg. 213/91, s. 204 (3).

(4)   No drill hole permitted under subsection (3) shall be drilled within one metre of another hole containing explosives. O. Reg. 213/91, s. 204 (4).

(5)   The professional engineer's specification shall be in writing. O. Reg. 213/91, s. 204 (5); O. Reg. 85/04, s. 20.

(6)   The employer responsible for blasting shall keep a copy of the specification at the project until the blasting to which the specification refers is completed. O. Reg. 213/91, s. 204 (6).

Drill hole size

205. (1)   If cartridges of explosives are to be used in a drill hole, the hole shall be made large enough that a cartridge can be inserted easily to the bottom of the hole. O. Reg. 213/91, s. 205 (1).

(2)   No drill hole shall be charged with explosives unless a properly prepared detonation agent is placed in the charge. O. Reg. 213/91, s. 205 (2).

(3)   Drill holes charged with explosives in one loading operation shall be fired in one operation. O. Reg. 213/91, s. 205 (3).

(4)   No drill hole that is charged with explosives shall be left unfired for any longer than is required in a continuing operation to complete the charging and blasting of adjacent holes. O. Reg. 213/91, s. 205 (4).

Non-sparking tool
206. Only a non-sparking tool or rod shall be used in the charging of a drill hole or in a drill hole containing explosives. O. Reg. 213/91, s. 206.

Roofing

Barrier
207. (1)   If a built-up roof is being constructed, repaired or resurfaced, a barrier shall be placed in the immediate work area at least two metres from the perimeter of the roof. O. Reg. 213/91, s. 207 (1).

(2)   The barrier shall consist of portable weighted posts supporting a taut chain, cable or rope that is located 1.1 metres above the roof level. O. Reg. 213/91, s. 207 (2).

Pipe support
208. (1)   A pipe that supplies hot tar or bitumen to a roof shall be securely fixed and supported to prevent its deflection. O. Reg. 213/91, s. 208 (1).

(2)   If a pipe discharges hot tar or bitumen within two metres of the edge of a roof, a guardrail shall be provided at the edge of the roof. O. Reg. 213/91, s. 208 (2).

Roof hoist
209. (1)   A hoist used on a roof,

      (a)   shall have a guardrail installed on both sides of the frame at the edge of the roof; and

(b)   shall be positioned in such a way that the hoist cable is vertical at all times while a load is being hoisted. O. Reg. 213/91, s. 209 (1).

(2)   Only a competent worker shall operate a hoist used on a roof. O. Reg. 213/91, s. 209 (2).

Counterweights

210. The counterweights on a roofer's hoist,

(a)   shall be suitable for the purpose;

(b)   shall not consist of roofing or other construction material;

(c)   shall be securely attached to the hoist; and

(d)   shall provide a safety factor against overturning of not less than three. O. Reg. 213/91, s. 210.

Hot Tar or Bitumen Roadtankers

211. (1)   Only a competent worker shall operate a hot tar or bitumen roadtanker or kettle. O. Reg. 213/91, s. 211 (1).

(2)   If a hot tar or bitumen roadtanker or kettle is fitted with a propane-fuelled heater,

(a)   the storage cylinder for propane shall not be placed closer than three metres to a source of fire or ignition;

(b)   the lines connecting the storage cylinder for propane to the heating device shall be located so that they do not come into contact with the hot tar or bitumen in the case of a spill or a failure of a component of the system; and

(c) a fire extinguisher with an Underwriters' Laboratories of Canada rating of at least 4A40BC shall be provided with the roadtanker or kettle. O. Reg. 213/91, s. 211 (2).

(3) A propane burner used on a bitumen roadtanker or kettle,

(a) shall have a thermal rating no greater than that recommended by the manufacturer of the roadtanker or kettle; and

(b) shall consist of components that are adequate for their intended use. O. Reg. 213/91, s. 211 (3).

(4) Hot tar or bitumen shall be transferred from a roadtanker to a kettle through enclosed piping. O. Reg. 213/91, s. 211 (4).

Demolition and Damaged Structures

Safeguards

212. (1) If a structure is so damaged that a worker is likely to be endangered by its partial or complete collapse,

(a) the structure shall be braced and shored; and

(b) safeguards appropriate in the circumstances shall be provided to prevent injury to a worker. O. Reg. 213/91, s. 212 (1).

(2) Safeguards shall be installed progressively from a safe area towards the hazard so that the workers installing the safeguards are not endangered. O. Reg. 213/91, s. 212 (2).

Entry

213. (1) Only a worker who is directly engaged in the demolition, dismantling or moving of a building or structure shall be in, on or near it. O. Reg. 213/91, s. 213 (1).

(2)   If the demolition or dismantling of a building or structure is discontinued, barriers shall be erected to prevent access by people to the remaining part of the building or structure. O. Reg. 213/91, s. 213 (2).

(3)   A worker shall enter only the part of a building or structure being demolished that will safely support the worker. O. Reg. 213/91, s. 213 (3).

Precautions

214. (1)   No building or structure shall be demolished, dismantled or moved until this section is complied with. O. Reg. 213/91, s. 214 (1).

(2)   Precautions shall be taken to prevent injury to a person on or near the project or the adjoining property that may result from the demolition, dismantling or moving of a building or structure. O. Reg. 213/91, s. 214 (2).

Services

(3)   All gas, electrical and other services that may endanger persons who have access to a building or structure shall be shut off and disconnected before, and shall remain shut off and disconnected during, the demolition, dismantling or moving of the building or structure. O. Reg. 213/91, s. 214 (3).

Substances

(4)   All toxic, flammable or explosive substances shall be removed from a building or structure that is to be demolished, dismantled or moved. O. Reg. 213/91, s. 214 (4).

215. (1)   Sections 216, 217, 218 and 220 do not apply with respect to a building or structure that is being demolished by,

       (a)   a heavy weight suspended by cable from a crane or similar hoisting device;

       (b)   a power shovel, bulldozer or other vehicle;

       (c)   the use of explosives; or

       (d)   a combination of methods described in clauses (a) to (c). O. Reg. 213/91, s. 215 (1).

(2)   The controls of a mechanical device used to demolish a building or structure shall be operated from a location that is as remote as is practicable from the building or structure. O. Reg. 213/91, s. 215 (2).

(3)   If a swinging weight is used to demolish a building or structure, the supporting cable of the weight shall be short enough or shall be so restrained that the weight does not swing against another building or structure. O. Reg. 213/91, s. 215 (3).

216. (1)   Demolition and dismantling of a building or structure shall proceed systematically and continuously from the highest to the lowest point unless a worker is endangered by this procedure. O. Reg. 213/91, s. 216 (1).

Skeleton structural frame

(2)   Despite subsection (1), the skeleton structural frame in a skeleton structural frame building may be left in place during the demolition or dismantling of the masonry if the masonry and any loose material are removed from the frame systematically and continuously from the highest to the lowest point. O. Reg. 213/91, s. 216 (2).

(3)   The work above a tier or floor of a building or structure shall be completed before the support of the tier or floor is affected by demolition or dismantling operations. O. Reg. 213/91, s. 216 (3).

Glass

217. No exterior wall of a building or structure shall be demolished until all glass is removed from windows, doors, interior partitions and components containing glass or is protected to prevent the glass from breaking during the demolition. O. Reg. 213/91, s. 217.

Masonry walls

218. (1)   Masonry walls of a building or structure being demolished or dismantled shall be removed in reasonably level courses. O. Reg. 213/91, s. 218 (1).

(2)   No materials in a masonry wall of a building or structure being demolished or dismantled shall be loosened or permitted to fall in masses that are likely to endanger,

    (a)   a person; or

    (b)   the structural stability of a scaffold or of a floor or other support of the building or structure. O. Reg. 213/91, s. 218 (2).

219. No worker shall stand on top of a wall, pier or chimney to remove material from it unless flooring, scaffolding or staging is provided on all sides of it not more than 2.4 metres below the place where the worker is working. O. Reg. 213/91, s. 219.

Structural members

220. No truss, girder or other structural member of a building or structure being demolished or dismantled shall be disconnected until,

    (a)   it is relieved of all loads other than its own weight; and

(b)   it has temporary support. O. Reg. 213/91, s. 220.

221. (1)   A basement, cellar or excavation left after a building or structure is demolished, dismantled or moved,

(a)   shall be backfilled to grade level; or

(b)   shall have fencing along its open sides. O. Reg. 213/91, s. 221 (1).

(2)   Subsection (1) does not apply to a basement or cellar that is enclosed by a roof, floor or other solid covering if all openings in the roof, floor or covering are covered with securely fastened planks. O. Reg. 213/91, s. 221 (2).

Part II.1 (ss. 221.1-221.19) Revoked: O. Reg. 96/11, s. 1.

PART III
EXCAVATIONS

Interpretation and Application

222. In this Part,

"engineered support system" means an excavation or trench shoring system, designed for a specific project or location, assembled in place and which cannot be moved as a unit;

"hydraulic support system" means a system capable of being moved as a unit, designed to resist the earth pressure from the walls of an excavation by applying a hydraulic counter pressure through the struts;

"prefabricated support system" means a trench box, trench shield or similar structure, composed of members connected to each other and capable of being moved as a unit, and designed to resist the pressure from the walls of an excavation but does not include a hydraulic support system;

"pressure", in relation to a wall of an excavation, means the lateral pressure of the earth on the wall calculated in accordance with generally accepted engineering principles and includes hydrostatic pressure and pressure due to surcharge. O. Reg. 213/91, s. 222.

223. This Part applies to all excavating and trenching operations. O. Reg. 213/91, s. 223.

Entry and Working Alone

224. No person shall enter or be permitted to enter an excavation that does not comply with this Part. O. Reg. 213/91, s. 224.

225. Work shall not be performed in a trench unless another worker is working above ground in close proximity to the trench or to the means of access to it. O. Reg. 213/91, s. 225.

Soil Types

226. (1) For the purposes of this Part, soil shall be classified as Type 1, 2, 3 or 4 in accordance with the descriptions set out in this section. O. Reg. 213/91, s. 226 (1).

(2) Type 1 soil,

(a) is hard, very dense and only able to be penetrated with difficulty by a small sharp object;

(b) has a low natural moisture content and a high degree of internal strength;

(c) has no signs of water seepage; and

         (d)   can be excavated only by mechanical equipment.
O. Reg. 213/91, s. 226 (2).

(3)   Type 2 soil,

    (a)   is very stiff, dense and can be penetrated with moderate difficulty by a small sharp object;

    (b)   has a low to medium natural moisture content and a medium degree of internal strength; and

    (c)   has a damp appearance after it is excavated. O. Reg. 213/91, s. 226 (3).

(4)   Type 3 soil,

    (a)   is stiff to firm and compact to loose in consistency or is previously-excavated soil;

    (b)   exhibits signs of surface cracking;

    (c)   exhibits signs of water seepage;

    (d)   if it is dry, may run easily into a well-defined conical pile; and

    (e)   has a low degree of internal strength. O. Reg. 213/91, s. 226 (4).

(5)   Type 4 soil,

    (a)   is soft to very soft and very loose in consistency, very sensitive and upon disturbance is significantly reduced in natural strength;

    (b)   runs easily or flows, unless it is completely supported before excavating procedures;

(c)   has almost no internal strength;

(d)   is wet or muddy; and

(e)   exerts substantial fluid pressure on its supporting
      system. O. Reg. 213/91, s. 226 (5).

Soil classification

227. (1)   The type of soil in which an excavation is made shall be
determined by visual and physical examination of the soil,

(a)   at the walls of the excavation; and

(b)   within a horizontal distance from each wall equal to the
      depth of the excavation measured away from the
      excavation. O. Reg. 213/91, s. 227 (1).

(2)   The soil in which an excavation is made shall be classified as
the type described in section 226 that the soil most closely
resembles. O. Reg. 213/91, s. 227 (2).

(3)   If an excavation contains more than one type of soil, the soil
shall be classified as the type with the highest number as described
in section 226 among the types present. O. Reg. 213/91, s. 227 (3).

Precautions Concerning Services

228. (1)   Before an excavation is begun,

(a)   the employer excavating shall ensure that all gas,
      electrical and other services in and near the area to be
      excavated are located and marked;

(b)   the employer and worker locating and marking the
      services described in clause (a) shall ensure that they
      are accurately located and marked; and

  (c) if a service may pose a hazard, the service shall be shut off and disconnected. O. Reg. 443/09, s. 6.

(2) If a service may pose a hazard and it cannot be shut off or disconnected, the owner of the service shall be requested to supervise the uncovering of the service during the excavation. O. Reg. 443/09, s. 6.

(3) Pipes, conduits and cables for gas, electrical and other services in an excavation shall be supported to prevent their failure or breakage. O. Reg. 443/09, s. 6.

Protection of Adjacent Structures

229. (1) If an excavation may affect the stability of an adjacent building or structure, the constructor shall take precautions to prevent damage to the adjacent building or structure. O. Reg. 213/91, s. 229 (1).

(2) A professional engineer shall specify in writing the precautions required under subsection (1). O. Reg. 213/91, s. 229 (2).

(3) Such precautions as the professional engineer specifies shall be taken. O. Reg. 213/91, s. 229 (3).

General Requirements

Water

230. Every excavation that a worker may be required to enter shall be kept reasonably free of water. O. Reg. 213/91, s. 230.

Clear space

231. An excavation in which a worker may work shall have a clear work space of at least 450 millimetres between the wall of the excavation and any formwork or masonry or similar wall. O. Reg. 213/91, s. 231.

232. (1)   The walls of an excavation shall be stripped of loose rock or other material that may slide, roll or fall upon a worker. O. Reg. 213/91, s. 232 (1).

(2)   The walls of an excavation cut in rock shall be supported by rock anchors or wire mesh if support is necessary to prevent the spalling of loose rock. O. Reg. 213/91, s. 232 (2).

Wall stability

233. (1)   A level area extending at least one metre from the upper edge of each wall of an excavation shall be kept clear of equipment, excavated soil, rock and construction material. O. Reg. 213/91, s. 233 (1).

(2)   The stability of a wall of an excavation shall be maintained where it may be affected by stockpiling excavated soil or rock or construction materials. O. Reg. 213/91, s. 233 (2).

(3)   No person shall operate a vehicle or other machine and no vehicle or other machine shall be located in such a way as to affect the stability of a wall of an excavation. O. Reg. 213/91, s. 233 (3).

Barrier

(4)   If a person could fall into an excavation that is more than 2.4 metres deep, a barrier at least 1.1 metres high shall be provided at the top of every wall of the excavation that is not sloped as described in clauses 234 (2) (e), (f) and (g). O. Reg. 213/91, s. 233 (4).

Support Systems

234. (1)   The walls of an excavation shall be supported by a support system that complies with sections 235, 236, 237, 238, 239 and 241. O. Reg. 213/91, s. 234 (1).

(2) Subsection (1) does not apply with respect to an excavation,

(a) that is less than 1.2 metres deep;

(b) that no worker is required to enter;

(c) that is not a trench and with respect to which no worker is required to be closer to a wall than the height of the wall;

(d) that is cut in sound and stable rock;

(e) made in Type 1 or Type 2 soil and whose walls are sloped to within 1.2 metres of its bottom with a slope having a minimum gradient of one horizontal to one vertical;

(f) made in Type 3 soil and whose walls are sloped from its bottom with a slope having a minimum gradient of one horizontal to one vertical;

(g) made in Type 4 soil and whose walls are sloped from its bottom with a slope having a minimum gradient of three horizontal to one vertical; or

(h) that is not a trench and is not made in Type 4 soil and with respect to which a professional engineer has given a written opinion that the walls of the excavation are sufficiently stable that no worker will be endangered if no support system is used. O. Reg. 213/91, s. 234 (2).

(3) The opinion in clause (2) (h) shall include details of,

(a) the specific project and the location thereon;

(b) any specific condition for which the opinion applies; and

(c)   the frequency of inspections. O. Reg. 213/91, s. 234 (3).

(4)   The constructor shall keep on the project a copy of every opinion given by a professional engineer for the purpose of clause (2) (h) while the project is in progress. O. Reg. 213/91, s. 234 (4).

Inspection

(5)   The professional engineer who gives an opinion described in clause (2) (h), or a competent worker designated by him or her, shall inspect the excavation to which the opinion relates as frequently as the opinion specifies. O. Reg. 213/91, s. 234 (5).

235. (1)   Subject to subsection (2), a support system shall consist of,

        (a)   timbering and shoring that meets the requirements of subsection 238 (2), if no hydrostatic pressure is present in the soil, and if the width and depth of the excavation are equal to or less than the width and depth indicated in the Table to section 238;

        (b)   a prefabricated support system that complies with sections 236 and 237;

        (c)   a hydraulic support system that complies with sections 236 and 237; or

        (d)   an engineered support system that complies with section 236. O. Reg. 213/91, s. 235 (1).

(2)   Where the excavation is a trench and the depth exceeds six metres or the width exceeds 3.6 metres, the support system shall consist of an engineered support system designed for the specific location and project. O. Reg. 213/91, s. 235 (2); O. Reg. 631/94, s. 7.

Design

236. (1) Every prefabricated, hydraulic or engineered support system shall be designed by a professional engineer. O. Reg. 213/91, s. 236 (1).

(2) Every prefabricated, hydraulic or engineered support system shall be constructed, installed, used and maintained in accordance with its design drawings and specifications. O. Reg. 213/91, s. 236 (2).

Design drawings and specifications

(3) The design drawings and specifications for a prefabricated, hydraulic or an engineered support system,

(a) shall indicate the size of the system and the type and grade of materials of which it is to be made;

(b) shall indicate the maximum depth and the types of soil for which it is designed;

(c) shall indicate the proper positioning of the system in the excavation, including the maximum allowable clearance between the walls of the support system and the walls of the excavation; and

(d) shall indicate how to install and remove the system.

(e) **Revoked:** O. Reg. 213/91, s. 236 (3); O. Reg. 85/04, s. 21.

(4) In addition to the requirements of subsection (3), the design drawings and specifications for a hydraulic support system,

(a) shall indicate the minimum working pressure required for the system; and

(b)   shall require the use of a device to ensure the protection of workers if a loss of hydraulic pressure occurs in the system. O. Reg. 213/91, s. 236 (4).

Variance

(5)   Before a variation from the design drawings and specifications for a prefabricated, hydraulic or an engineered support system is permitted, the variation shall be approved in writing by a professional engineer. O. Reg. 213/91, s. 236 (5).

(6)   If the soil conditions on a project differ from those assumed by the professional engineer in designing a prefabricated, hydraulic or an engineered support system, a professional engineer shall modify the design drawings and specifications for the actual soil conditions or shall approve the support system for use in the actual soil conditions. O. Reg. 213/91, s. 236 (6).

(7)   The constructor shall keep the design drawings and specifications for a prefabricated, hydraulic or an engineered support system at a project while the system is on the project. O. Reg. 213/91, s. 236 (7).

(8)   **Revoked:** O. Reg. 443/09, s. 7.

Prohibition Type 4

237. (1)   Subject to subsection (2),

(a)   no prefabricated or hydraulic support system shall be used in type 4 soil;

(b)   the space between the walls of a prefabricated support system and the walls of the excavation shall be restricted to the minimum clearance required for the forward progression of the support system; and

(c) the walls of a hydraulic support system shall touch the walls of the excavation. O. Reg. 631/94, s. 8.

Underground pipe break

(2) A prefabricated or hydraulic support system may be used for repairing underground pipe breaks if the system,

(a) meets the requirements of section 236;

(b) has four side walls;

(c) is designed for a maximum depth of 3.6 metres;

(d) is not used at a greater depth than 3.6 metres;

(e) is designed to resist all hydrostatic and earth pressures found in type 3 and type 4 soils;

(f) is installed so as to extend to the bottom of the excavation;

(g) is installed so that the walls of the system touch the walls of the excavation; and

(h) is not pulled forward after being installed in the excavation. O. Reg. 631/94, s. 8.

Drawings/specifications submission

(3) Before a support system is used as described in subsection (2), the constructor shall submit two copies of its design drawings and specifications to the office of the Ministry of Labour nearest to the project. O. Reg. 631/94, s. 8.

238. (1) In this section,

"cleat" means a member of shoring that directly resists the downward movement of a wale or strut;

"o/c" means the maximum distance measured from the centre of one member of sheathing, wale or strut to the centre of the adjacent member of sheathing, wale or strut;

"post" means a vertical member of shoring that acts as a spacer between the wales;

"10 millimetres gap" means that the space between two adjacent members of sheathing is a maximum of ten millimetres. O. Reg. 213/91, s. 238 (1).

Timbering, shoring

(2)   Timbering and shoring referred to in clause 235 (1) (a) for the walls of an excavation with a depth and located in a soil type described in Column 1 of the Table to this section shall meet the corresponding specifications set out in Columns 2 to 4 of the Table. O. Reg. 213/91, s. 238 (2).

Sheathing

(3)   Every piece of sheathing referred to in the Table to this section shall be made of sound Number 1 Grade spruce and,

(a)   shall be placed against the side of the excavation so that it is vertical;

(b)   shall be secured in place by wales; and

(c)   shall be driven into the soil and firmly secured in place if the excavation is made in Type 3 or 4 soil. O. Reg. 213/91, s. 238 (3).

Struts

(4)   Every strut referred to in the Table to this section shall be made of sound number 1 structural grade spruce and,

(a)   shall be placed in the excavation so that it is horizontal and at right angles to the wales;

(b)   shall be cut to the proper length and held in place by at least two wedges driven between the strut and the wales; and

(c)   shall be cleated with cleats that extend over the top of the strut and rest on the wales or that are attached securely to the wales by spikes or bolts. O. Reg. 213/91, s. 238 (4).

Wales

(5)   Every wale referred to in the Table to this section shall be made of sound number 1 structural grade spruce and,

(a)   shall be placed in the excavation so that it is parallel to the bottom, or proposed bottom, of the excavation; and

(b)   shall be supported by either cleats secured to the sheathing or posts set on the wale next below it or, if it is the lowest wale, on the bottom of the excavation. O. Reg. 213/91, s. 238 (5).

TABLE
EXCAVATION SHORING AND TIMBERING (METRIC SIZES)

Column 1		Column 2	Column 3				Column 4
Excavation Depth	Soil Type	Sheathing	Struts		Strut Spacing		Wales
			Width of Excavation at Strut Location				
			Up to 1.8 m	1.8 m to 3.6 m	Vertical	Horizontal	
3.0 m or less	1	50 mm × 200 mm at 1.2 m o/c	150 mm × 150 mm	200 mm × 200 mm	1.2 m	* 2.4 m	*200 mm × 200 mm
	2	50 mm × 200 mm at 1.2 m o/c	150 mm × 150 mm	200 mm × 200 mm	1.2 m	* 2.4 m	*200 mm × 200 mm
	3	50 mm × 200 mm at 10 mm gap	200 mm × 200 mm	200 mm × 200 mm	1.2 m	2.4 m	250 mm × 250 mm
	4	75 mm × 200 mm at 10 mm gap	200 mm × 200 mm	250 mm × 250 mm	1.2 m	2.4 m	300 mm × 300 mm
Over 3.0 m to 4.5 m	1	50 mm × 200 mm with 10 mm gap	200 mm × 200 mm	200 mm × 200 mm	1.2 m	2.4 m	200 mm × 200 mm
	2	50 mm × 200 mm with 10 mm gap	200 mm × 200 mm	200 mm × 200 mm	1.2 m	2.4 m	250 mm × 250 mm
	3	50 mm × 200 mm with 10 mm gap	250 mm × 250 mm	250 mm × 250 mm	1.2 m	2.4 m	250 mm × 250 mm
Over 3.0 m to 4.0 m	4	75 mm × 200 mm with 10 mm gap	300 mm × 300 mm	300 mm × 300 mm	1.2 m	2.4 m	300 mm × 300 mm
Over 4.5 m to 6.0 m	1	50 mm × 200 mm with 10 mm gap	200 mm × 200 mm	200 mm × 200 mm	1.2 m	2.4 m	200 mm × 200 mm
	2	50 mm × 200 mm with 10 mm gap	250 mm × 250 mm	250 mm × 250 mm	1.2 m	2.4 m	250 mm × 250 mm
	3	50 mm × 200 mm with 10 mm gap	300 mm × 300 mm	300 mm × 300 mm	1.2 m	2.4 m	300 mm × 300 mm

* Note: For excavations to 3 m deep in soil types 1 and 2, the wales can be omitted if the struts are used at 1.2 m horizontal spacings. O. Reg. 213/91, s. 238, Table; O. Reg. 631/94, s. 9.

Installation

239. (1) A support system for the walls of an excavation shall be installed,

- (a) progressively in an excavation in Type 1, 2 or 3 soil; and

- (b) in advance of an excavation in Type 4 soil, if practicable. O. Reg. 213/91, s. 239 (1).

(2) A support system for the walls of an excavation shall provide continuous support for it. O. Reg. 213/91, s. 239 (2).

Removal

(3) No support system for the walls of an excavation shall be removed until immediately before the excavation is backfilled. O. Reg. 213/91, s. 239 (3).

(4) A competent person shall supervise the removal of a support system for the walls of an excavation. O. Reg. 213/91, s. 239 (4).

Ladder

240. If a support system is used for the walls of an excavation, a ladder for access to or egress from the excavation shall be placed within the area protected by the support system. O. Reg. 213/91, s. 240.

Extension

241. (1) A support system for the walls of an excavation shall extend at least 0.3 metres above the top of the excavation unless otherwise permitted or required by this section. O. Reg. 213/91, s. 241 (1).

(2) If an excavation is located where there is vehicular or pedestrian traffic and if the excavation will be covered when work on or in it is not in progress, the support system for the walls of the excavation shall extend at least to the top of the excavation. O. Reg. 213/91, s. 241 (2).

(3)   If the upper portion of the walls of an excavation are sloped for the soil types as described in clauses 234 (2) (e), (f) and (g) and the lower portion of the walls are vertical or near vertical, the walls shall be supported by a support system which extends at least 0.5 metres above the vertical walls. O. Reg. 213/91, s. 241 (3).

Trench-jack, trench-brace

242. (1)   A metal trench-jack or trench-brace may be used in place of a timber strut,

    (a)   if the allowable working load of the trench-jack or trench-brace is equal to or greater than that of the timber strut; and

    (b)   if the size of the replaced timber strut is shown on the trench-jack or trench-brace. O. Reg. 213/91, s. 242 (1).

(2)   The allowable working load of a metal trench-jack or trench-brace shall be determined by a professional engineer in accordance with good engineering practice and shall be legibly cast or stamped on the trench-jack or trench-brace. O. Reg. 213/91, s. 242 (2).

(3)   No metal trench-jack or trench-brace shall be extended beyond the length used to establish its maximum allowable working load. O. Reg. 213/91, s. 242 (3).

(4)   Every metal trench-jack or trench-brace, when it is used,

    (a)   shall be placed against the wales in such a way that the load from the wales is applied axially to the trench-jack or trench-brace; and

    (b)   shall be adequately supported so that it does not move out of position. O. Reg. 213/91, s. 242 (4).

PART IV
TUNNELS, SHAFTS, CAISSONS AND COFFERDAMS

Application

243. This Part applies with respect to,

    (a)   tunnels and shafts other than those located at or used in connection with a mine; and

    (b)   caissons and cofferdams. O. Reg. 213/91, s. 243.

Land Requirements

244. A tunnel or shaft shall be commenced or started only where sufficient land space is available to permit compliance with Parts IV and V. O. Reg. 213/91, s. 244.

Notice

Notice
245. (1)   An employer who will be constructing a tunnel, shaft, caisson or cofferdam shall file a notice with a Director before beginning work on a tunnel, shaft, caisson or cofferdam. O. Reg. 213/91, s. 245 (1); O. Reg. 145/00, s. 33 (1).

    (2)   The notice shall,

        (a)   describe the work;

        (b)   provide specifications and drawings showing profiles, transverse sections and plans for the tunnel, shaft, caisson or cofferdam signed and sealed by the professional engineer who designed the support system for the tunnel, shaft, caisson or cofferdam;

(c)   provide complete details of all temporary and permanent ground support;

(d)   state the name, mailing address, address for service and telephone number of the constructor, of the owner and of the employer in charge of the work;

(e)   state the name of the supervisor in charge of the work and the supervisor's mailing address, address for service and telephone number;

(f)   provide the municipal address of the work or include a description of its location relative to the nearest highway such that the Director is able to locate the work;

(g)   state the starting date and the anticipated duration of the work;

(h)   state the estimated total cost for labour and materials for the work; and

(i)   list all designated substances that may be used, handled or disturbed by the work. O. Reg. 213/91, s. 245 (2); O. Reg. 145/00, s. 33 (2).

Working Alone and Entry

246. Work shall not be performed in a shaft, tunnel, caisson or cofferdam unless another worker is working above ground in close proximity to the shaft, tunnel, caisson or cofferdam or to the means of access to it. O. Reg. 213/91, s. 246.

Well, caisson entry

247. (1)   No worker shall enter a well or augured caisson where the excavation is deeper than 1.2 metres unless,

   (a)   a steel liner of adequate capacity is installed in the well or caisson;

   (b)   the requirements of Ontario Regulation 632/05 (Confined Spaces) made under the Act are complied with; and

   (c)   the worker is inside the steel liner and is wearing a fall arrest system with a full body harness secured to a fixed support. O. Reg. 213/91, s. 247 (1); O. Reg. 628/05, s. 4; O. Reg. 96/11, s. 2.

   (2)   A steel liner,

   (a)   shall extend sixty centimetres above ground level and to within 1.2 metres of the point in the well or caisson where work is being done;

   (b)   shall be supported on two sides by steel wire rope and steel beams; and

   (c)   shall have a diameter which is not less than 100 millimetres less than the diameter of the excavation. O. Reg. 213/91, s. 247 (2).

Fire Protection

Notices

248. Notices describing how to sound a fire alarm shall be posted in conspicuous places on a project to which this Part applies. O. Reg. 213/91, s. 248.

Location

249. (1)   A means of extinguishing fire shall be provided,

   (a)   at the top and bottom of every shaft;

   (b)   if a project consists of or includes a tunnel, at each panel board for electricity, on each electric-powered locomotive and at each battery charging station; and

   (c)   within thirty metres of each work face of a tunnel and of each location where a fire hazard exists. O. Reg. 213/91, s. 249 (1).

(2)   The means of extinguishing fire shall be inspected at least once a week to ensure that it is in working order. O. Reg. 213/91, s. 249 (2).

Fire suppression

250. (1)   A fire suppression system for equipment that contains flammable hydraulic fluids shall be provided while the equipment is underground. O. Reg. 213/91, s. 250 (1).

(2)   A fire suppression system shall include a dry chemical fire extinguisher with an Underwriters' Laboratories of Canada 4A40BC rating. O. Reg. 213/91, s. 250 (2).

Standpipe, line, hose

251. (1)   If the diameter of a tunnel will be equal to or greater than 1.5 metres when it is completed, a standpipe, a fire line and a hose shall be provided in the tunnel. O. Reg. 213/91, s. 251 (1).

(2)   A siamese connection shall be provided on the fire line at the surface of the shaft. O. Reg. 213/91, s. 251 (2).

Standpipe

252. (1)   Every standpipe in a tunnel,

> (a)   shall be made of metal pipe that has at least a fifty-one millimetres inside diameter; and

> (b)   shall have a connection for the use of the local fire department outside the shaft or tunnel to which there is clear and ready access at all times. O. Reg. 213/91, s. 252 (1).

(2)   Every standpipe in a shaft shall be installed progressively as the shaft is excavated. O. Reg. 213/91, s. 252 (2).

Fire-line

253. (1)   Every fire line in a tunnel,

> (a)   shall be made of metal pipe that has at least a fifty-one millimetres inside diameter; and

> (b)   shall have, at intervals of not more than forty-five metres along it, an outlet with a valve. O. Reg. 213/91, s. 253 (1).

(2)   Every fire line in a tunnel shall be installed progressively as the tunnel is excavated. O. Reg. 213/91, s. 253 (2).

Fire-hose

254. (1)   Every hose in a tunnel,

> (a)   shall have at least a thirty millimetres inside diameter;

> (b)   shall have a combination straight stream and fog nozzle; and

> (c)   shall be at least twenty-three metres long. O. Reg. 213/91, s. 254 (1).

(2)   A hose shall be provided in a tunnel at forty-six metre intervals horizontally along it. O. Reg. 213/91, s. 254 (2).

(3)   Every hose shall be stored on a rack when it is not in use so as to be readily available. O. Reg. 213/91, s. 254 (3).

Flammable liquid, gas

255. (1)   No flammable liquid or gas shall be brought underground except as permitted by this section. O. Reg. 213/91, s. 255 (1).

(2)   A compressed gas storage cylinder to which gas welding or flame-cutting equipment is attached may be brought underground. O. Reg. 213/91, s. 255 (2).

Fuel

(3)   Fuel may be brought underground if,

   (a)   it is in a tank that is supplied with and that forms a part of an engine or heating device; or

   (b)   it is in a container and is intended for transfer into a tank described in clause (a). O. Reg. 213/91, s. 255 (3).

(4)   The maximum amount of fuel that may be brought underground in a container referred to in clause (3) (b) is the amount required for eight hours use of the engine or heating device. O. Reg. 213/91, s. 255 (4).

Storage

256. (1)   A flammable liquid or gas shall be stored,

   (a)   as far as is practicable from a shaft; and

   (b)   in a place from which it is impossible for spilled liquid to flow underground. O. Reg. 213/91, s. 256 (1).

Lube oils

(2)   Lubricating oil shall be stored in a suitable building or storage tank located in a place from which spilled liquid cannot run toward any shaft or tunnel. O. Reg. 213/91, s. 256 (2).

Hydraulic oil

257. Oil for use in hydraulic-powered equipment underground shall be of the type that,

(a)   is not readily flammable; and

(b)   does not readily support combustion. O. Reg. 213/91, s. 257.

Combustibles

258. (1)   No combustible equipment, including welding cable and air-hoses, shall be stored underground unless the equipment is required for immediate use. O. Reg. 213/91, s. 258 (1).

Electrical cable, gas hose

(2)   No electrical cable or gas hose shall be taken or used underground unless,

(a)   it has an armoured casing or jacket made of a material that is not readily flammable and that does not readily support combustion; and

(b)   it is marked to indicate that it has the casing or jacket required by clause (a). O. Reg. 213/91, s. 258 (2).

Rubbish

259. (1)   No combustible rubbish, used or decayed timber, scrap wood or paper shall be accumulated underground. O. Reg. 213/91, s. 259 (1).

(2)   Material described in subsection (1) shall be promptly removed from underground. O. Reg. 213/91, s. 259 (2).

Facilities for Workers

Heated room

260. (1)   A heated room shall be provided for the use of underground workers. O. Reg. 213/91, s. 260 (1).

Change room

(2)   The wet clothes of workers employed underground shall be dried using sanitary means in a change room on the project. O. Reg. 213/91, s. 260 (2).

(3)   A change room,

    (a)   shall have an open floor area no smaller than the greater of,

        (i)   ten square metres, and

        (ii)   one square metre per worker on a shift;

    (b)   shall be equipped with mechanical ventilation that provides no less than six air changes per hour;

    (c)   shall have suitable drainage facilities;

    (d)   shall be kept at a temperature of at least 27 degrees celsius; and

    (e)   shall have, for every worker employed underground, a locker that locks. O. Reg. 213/91, s. 260 (3).

Cleaning

(4)   Every change room shall be scrubbed once every twenty-four hours. O. Reg. 213/91, s. 260 (4).

Showers, washbasins

(5)   If workers are employed underground, a change room shall be provided with one shower and one washbasin for each group of ten or fewer workers. O. Reg. 213/91, s. 260 (5).

(6)   Showers and washbasins provided in a change room shall be supplied with hot and cold water, soap or hand cleaner and paper towels or individual hand towels. O. Reg. 213/91, s. 260 (6).

First Aid

First aid

261. The supervisor in charge of a project shall appoint at least one competent worker to be available to give first aid at a shaft or tunnel. O. Reg. 213/91, s. 261.

262. (1)   A first aid kit shall be kept in the immediate vicinity of the above-ground entrance to every shaft, tunnel, caisson or cofferdam. O. Reg. 213/91, s. 262 (1).

(2)   At least one first aid kit shall be kept underground in every shaft and tunnel. O. Reg. 213/91, s. 262 (2).

Stretcher

263. (1)   At least one stretcher for each group of twenty-five or fewer workers who are underground shall be kept at every tunnel, shaft or cofferdam. O. Reg. 213/91, s. 263 (1).

(2)   Every stretcher shall be a wire-basket type and shall be designed and equipped to permit the safe hoisting and transport of a worker. O. Reg. 213/91, s. 263 (2).

Rescue of Workers

Procedures

264. (1)   Before a project begins, an employer shall establish in writing emergency procedures for the rescue of underground workers. O. Reg. 213/91, s. 264 (1).

(2)   Copies of the rescue procedures signed by the employer and supervisor of the underground workers shall be posted in conspicuous places on the project. O. Reg. 213/91, s. 264 (2).

(3)   The emergency procedures shall be practised in preparation for an emergency and shall be followed in an emergency. O. Reg. 213/91, s. 264 (3).

265. (1)   At least four workers at a project or, if fewer than four workers work at the project, all workers shall be trained in and readily available to perform rescues of underground workers. O. Reg. 213/91, s. 265 (1).

(2)   Rescue workers shall be provided with suitable equipment to perform rescues. O. Reg. 213/91, s. 265 (2).

(3)   Rescue workers shall be trained by a competent person appointed by a Director. O. Reg. 213/91, s. 265 (3); O. Reg. 145/00, s. 34 (1).

(4)   A Director who makes an appointment described in subsection (3) shall, in doing so, consider any recommendations of the representatives of labour and of management. O. Reg. 145/00, s. 34 (2).

(5)   Rescue workers shall be trained within thirty days before tunnelling operations begin and retrained at least every thirty days after the initial training. O. Reg. 213/91, s. 265 (5).

(6)   Before a project begins, the supervisor of the construction of a tunnel shall designate a rescue worker who shall inspect and test all rescue equipment every thirty days. O. Reg. 213/91, s. 265 (6).

266. (1)   This section applies if, on a project, there is a tunnel and shaft whose combined length exceeds forty-five metres. O. Reg. 213/91, s. 266 (1).

Self-contained breathing apparatus

(2)   Every rescue worker shall be provided with a self-contained breathing apparatus that meets the requirements of subsection (5) and subsection (6), (7) or (8), as is appropriate to the length of the underground work place. O. Reg. 213/91, s. 266 (2).

(3)   A competent person referred to in subsection 265 (3) shall train rescue workers in the proper operation of the self-contained breathing apparatus. O. Reg. 213/91, s. 266 (3).

(4)   The training required by subsection (3) shall be repeated at least every thirty days. O. Reg. 213/91, s. 266 (4).

(5)   The self-contained breathing apparatus shall have a full face mask. O. Reg. 213/91, s. 266 (5).

(6)   For use in an underground work place that is less than 100 metres long, the minimum rated duration of use for a self-contained breathing apparatus shall be one-half hour. O. Reg. 213/91, s. 266 (6).

(7)   For use in an underground work place that is 100 metres or more but less than 150 metres long, the minimum rated duration of use for a self-contained breathing apparatus shall be one hour. O. Reg. 213/91, s. 266 (7).

(8)   For use in an underground work place that is 150 metres or more long, the minimum rated duration of use for a self-contained

breathing apparatus shall be one and one-half hours. O. Reg. 213/91, s. 266 (8).

(9) All self-contained breathing apparatuses intended for rescue work on a project shall be the same model and made by the same manufacturer. O. Reg. 213/91, s. 266 (9).

(10) All self-contained breathing apparatuses shall be kept in close proximity to the means of access to an underground work place and shall be readily available. O. Reg. 213/91, s. 266 (10).

(11) A sufficient number, four as a minimum, of self-contained breathing apparatuses shall be available on the project to provide for all rescue work that may be required. O. Reg. 213/91, s. 266 (11).

(12) A competent person shall inspect every self-contained breathing apparatus at least once a month or as often as is required by the manufacturer to ensure it is in proper condition. O. Reg. 213/91, s. 266 (12).

Self-rescue respirator

267. Every worker who is in, or may be required to enter, a tunnel or a shaft leading to it shall be provided with a self-rescue respirator for the worker's exclusive use which is suitable for protection against hazardous gases. O. Reg. 631/94, s. 10.

268. (1) A worker's self-rescue respirator shall be kept in the vicinity of the worker while he or she is in a tunnel or shaft. O. Reg. 213/91, s. 268 (1).

(2) All workers on a tunnel project shall be instructed in the proper use, care, maintenance and limitations of the self-rescue respirator in accordance with the manufacturer's specifications. O. Reg. 213/91, s. 268 (2).

Communications

Telephone

269. (1)   Subject to subsection (2), a telephone connected to a public telephone system shall be installed at a project that is to be over fourteen days duration. O. Reg. 213/91, s. 269 (1).

Radio telephone

(2)   If it is not practicable to install at a project a telephone connected to a public telephone system, a radio telephone shall be available that permits communication with an office of the constructor that has a telephone connected to a public telephone system. O. Reg. 213/91, s. 269 (2).

(3)   At a project of fourteen or fewer days duration, before work is begun, a public telephone or a radio telephone shall be installed or shall be arranged for nearby if,

   (a)   the services of a police or fire department or ambulance are reasonably available; and

   (b)   prompt direct telephone communication is possible with the police or fire department or ambulance. O. Reg. 213/91, s. 269 (3).

Location

270. (1)   A telephone system shall be provided at a tunnel if the work at the face of the tunnel is or will be done twenty-three metres or more from,

   (a)   the top of the service shaft; or

   (b)   the opening into the tunnel, if the tunnel is not constructed from a service shaft. O. Reg. 213/91, s. 270 (1).

(2) A telephone system shall be installed before work on the tunnel is begun. O. Reg. 213/91, s. 270 (2).

(3) A telephone system shall consist of telephones that are located,

    (a) in the office of the supervisor in charge of the project;

    (b) at the top and bottom of the service shaft or at the opening into the tunnel, if the tunnel is not constructed from a service shaft;

    (c) at all other means of access to the service shaft, if any; and

    (d) at intervals not exceeding thirty metres in every area of the tunnel where work is being performed. O. Reg. 213/91, s. 270 (3).

Notice

(4) A notice shall be posted by each telephone,

    (a) indicating how to call every other telephone in the system;

    (b) describing the emergency signal to be used; and

    (c) stating that a worker who hears the emergency signal shall answer the telephone. O. Reg. 213/91, s. 270 (4).

(5) A telephone system shall be installed in such a way that a conversation can be carried on between any two telephones in the system. O. Reg. 213/91, s. 270 (5).

(6) The voice communication circuits used in a telephone system shall be independent from the circuits used to signal from one telephone to another. O. Reg. 213/91, s. 270 (6).

Communication

271. During the construction of a shaft, an effective means of communicating between the lowest point of the shaft and the surface shall be provided. O. Reg. 213/91, s. 271.

Signals

272. A completed service shaft more than six metres deep shall have a means, other than a telephone, of exchanging distinct and definite signals between the top and bottom of the shaft. O. Reg. 213/91, s. 272.

Notification, signals

273. (1) If a person is about to be conveyed by a hoist in a shaft, the pit bottom worker shall notify the hoist operator before the person enters the conveyance. O. Reg. 213/91, s. 273 (1).

(2) A hoist operator shall acknowledge every signal received by repeating the signal. O. Reg. 213/91, s. 273 (2).

(3) A signal to a hoist operator to move a conveyance shall be given only from the landing from which the conveyance is being moved. O. Reg. 213/91, s. 273 (3).

Code of signals

(4) The following signals shall be used to give signals between a hoist operator, the top or bottom of a shaft and all landings in the shaft:

Code of Signals

Where the conveyance is in motion –	
1 signal	STOP
Where the conveyance is stationary –	
1 signal	HOIST
2 signals together	LOWER
3 signals together (to be given before any person enters the conveyance)	Person will be on conveyance. OPERATE CAREFULLY.

O. Reg. 213/91, s. 273 (4).

(5)   The supervisor in charge of a project may establish signals in addition to those set out in subsection (4) if required for the operation of a hoist on the project. O. Reg. 213/91, s. 273 (5).

(6)   A notice setting out the signals used for a hoist shall be securely posted,

(a)   where it is readily visible to the hoist operator; and

(b)   at each landing of the hoistway. O. Reg. 213/91, s. 273 (6).

(7)   The notice shall be on a board or a metal plate that is not less than 450 millimetres by 450 millimetres and shall be written in letters that are at least thirteen millimetres high. O. Reg. 213/91, s. 273 (7).

Lighting and Electricity Supply

274. All electrical circuits of 100 volts or more shall be in an insulated cable that consists of at least two conductors and a grounding conductor. O. Reg. 627/05, s. 8.

Grounding
275. All electrical pumps and electrical tools shall be either adequately grounded or double-insulated. O. Reg. 213/91, s. 275.

Lighting
276. (1) An area of a tunnel or shaft that is not adequately lit by natural light shall be electrically illuminated. O. Reg. 213/91, s. 276 (1).

(2) Flashlights shall be readily available at the top and bottom of every shaft and near the work face of a tunnel. O. Reg. 213/91, s. 276 (2).

Emergency lighting system
(3) If electric lighting is used in a tunnel or shaft, an emergency lighting system shall be installed in the tunnel or shaft. O. Reg. 213/91, s. 276 (3).

(4) An emergency lighting system,

(a) shall be connected to the electrical supply so that in the event of the failure of the electrical supply, the system will automatically turn on;

(b) shall be provided with a testing switch, if the system is battery-powered; and

(c) shall be tested at least as frequently as is recommended by its manufacturer to ensure that the system will function in an emergency. O. Reg. 213/91, s. 276 (4).

277. Revoked: O. Reg. 627/05, s. 9.

Shafts

Size

278. (1)   Every shaft shall be large enough that its walls can be adequately shored and shall have enough clear space for work to be done. O. Reg. 213/91, s. 278 (1).

(2)   In a service shaft that is more than six metres deep or that serves a tunnel more than fifteen metres long,

   (a)   the minimum inside dimension of the shaft, measured between the wales or other wall supports, shall be 2.4 metres for a cylindrical shaft and 1.5 metres for a shaft that is not cylindrical; and

   (b)   the minimum transverse cross-sectional area of a shaft that is not cylindrical shall be 5.7 square metres. O. Reg. 213/91, s. 278 (2).

Support

279. (1)   The walls of a shaft shall be supported by shoring and bracing adequate to prevent their collapse. O. Reg. 213/91, s. 279 (1).

(2)   Subsection (1) does not apply to the walls of a shaft that is less than 1.2 metres deep or is cut in sound rock. O. Reg. 213/91, s. 279 (2).

Professional engineer's opinion

(3)   If a shaft is to be cut in sound rock, the constructor shall obtain a written opinion from a professional engineer as to whether the walls of the shaft need to be supported by rock bolts or wire mesh to prevent the spalling of loose rock. O. Reg. 213/91, s. 279 (3).

(4)   The walls of a shaft cut in sound rock shall be supported by rock bolts or wire mesh where necessary in the opinion of the professional engineer. O. Reg. 213/91, s. 279 (4).

Strength

280. (1)   Shoring and bracing for a shaft that is more than 1.2 metres deep shall be capable of withstanding all loads likely to be applied to them. O. Reg. 213/91, s. 280 (1).

(2)   The shoring and bracing,

(a)   shall be designed by a professional engineer in accordance with good engineering practice; and

(b)   shall be constructed in accordance with the professional engineer's design. O. Reg. 213/91, s. 280 (2).

Drawings

(3)   Design drawings by a professional engineer for the shoring and bracing shall show the size and specifications of the shoring and bracing including the type and grade of all materials to be used in their construction. O. Reg. 213/91, s. 280 (3).

(4)   **Revoked:** O. Reg. 443/09, s. 8.

(5)   The constructor shall keep a copy of design drawings for the shoring and bracing at the project while the shoring and bracing are in use. O. Reg. 213/91, s. 280 (5).

281. (1)   If a square or rectangular shaft is not more than six metres deep and has walls that are not more than 3.6 metres wide, the walls,

(a)   shall be fully sheathed with Number 1 Grade spruce planks that are at least fifty-one millimetres thick by 152 millimetres wide and are placed side by side; and

    (b)   shall be supported by wales and struts. O. Reg. 213/91, s. 281 (1); O. Reg. 631/94, s. 11.

(2) Wales and struts,

    (a)   shall be made of number 1 structural grade spruce planks that are,

        (i)   at least 152 millimetres by 152 millimetres, for a shaft that is not more than 2.7 metres deep,

        (ii)   at least 203 millimetres by 203 millimetres, for a shaft that is more than 2.7 metres but not more than 4.3 metres deep, and

        (iii)   at least 254 millimetres by 254 millimetres, for a shaft that is more than 4.3 metres but not more than six metres deep;

    (b)   shall be spaced not more than 1.2 metres apart vertically; and

    (c)   shall be adequately supported by vertical posts that extend to the bottom of the shaft. O. Reg. 213/91, s. 281 (2).

Barrier

282. (1) An adequate barrier that is at least 1.1 metres high shall be provided around the top of an uncovered shaft. O. Reg. 213/91, s. 282 (1).

(2) A barrier around the top of an uncovered shaft that is more than 2.4 metres deep,

    (a)   shall consist of a top rail, an intermediate rail and a toe-board; and

(b)   shall be made of thirty-eight by 140 millimetres lumber securely fastened to vertical supports that are spaced at intervals of not more than 2.4 metres. O. Reg. 213/91, s. 282 (2).

(3)   A barrier shall be kept free of splinters and protruding nails. O. Reg. 213/91, s. 282 (3).

(4)   A gate in a barrier around the top of an uncovered shaft shall be kept closed and latched. O. Reg. 213/91, s. 282 (4).

Ground slope
(5)   The ground adjacent to a barrier around the top of a shaft shall be sloped away from the barrier. O. Reg. 213/91, s. 282 (5).

283. A shaft shall be kept clear of ice and loose objects that may endanger a worker. O. Reg. 213/91, s. 283.

284. A shaft shall be kept reasonably free of water when a worker is required to be in the shaft. O. Reg. 213/91, s. 284.

Access, egress
285. Every shaft shall have a means of access and egress by stairway, ladder or ladderway for its full depth during its construction and when it is completed. O. Reg. 213/91, s. 285.

Landings
286. (1)   A stairway, ladder or ladderway for a shaft that is more than six metres deep,

(a)   shall have landings or rest platforms spaced at intervals not greater than 4.5 metres;

(b)   shall be off-set at each landing or rest platform; and

(c)   shall be located in a sheathed compartment that is constructed in such a way that a worker who falls while

on the stairway, ladder or ladderway will land on the
landing or rest platform below. O. Reg. 213/91,
s. 286 (1).

(2)   Every landing and rest platform shall be wide enough to permit
at least two workers to pass on it safely. O. Reg. 213/91, s. 286 (2).

(3)   Every opening and ladderway shall be wide enough to permit
the passage of a worker wearing rescue equipment and shall be at
least 750 cm by 750 cm. O. Reg. 631/94, s. 12.

Lining

287. (1)   Every conveyance located in a service shaft that is more than
six metres deep shall be separated from a stairway, ladder or
ladderway in the shaft by a lining described in subsection (3).
O. Reg. 213/91, s. 287 (1).

(2)   Subsection (1) does not apply with respect to a conveyance
located in a service shaft if the hoisting area is so remote from the
stairway, ladder or ladderway that it is not possible for a load,
bucket or device being hoisted or lowered to come into contact with
the stairway, ladder or ladderway. O. Reg. 213/91, s. 287 (2).

(3)   A lining shall consist of solid planks at least fifty-one
millimetres thick and spaced not more than ten millimetres apart.
O. Reg. 213/91, s. 287 (3).

Hoistways

288. (1)   This section applies with respect to a hoistway that is more
than six metres deep in which hoisting is carried out by mechanical
power. O. Reg. 213/91, s. 288 (1).

Gate

(2)   Every landing on a hoistway shall have a gate located within 200 millimetres of the hoistway that,

(a)   extends the full width of the hoistway from within fifty millimetres of the floor level to a height of at least 1.8 metres;

(b)   is constructed without any gaps that would permit the entry of a ball thirty-eight millimetres in diameter; and

(c)   is equipped with a light readily visible to the hoist operator indicating when the gate is closed. O. Reg. 213/91, s. 288 (2).

(3)   Subsection (2) does not apply to a landing at the bottom of a hoistway if the landing has one or more red lights that,

(a)   are located where a person approaching the hoistway from a tunnel or from the lower end of a stair or ladder can see at least one of them; and

(b)   are controlled by a switch readily accessible to a shaft attendant. O. Reg. 213/91, s. 288 (3).

(4)   A gate required by subsection (2) shall be kept closed unless a conveyance is stopped at the landing. O. Reg. 213/91, s. 288 (4).

(5)   The red lights referred to in subsection (3) shall be continuously flashed off and on during a hoisting operation. O. Reg. 213/91, s. 288 (5).

Inspection

289. (1)   All parts of a hoisting apparatus used in a hoistway or shaft shall be able to be conveniently inspected. O. Reg. 213/91, s. 289 (1).

(2)   Every hoist drum shall have a flange at each end to keep the hoist rope on the drum. O. Reg. 213/91, s. 289 (2).

Hoist operator duties

290. (1)   A hoist operator shall operate and watch over a hoist and all machinery associated with the hoist to detect any hazardous conditions. O. Reg. 213/91, s. 290 (1).

(2)   A hoist operator shall report immediately to the supervisor in charge of the project any defects in the hoisting machinery and safety appliances. O. Reg. 213/91, s. 290 (2).

(3)   The hoist operator shall test all safety devices on a hoisting apparatus to ensure that they function and shall perform the tests,

  (a)   before a conveyance is first put into service on a project;

  (b)   at least once every three months after being put into service on the project; and

  (c)   daily, if the hoisting apparatus is used to hoist persons. O. Reg. 213/91, s. 290 (3).

(4)   The hoist operator shall make a record of tests performed under subsection (3). O. Reg. 213/91, s. 290 (4).

(5)   The hoist operator shall keep available for inspection at the project the record of tests performed under subsection (3). O. Reg. 213/91, s. 290 (5).

Competent worker

291. (1)   No person other than a competent worker appointed by the supervisor in charge of a project shall operate a hoist in a hoistway or shaft. O. Reg. 213/91, s. 291 (1).

(2)   No person, other than a worker required to do so as a part of the worker's job, shall enter or attend the machine room of a hoist. O. Reg. 213/91, s. 291 (2).

Hoist operator duty, inspection

292. A hoist operator shall inspect the hoisting machinery and safety appliances connected to it at least once a day and shall make a record of the inspection in a log book. O. Reg. 213/91, s. 292.

Hoist operator duties

293. (1)   A hoist operator and all shaft attendants shall understand the signal code established for the hoist. O. Reg. 213/91, s. 293 (1).

(2)   No hoist operator shall converse with another person while the hoist is in motion or signals are being given. O. Reg. 213/91, s. 293 (2).

(3)   No hoist operator shall turn over the controls of a hoist to another person while a conveyance is in motion. O. Reg. 213/91, s. 293 (3).

(4)   No hoist operator shall operate a hoist,

    (a)   unless it is equipped with,

        (i)   indicators showing the position of the conveyance on the hoist, and

        (ii)   brakes and distance markers on the hoisting ropes and cables;

    (b)   in a compartment of a shaft in which work is being done unless the hoist is being operated for the purpose of work in the compartment. O. Reg. 213/91, s. 293 (4).

(5)   After a hoist has been stopped for repairs, a hoist operator shall run an empty conveyance up and down the shaft at least once

and shall determine that the hoist is in good working order before carrying a load in it. O. Reg. 213/91, s. 293 (5).

Supervisor duties

294. (1)   The supervisor in charge of a project,

(a)   shall establish the maximum speed for a conveyance transporting persons in a hoistway; and

(b)   shall determine the maximum number of persons and the maximum weight of material that may be carried safely on a conveyance in a hoistway. O. Reg. 213/91, s. 294 (1).

(2)   A notice setting out the maximums referred to in subsection (1) shall be conspicuously posted near each hoistway entrance. O. Reg. 213/91, s. 294 (2).

(3)   No person shall load a conveyance in a hoistway beyond the maximum limits established under clause (1) (b). O. Reg. 213/91, s. 294 (3).

(4)   A hoist operator shall operate a hoist in accordance with the notice posted under subsection (2). O. Reg. 213/91, s. 294 (4).

Appointment of shaft attendants

295. (1)   The supervisor in charge of a project shall appoint shaft attendants for a shaft where a hoist is being used. O. Reg. 213/91, s. 295 (1).

(2)   No shaft attendant shall be less than nineteen years of age. O. Reg. 213/91, s. 295 (2).

(3)   At least one shaft attendant shall be on duty at the top of a shaft if a hoist, crane or similar hoisting device is being used or if a

worker is present in the shaft or in a tunnel connected to the shaft. O. Reg. 213/91, s. 295 (3).

(4)   A shaft attendant,

(a)   shall give the hoist operator the signals for starting and stopping the hoist;

(b)   shall warn workers of hazards in or near the shaft; and

(c)   as far as is practicable, shall remove known hazards. O. Reg. 213/91, s. 295 (4).

Signals

296. (1)   The supervisor in charge of a project shall, before a hoist is used on the project, establish a communication system of signals to be used between a hoist operator, shaft attendants and any other attendants working at a hoist. O. Reg. 213/91, s. 296 (1).

(2)   The supervisor in charge of a project shall ensure that all hoist operators, shaft attendants and other attendants working at a hoist know and understand the signals. O. Reg. 213/91, s. 296 (2).

Appointment of workers

297. (1)   The supervisor in charge of a project shall appoint workers to control the movement of materials to and from a conveyance on a hoist at every landing and at the bottom of a shaft. O. Reg. 213/91, s. 297 (1).

(2)   A worker appointed under subsection (1) shall control and direct the movement of materials to and from a conveyance. O. Reg. 213/91, s. 297 (2).

Worker transportation

298. No worker shall be transported in a conveyance or a hoist while it is being used to carry materials or equipment other than hand tools or similar small objects. O. Reg. 213/91, s. 298.

Overhead protection

299. The path of travel of an object being hoisted from or lowered into a shaft by a crane shall not pass over a manway unless the manway has adequate overhead protection. O. Reg. 213/91, s. 299.

Cage, car

300. (1) A service shaft that will be over thirty metres deep when completed shall have a hoist with a conveyance consisting of a cage or car suitable for transporting workers. O. Reg. 213/91, s. 300 (1).

Hoist

(2) A hoist shall be installed in the service shaft as soon as is practicable. O. Reg. 213/91, s. 300 (2).

(3) A hoist,

(a) shall have a headframe that is grounded for protection against lightning and is designed by a professional engineer;

(b) shall have guides to control the movement of the conveyance;

(c) shall have a device that automatically stops the conveyance when it runs beyond the limit of its normal travel; and

(d) shall have a brake on the hoisting machine that automatically stops and holds the conveyance if the hoist fails or the power to the hoist is interrupted. O. Reg. 213/91, s. 300 (3).

(4)   A shaft in sound rock may be excavated to a depth of not more than thirty metres before the headframe and guides are installed on the hoist. O. Reg. 213/91, s. 300 (4).

Stopping device

301. (1)   Every conveyance on a hoist used for transporting workers in a shaft shall have a suitable device that, if the cable breaks or becomes slack,

(a)   automatically prevents the conveyance from falling; and

(b)   is capable of holding the conveyance stationary when it contains the maximum number of passengers it is permitted to carry. O. Reg. 213/91, s. 301 (1).

(2)   Subsection (1) does not apply with respect to a bucket or a skip operated in accordance with sections 303 and 305. O. Reg. 213/91, s. 301 (2).

(3)   A device shall be installed to warn the hoist operator when a conveyance transporting workers in a shaft has reached the normal limit of its travel. O. Reg. 213/91, s. 301 (3).

Cage, car

302. (1)   A cage or car on a hoist used for transporting workers in a shaft,

(a)   shall be at least 1.8 metres high;

(b)   shall be solidly enclosed, except for openings for access and egress;

(c)   shall have a maximum of two openings for access and egress;

      (d)   shall have a gate at each opening for access and egress; and

      (e)   shall have a protective cover suitable to protect passengers from falling objects. O. Reg. 213/91, s. 302 (1).

  (2)   A gate for access and egress,

      (a)   shall be constructed without any gaps that would permit the entry of a ball thirty-eight millimetres in diameter;

      (b)   shall extend the full width of the opening and from within fifty millimetres of the floor of the cage or car to a height of at least 1.8 metres; and

      (c)   shall not open outward. O. Reg. 213/91, s. 302 (2).

  (3)   A protective cover referred to in clause (1) (e) shall have a trap door for emergency access which measures not less than 600 millimetres by 600 millimetres. O. Reg. 213/91, s. 302 (3).

Worker transport

303. (1)   Subject to subsection (2), a bucket or similar conveyance shall not be used to transport a worker in a shaft. O. Reg. 213/91, s. 303 (1).

  (2)   A bucket or similar conveyance may be used to transport a worker in a shaft for the purpose of inspecting the hoistway if no other method of access to the parts of the hoistway is available. O. Reg. 213/91, s. 303 (2).

  (3)   A bucket referred to in subsection (2),

      (a)   shall be at least 1.2 metres deep;

(b) shall have smoothly-contoured outer surfaces to prevent it from tipping or becoming snagged by an obstacle during hoisting or lowering; and

(c) shall not be self-opening. O. Reg. 213/91, s. 303 (3).

(4)   If a pivoted bucket that is manually-dumped and is not self-guided is being used to transport a worker, the bucket,

(a) shall be equipped with a lock to prevent tipping; and

(b) shall be pivoted in such a way that it does not automatically invert when the lock is released. O. Reg. 213/91, s. 303 (4).

(5)   A bucket that is not controlled by a cross head running in vertical guides shall not be hoisted or lowered at a speed greater than 0.5 metres per second when it is transporting a worker. O. Reg. 213/91, s. 303 (5).

Door
304. (1)   A hinged door that opens upward shall be provided over the opening at the top of a shaft. O. Reg. 213/91, s. 304 (1).

(2)   The door shall be closed while a worker is entering or leaving a bucket over the opening at the top of the shaft. O. Reg. 213/91, s. 304 (2).

Worker transport
305. A skip shall not be used to transport a worker unless,

(a) the worker is inspecting guiderails or shaft supports; and

(b) the skip is protected by an overwind device to prevent the skip from being hoisted to the dump position. O. Reg. 213/91, s. 305.

Tunnels

Clear space

306. (1)   A tunnel shall have enough clear space for the passage of vehicles and the movement of workers. O. Reg. 213/91, s. 306 (1).

(2)   The diameter of a circular or elliptical tunnel and the width and height of a square or rectangular tunnel shall be at least 760 millimetres. O. Reg. 213/91, s. 306 (2).

(3)   A clear space of at least 450 millimetres shall be left between the side of a tunnel and the nearer side of,

    (a)   all trackless haulage equipment being used; and

    (b)   all locomotives, haulage cars and machines operating on a track. O. Reg. 213/91, s. 306 (3).

(4)   A circular or elliptical tunnel shall have safety platforms at sixty metre intervals along it. O. Reg. 213/91, s. 306 (4).

(5)   A safety platform shall be long enough for a crew of workers to stand on, shall be constructed above the tunnel invert and shall be clear of passing equipment. O. Reg. 213/91, s. 306 (5).

Support

307. (1)   Except for a tunnel cut in sound rock, the sides and roof of a tunnel shall be supported by timbers set on ribs or beams or by an equivalent system of lining. O. Reg. 213/91, s. 307 (1).

(2)   If a tunnel is to be cut in sound rock, the constructor shall obtain a written opinion from a professional engineer as to whether the sides and roof of the tunnel need to be supported by rock bolts or wire mesh to prevent the spalling of loose rock. O. Reg. 213/91, s. 307 (2).

(3) The sides and roof of a tunnel cut in sound rock,

   (a) shall be supported, where necessary in the opinion of the professional engineer, by rock bolts or wire mesh;

   (b) shall be inspected daily by a competent worker; and

   (c) shall have all loose pieces of rock removed. O. Reg. 213/91, s. 307 (3).

(4) If the permanent lining of a tunnel will, when completed, consist of a primary lining and a secondary lining, the primary lining shall be strong enough to support the sides and roof of the tunnel until the secondary lining is installed. O. Reg. 213/91, s. 307 (4).

(5) If the permanent lining of a tunnel consists only of a concrete cast-in-place lining, the tunnel shall not be excavated beyond the leading edge of the permanent lining unless adequate temporary shoring is installed as soon as is practicable. O. Reg. 213/91, s. 307 (5).

(6) The primary supports of a tunnel,

   (a) shall be designed by a professional engineer in accordance with good engineering practice to withstand all loads likely to be applied to them; and

   (b) shall be constructed in accordance with the design. O. Reg. 213/91, s. 307 (6).

(7) The constructor shall keep available for inspection at a project the design drawings for the primary supports. O. Reg. 213/91, s. 307 (7); O. Reg. 85/04, s. 23.

Water-free

308. A tunnel shall be kept reasonably free of water when a worker is required to be in the tunnel. O. Reg. 213/91, s. 308.

Tunnel Equipment

Precautions

309. When a haulage locomotive, trackless haulage equipment or a hoist in a shaft or tunnel is left unattended,

(a)   its controls shall be left in the neutral position; and

(b)   its brakes shall be set or other measures, such as blocking, shall be taken to prevent its moving. O. Reg. 213/91, s. 309.

Brakes, bell, control

310. (1)   A haulage locomotive shall have suitable brakes, an audible bell and controls that can be operated only by a worker at the driver's station. O. Reg. 213/91, s. 310 (1).

(2)   A haulage locomotive shall be designed so that power for its driving mechanism is cut off unless the control regulating the power is continuously operated by a worker at the driver's station. O. Reg. 213/91, s. 310 (2).

(3)   The driver of a haulage locomotive shall sound the bell when the locomotive is set in motion or is approaching someone. O. Reg. 213/91, s. 310 (3).

(4)   No person other than the driver shall ride on a haulage locomotive. O. Reg. 213/91, s. 310 (4).

311. No worker shall ride on a haulage train except in a car provided to carry passengers. O. Reg. 213/91, s. 311.

312. A haulage car shall have a device to prevent uncontrolled travel by the car. O. Reg. 213/91, s. 312.

Track

313. (1) Track for haulage equipment shall be securely fastened to the ties on which it is laid. O. Reg. 213/91, s. 313 (1).

(2) If the ties interfere with the use of the bottom of the tunnel as a walkway, a solid walkway that is at least 300 millimetres wide shall be provided. O. Reg. 213/91, s. 313 (2).

Compressor inlet

314. (1) The air inlet to an air compressor shall be located in such a position that fumes or noxious contaminants are not drawn in with the air to be compressed. O. Reg. 213/91, s. 314 (1).

(2) A valve connected to a vessel used for storing compressed air,

(a) shall be connected at the lowest point of the vessel to permit the discharge of the compressed air; and

(b) shall be opened at least once each shift for the purpose of ejecting oil, water and other matter from the vessel. O. Reg. 213/91, s. 314 (2).

Pumping equipment

315. (1) A project shall have pumping equipment of sufficient capacity to handle the pumping requirements of the project. O. Reg. 213/91, s. 315 (1).

(2) Pumping equipment shall be connected to an adequate source of energy. O. Reg. 213/91, s. 315 (2).

(3) Sufficient spare pumping equipment and an alternative source of energy for it shall be readily available at the project in case of emergency. O. Reg. 213/91, s. 315 (3).

Internal combustion engine

316. No internal combustion engine shall be used in a tunnel on a project without the prior written consent of a Director. O. Reg. 213/91, s. 316; O. Reg. 145/00, s. 36.

Explosives

Work continuance

317. Before blasting begins in a shaft, tunnel, caisson or cofferdam that is located within the greater of 4.5 metres and twice the length of the longest drill rod used away from another shaft, tunnel, caisson or cofferdam, the worker in charge of the blasting operations shall determine whether work in the adjacent shaft, tunnel, caisson or cofferdam can safely continue during blasting operations. O. Reg. 213/91, s. 317.

Transport vehicle

318. (1) No vehicle or conveyance being used to transport explosives or blasting agents shall carry any other cargo or any person other than the vehicle operator. O. Reg. 213/91, s. 318 (1).

Detonator

(2) No detonator shall be transported in a vehicle or conveyance while it is carrying explosives or other blasting agents. O. Reg. 213/91, s. 318 (2).

(3) Where mechanical track haulage is used in a tunnel, explosives or blasting agents shall not be transported on the locomotive or in the same car as the detonators. O. Reg. 213/91, s. 318 (3).

Transport, mechanical haulage

319. (1)   A vehicle or conveyance, including trackless equipment, that is transporting explosives or blasting agents in a tunnel by mechanical haulage,

   (a)   shall be given an uninterrupted and a clear passage of travel;

   (b)   shall be conspicuously marked by signs or red flags that are easily visible from the front and the rear;

   (c)   shall not travel at a speed greater than six kilometres per hour; and

   (d)   shall not be left unattended. O. Reg. 213/91, s. 319 (1).

   (2)   Explosives and blasting agents referred to in subsection (1),

Storage

   (a)   shall be in a box made of wood or be separated from every metal part of the vehicle or conveyance in which they are being transported by a lining made of wood; and

   (b)   shall be arranged or secured so as to prevent any part of an explosive or blasting agent from being dislodged. O. Reg. 213/91, s. 319 (2).

Notification

320.   If explosives or blasting agents are to be transported in a shaft, the worker in charge of blasting operations shall notify the hoist operator and shaft attendants before the explosives or blasting agents are put in the conveyance. O. Reg. 213/91, s. 320.

Flashlights

321. A flashlight shall be provided to every worker who is engaged in blasting operations in a tunnel or is in an area from which the means of egress passes a place where blasting is to be done.
O. Reg. 213/91, s. 321.

Drilling, charging operations

322. Drilling or charging operations in a shaft or tunnel shall not be done simultaneously,

    (a) above or below one another on the same face; or

    (b) within a 7.5 metre horizontal distance from one another.
O. Reg. 213/91, s. 322.

Electric firing

323. (1) Explosives and blasting agents shall be fired electrically.
O. Reg. 213/91, s. 323 (1).

(2) Despite subsection (1), tape fuse may be used to fire explosives and blasting agents if block holing is to be done.
O. Reg. 213/91, s. 323 (2).

Firing cables, wires

324. (1) If a portable direct current battery or a blasting machine is the source of current for blasting, the firing cables or wires,

    (a) shall not be connected to the source of current until immediately before the charges are fired; and

    (b) shall be disconnected immediately after the charges are fired. O. Reg. 213/91, s. 324 (1).

(2)   All firing cables or wires leading to a face shall be short-circuited while the leads from the blasting caps are being connected to one another and to the firing cables. O. Reg. 213/91, s. 324 (2).

(3)   No short-circuit of a firing cable or wire shall be removed until all workers have retreated from the face and are so located that, should a premature explosion occur, the workers are not endangered. O. Reg. 213/91, s. 324 (3).

(4)   A short-circuit shall be replaced immediately after the firing cables or wires are disconnected from the blasting machine or the blasting switch is opened. O. Reg. 213/91, s. 324 (4).

(5)   Separate firing cables or wires for firing charges shall be used for each work location. O. Reg. 213/91, s. 324 (5).

(6)   Firing cables or wires,

   (a)   shall be located as far as is practicable from every other electrical circuit; and

   (b)   shall not be permitted to come in contact with power, lighting or communication cables, or pipes, rails or other continuous metal grounded surfaces. O. Reg. 213/91, s. 324 (6).

Device for firing charge
325. (1)   Every device, other than a portable hand-operated device, used for firing a charge shall meet the requirements of this section. O. Reg. 213/91, s. 325 (1).

(2)   No person other than a competent worker shall use a device used for firing a charge. O. Reg. 213/91, s. 325 (2).

(3) A device used for firing a charge shall have a switch mechanism that automatically returns by gravity to the open position. O. Reg. 213/91, s. 325 (3).

(4) The live side of a device used for firing a charge shall be installed in a fixed locked box which is accessible only to the worker doing the blasting. O. Reg. 213/91, s. 325 (4).

(5) The lock on the box referred to in subsection (4) shall be able to be closed only when the contacts of the device are open and a short-circuiting device is in place. O. Reg. 213/91, s. 325 (5).

(6) The leads to the face shall be short-circuited when the contacts of the device are in the open position. O. Reg. 213/91, s. 325 (6).

Blasting circuit
326. (1) A circuit used for blasting shall originate from an isolated ungrounded power source and shall be used only for blasting. O. Reg. 213/91, s. 326 (1).

(2) Subsection (1) does not apply with respect to blasting done with a portable hand-operated device. O. Reg. 213/91, s. 326 (2).

Return after blast
327. (1) When a charge is fired and after a shot is heard, every worker in a place of refuge from a blast shall remain there and not return to the blast area for at least ten minutes. O. Reg. 213/91, s. 327 (1).

(2) If a charge is fired and no shot is heard, before the circuit is repaired,

    (a) the blasting circuit shall be locked in the open position; and

(b)   the lead wires shall be short-circuited. O. Reg. 213/91, s. 327 (2).

(3)   A worker who suspects a misfire of an explosive or a blasting agent shall report it to the supervisor in charge of the project. O. Reg. 213/91, s. 327 (3).

(4)   A charge of an explosive or a blasting agent that has misfired shall be left in place and blasted as soon as it is discovered. O. Reg. 213/91, s. 327 (4).

328. When a blasting operation is completed, the blasting switch shall be locked in the open position, the lead wires short-circuited and the blasting box locked. O. Reg. 213/91, s. 328.

Ventilation

Fresh air
329. An adequate supply of fresh air shall be provided and circulated throughout an underground work place. O. Reg. 213/91, s. 329.

Testing
330. (1)   An underground work place shall be tested regularly for noxious or toxic gases, fumes or dust. O. Reg. 213/91, s. 330 (1).

(2)   A competent worker shall regularly test the air and the mechanical ventilation for an underground work place to ensure that the mechanical ventilation is adequate. O. Reg. 213/91, s. 330 (2).

Respiratory equipment
(3)   When the results of the tests referred to in subsection (2) indicate there is a need for respiratory protective equipment, the employer shall provide respiratory protective equipment. O. Reg. 213/91, s. 330 (3).

331. (1)   Mechanical ventilation shall be provided in a shaft in which an internal combustion engine or other device which emits a noxious gas or fume operates. O. Reg. 213/91, s. 331 (1).

(2)   Subsection (1) does not apply if the noxious gas or fume is discharged outside the shaft in such a way that its return to the shaft is prevented. O. Reg. 213/91, s. 331 (2).

PART V
WORK IN COMPRESSED AIR

Interpretation and Application

332. In this Part,

"air lock" means a chamber designed for the passage of persons or materials from one place to another place that has a different air pressure from the first;

"compressed air" means air whose pressure is mechanically raised to more than atmospheric pressure;

"decompression sickness", in relation to a worker, means a condition of bodily malfunction caused by a change from a higher to a lower air pressure and includes the condition commonly known as "the bends";

"kilopascals", except in section 376, means kilopascals relative to atmospheric pressure;

"maximum air pressure", in relation to a worker, means the greatest level of air pressure to which a worker is subjected for a period of more than five minutes;

"medical lock" means a chamber in which workers may be subjected to changes in air pressure for medical purposes;

"superintendent" means the person appointed by a constructor to be supervisor over and in charge of work done in compressed air;

"work chamber" means a part of a project that is used for work in compressed air but does not include an air lock or a medical lock. O. Reg. 213/91, s. 332.

333. This Part applies with respect to work done in compressed air, other than work done in diving bells or work done by divers. O. Reg. 213/91, s. 333.

General Requirements

334. (1)   No constructor or employer shall begin work at a project where a worker may be subjected to compressed air until the requirements of this section are met. O. Reg. 213/91, s. 334 (1).

Notice to Director

(2)   The employer of workers who may be subjected to compressed air at a project shall give a Director written notice of the intended use of compressed air on the project at least fourteen days before beginning work on the project. O. Reg. 213/91, s. 334 (2); O. Reg. 145/00, s. 37 (1).

(3)   Before work is begun in compressed air, the employer shall obtain written permission from a Director. O. Reg. 213/91, s. 334 (3); O. Reg. 145/00, s. 37 (2).

Notice to authorities

335. (1)   Before work is begun in compressed air at a project, a constructor shall give written notice,

    (a)   to the local police department and the fire department and public hospital nearest to the project; and

    (b)   to a Director, together with the names and addresses of those to whom notice is given under clause (a). O. Reg. 213/91, s. 335 (1); O. Reg. 145/00, s. 38.

(2)   A notice shall set out,

    (a)   the location of the project;

    (b)   the name, address and telephone number of the project physician and the superintendent; and

    (c)   the location of a medical lock for the project and of every other readily-available medical lock. O. Reg. 213/91, s. 335 (2).

Notice of completion

(3)   The employer shall give notice of the completion of work in compressed air at the project to those who were given notice under clause (1) (a). O. Reg. 213/91, s. 335 (3).

Superintendent

336. (1)   The employer shall appoint a competent person as superintendent of all work in compressed air at a project. O. Reg. 213/91, s. 336 (1).

(2)   The superintendent, before a worker is first subjected to compressed air,

    (a)   shall ensure that the worker is fully instructed,

        (i)   in the hazards of working in compressed air, and

      (ii)   in the measures to be taken to safeguard the health and safety of the worker and other workers on the project; and

   (b)   shall obtain an acknowledgement signed by the worker who is receiving the instruction stating that the worker has been so instructed. O. Reg. 213/91, s. 336 (2).

Lock tender

337. (1)   A superintendent at a project shall designate for each shift at least one competent worker as lock tender who shall attend to the controls of an air lock. O. Reg. 213/91, s. 337 (1).

(2)   A lock tender must be able to speak, read and write English competently. O. Reg. 213/91, s. 337 (2).

(3)   A superintendent at a project shall ensure that at least one competent worker in addition to the lock tender is available in an emergency to perform the duties of the lock tender while a worker is working in compressed air. O. Reg. 213/91, s. 337 (3).

Records

338. (1)   The superintendent shall keep available at a project for inspection by an inspector,

   (a)   all Form 1 reports by a project physician;

   (b)   all records required under section 373 of air pressure in air locks on the project; and

   (c)   all records required under section 394 to be kept by a lock tender. O. Reg. 213/91, s. 338 (1).

(2)   The superintendent shall send all Form 1 reports to a Director promptly when work in compressed air at the project is finished. O. Reg. 213/91, s. 338 (2); O. Reg. 145/00, s. 39.

Badge

339. (1) A worker who works in compressed air shall wear for at least twenty-four hours after working in compressed air a sturdy metal or plastic badge that meets the requirements of subsection (2). O. Reg. 213/91, s. 339 (1).

(2) A badge shall measure at least fifty millimetres in diameter and shall set out,

- (a) the name of the constructor of the project;

- (b) the name and telephone number of the project physician;

- (c) the location of a medical lock at the project; and

- (d) the words, "compressed air worker – in case of decompression sickness take immediately to a medical lock". O. Reg. 213/91, s. 339 (2).

(3) The constructor at a project shall provide workers with the badge required under subsection (1). O. Reg. 213/91, s. 339 (3).

Communications

Telephone system

340. (1) A telephone system for work in compressed air shall be provided at a project. O. Reg. 213/91, s. 340 (1).

Locations

(2) A telephone system shall consist of telephones located,

- (a) at a location as close as is practicable to the work face;

- (b) in every work chamber near a door that leads to an air lock;

(c)   in every air lock;

(d)   near every lock tender's work position;

(e)   adjacent to every compressor plant; and

(f)   in the superintendent's office. O. Reg. 213/91, s. 340 (2).

Buzzer, bell system

341. (1)   An electric buzzer or bell system for work in compressed air shall be provided at a project. O. Reg. 213/91, s. 341 (1).

(2)   An electric buzzer or bell system shall consist of a switch and a buzzer or bell located,

(a)   in every work chamber near a door that leads to an air lock;

(b)   in every air lock; and

(c)   near every lock tender's work position. O. Reg. 213/91, s. 341 (2).

(3)   The following code shall be used to give signals between a work chamber, an air lock and the lock tender's work position:

| 1 signal | When no people are in the air lock, MATERIAL IS COMING OUT.

 When people are in the air lock, STOP COMPRESSING. |
| 3 signals | PEOPLE ARE COMING OUT OF THE AIR LOCK. |

O. Reg. 213/91, s. 341 (3).

Code posting

(4)   A copy of the signal code shall be posted near every switch of an electric buzzer or bell system. O. Reg. 213/91, s. 341 (4).

Acknowledgement

(5)   A lock tender shall acknowledge every signal received on an electric buzzer or bell system by returning the same signal. O. Reg. 213/91, s. 341 (5).

Fire Prevention

Acetylene

342. (1)   No person shall use acetylene while working in compressed air. O. Reg. 213/91, s. 342 (1).

Smoking

(2)   No person shall smoke or be permitted to smoke in an air lock or work chamber, other than in an area designated as a smoking area by the superintendent. O. Reg. 213/91, s. 342 (2).

Precautions

343. Before a flame-cutting, gas-welding or similar source of ignition is introduced into a work chamber that is in the vicinity of a combustible material,

(a) a firewatch shall be established and maintained;

(b) a fire hose shall be prepared for use;

(c) the fire hose shall be tested to ensure there is an adequate supply of water and water pressure to extinguish a fire; and

(d) a fire extinguisher suitable for the hazard shall be provided nearby. O. Reg. 213/91, s. 343.

Combustible material

344. As far as practicable, no combustible material shall be installed in or stored in an air lock or work chamber. O. Reg. 213/91, s. 344.

Standpipe

345. (1) A standpipe connected to a source of water or connected to other pipes above ground shall be installed in every air lock and work chamber at a project. O. Reg. 213/91, s. 345 (1).

(2) A standpipe shall have,

(a) valves that isolate the standpipe from the rest of the fire prevention system;

(b) a fitting that is controlled by a valve installed on the standpipe on the work chamber side of the bulkhead and by a valve inside the material lock;

(c) a fitting and valve similar to that described in clause (b) installed at the end of the standpipe nearest to the work face; and

(d)   the location of the fittings and valves clearly marked.
O. Reg. 213/91, s. 345 (2).

(3)   A fitting described in clause (2) (b) shall be such that a fire
hose of the local fire department can be connected to it. O. Reg.
213/91, s. 345 (3).

Lighting and Electrical Supply

Electrical wiring
346. Electrical wiring passing through an air lock or the bulkheads
adjacent to an air lock, other than telephone and signal system
wiring, shall be installed in a rigid metal conduit. O. Reg. 213/91,
s. 346.

Lighting
347. (1)   A lighting system shall be provided in each work chamber.
O. Reg. 213/91, s. 347 (1).

(2)   Electric light bulbs used in an air lock shall be enclosed in a
glass and metal protective screen cover. O. Reg. 213/91,
s. 347 (2).

Flashlights
(3)   Flashlights shall be readily available at the entrance to an air
lock, on the atmospheric side in an air lock and at every telephone
required by section 340. O. Reg. 213/91, s. 347 (3).

Auxiliary source
348. An auxiliary source of supply of electricity that is not a portable
emergency source of supply shall be provided for the lighting
system. O. Reg. 213/91, s. 348.

Emergency electrical lighting system

349. (1)   An emergency electrical lighting system shall be provided and maintained in each air lock or work chamber. O. Reg. 213/91, s. 349 (1).

(2)   An emergency electrical lighting system,

(a)   shall be connected to the electrical supply so that it automatically turns on in the event of the failure of the electrical supply; and

(b)   shall have a testing switch, if the system is battery-powered. O. Reg. 213/91, s. 349 (2).

(3)   An emergency electrical lighting system shall be tested at intervals that are at least as frequent as recommended by the manufacturer and that are adequate to ensure that it will function in an emergency. O. Reg. 213/91, s. 349 (3).

Sanitation

Water, toilet

350. A work chamber shall be provided with a reasonable supply of drinking water and at least one chemical toilet. O. Reg. 213/91, s. 350.

Medical Requirements

Project Physician

351. (1)   An employer who is constructing a tunnel or caisson in which a worker works or will work in compressed air shall employ as project physician at least one legally qualified medical practitioner. O. Reg. 213/91, s. 351 (1).

(2)   The project physician shall conduct such medical examinations of workers as in his or her opinion are necessary and

shall establish a medical treatment program for the workers.
O. Reg. 213/91, s. 351 (2).

(3) A project physician shall be reasonably available to render medical treatment or advice on the treatment of decompression sickness while a worker is working in compressed air. O. Reg. 213/91, s. 351 (3).

(4) The employer shall ensure that the project physician instruct workers on the hazards of working in compressed air and the necessary precautions to be taken to avoid decompression sickness. O. Reg. 213/91, s. 351 (4).

(5) If the pressure in a work chamber at a project may exceed 350 kilopascals for a period of more than five minutes, a project physician shall establish procedures to control decompression sickness including,

    (a) the maximum length of work periods for the workers in the chamber;

    (b) the minimum length of rest periods for workers in the chamber; and

    (c) compression and decompression procedures. O. Reg. 213/91, s. 351 (5).

352. (1) No worker shall work or be permitted to work in compressed air on a project unless,

    (a) the project physician has complied with subsection (4); and

     (b)   the project physician indicates on Form 1 that the worker is physically fit to work in compressed air. O. Reg. 213/91, s. 352 (1).

(2)   Subsection (1) does not apply with respect to an inspector or with respect to a worker accompanying an inspector at the inspector's request. O. Reg. 213/91, s. 352 (2).

Medical examination

(3)   Every worker working in compressed air at a project shall have a medical examination performed by the project physician before beginning work in compressed air and every two months thereafter while the worker is working in compressed air to determine the worker's fitness for working in compressed air. O. Reg. 213/91, s. 352 (3).

(4)   The project physician shall complete Form 1 for the worker, stating whether the worker is physically fit to work in compressed air and ensure that the superintendent receives a copy. O. Reg. 213/91, s. 352 (4).

(5)   The medical examination shall include,

     (a)   a physical examination;

     (b)   a test under compressed air, if the worker has not previously worked in compressed air; and

     (c)   such clinical tests as the project physician may require. O. Reg. 213/91, s. 352 (5).

(6)   The clinical tests referred to in clause (5) (c) shall include x-rays of the chest and shoulders, and hip and knee joints taken at least once every five years. O. Reg. 213/91, s. 352 (6).

(7)   If a worker undergoes a medical examination, the employer shall pay,

   (a)   the worker's costs for any medical examinations and tests; and

   (b)   the worker's reasonable travel costs respecting any medical examinations and tests. O. Reg. 213/91, s. 352 (7).

(8)   The time the worker spends to undergo medical examinations and tests, including travel time, shall be deemed to be work time for which the worker shall be paid by the employer at the worker's regular or premium rate, as may be proper. O. Reg. 213/91, s. 352 (8).

(9)   The project physician conducting the physical examination or clinical tests or under whose supervision the examination or tests are made shall advise the employer whether the worker is fit or is fit with limitations or unfit for work in compressed air, without giving or disclosing to the employer the records or results of the examination or tests. O. Reg. 213/91, s. 352 (9).

(10) The employer shall act on the advice given by the physician under subsection (9). O. Reg. 213/91, s. 352 (10).

(11) Where a project physician advises the employer that a worker, because of a condition resulting from work in compressed air, is fit with limitations or is unfit, the project physician shall forthwith communicate such advice to the Chief Physician, Occupational Health Medical Service of the Ministry. O. Reg. 213/91, s. 352 (11).

Records

(12) The records of medical examinations, tests, medical treatment and worker exposure to compressed air made or obtained by the

project physician under sections 351 and this section shall be kept in a secure place by the project physician who has conducted the examinations and tests or under whose supervision the examinations and tests have been made, for at least six years. O. Reg. 213/91, s. 352 (12).

(13) After six years, the project physician may forward the records to the Chief Physician, Occupational Health Medical Service of the Ministry, or a physician designated by the Chief Physician, and, in any event, the records shall not be destroyed for a period the greater of forty years from the time such records were first made or twenty years from the time the last of such records were made. O. Reg. 213/91, s. 352 (13).

Feeling unwell
353. (1) A worker who is about to work in compressed air and who does not feel well for any reason shall report the fact as soon as is practicable to the superintendent or a project physician before working in compressed air. O. Reg. 213/91, s. 353 (1).

(2) A worker who is working in compressed air and who does not feel well for any reason shall report the fact as soon as practicable to the superintendent or a project physician. O. Reg. 213/91, s. 353 (2).

Return to work
354. A worker who is absent for a period of ten or more days from working in compressed air shall not resume work in compressed air until a project physician indicates on Form 1 that the worker is physically fit to resume work in compressed air. O. Reg. 213/91, s. 354.

Medical Locks

First aid

355. (1)   A first aid room shall be provided in close proximity to each medical lock at a project. O. Reg. 213/91, s. 355 (1).

(2)   A first aid room shall contain all equipment necessary for first aid for workers working in compressed air and facilities adequate for conducting medical examinations. O. Reg. 213/91, s. 355 (2).

Medical lock

356. (1)   A constructor shall supply at least one medical lock at a project where work in compressed air is done and shall maintain it ready for operation while work in compressed air is being done. O. Reg. 213/91, s. 356 (1).

Certificate of inspection

(2)   A certificate of inspection issued under the Boilers and Pressure Vessels Act for a working pressure of at least 520 kilopascals is required for every medical lock on a project. O. Reg. 213/91, s. 356 (2).

357. (1)   A medical lock shall be not less than 1.8 metres high at its centre line. O. Reg. 213/91, s. 357 (1).

(2)   A medical lock shall be divided into two pressure compartments. O. Reg. 213/91, s. 357 (2).

(3)   Each compartment of a medical lock shall have air valves that are arranged so that the compartment can be pressurized and depressurized from inside and outside the lock. O. Reg. 213/91, s. 357 (3).

(4)   An observation window shall be installed in each door and in the rear wall of a medical lock. O. Reg. 213/91, s. 357 (4).

(5)   A medical lock shall be equipped with,

   (a)   a pressure release valve which will automatically blow-off at a pressure not greater than seventy kilopascals more than the operating pressure of the work chamber;

   (b)   a pressure gauge, a thermometer, a telephone, a cot, seating and a radiant heater; and

   (c)   a cot mattress, mattress cover and blankets all of which are made of material that is not readily flammable. O. Reg. 213/91, s. 357 (5).

(6)   The pressure release valve shall be tested and calibrated before the medical lock is used. O. Reg. 213/91, s. 357 (6).

(7)   A medical lock shall be maintained at a temperature of at least 18 degrees celsius, well-lit and well-ventilated and kept clean and sanitary. O. Reg. 213/91, s. 357 (7).

Project Physician
358. (1)   A project physician shall control the medical treatment of workers in a medical lock at a project. O. Reg. 213/91, s. 358 (1).

(2)   While a worker is working in compressed air and for twenty-four hours afterwards, at least one worker experienced in the decompression of persons suffering from decompression sickness,

   (a)   shall be present on the project, if the work in compressed air was done at a pressure greater than 100 kilopascals; or

   (b)   shall be readily available, if the work in compressed air was done at a pressure of 100 kilopascals or less. O. Reg. 213/91, s. 358 (2).

Air Compressors

Competent worker in charge

359. (1)   The superintendent shall designate at least one competent worker to be in charge of the compressors compressing air for a work chamber and air lock. O. Reg. 213/91, s. 359 (1).

(2)   **Revoked:** O. Reg. 88/13, s. 3.

(3)   A competent worker designated under subsection (1) shall attend to the compressors,

   (a)   while a person is in compressed air in the work chamber or air lock; and

   (b)   for twenty-four hours after a person has been in compressed air with a pressure exceeding 100 kilopascals in the work chamber or air lock. O. Reg. 213/91, s. 359 (3).

(4)   **Revoked:** O. Reg. 88/13, s. 3.

Air compressors

360. (1)   At least two air compressors shall be provided for every work chamber and air lock at a project. O. Reg. 213/91, s. 360 (1).

Capacity

(2)   The air compressors for a work chamber or an air lock shall have capacity enough to ensure that, if one compressor is not operating, the remaining compressors are capable of supplying the air required for the work chamber or air lock. O. Reg. 213/91, s. 360 (2).

Energy sources

361. (1)   The energy required to furnish compressed air to a work chamber or an air lock shall be readily available at a project from at least two independent sources. O. Reg. 213/91, s. 361 (1).

(2)   The two sources of energy shall be arranged so that, should the principal energy source fail, an auxiliary source automatically energizes the compressor. O. Reg. 213/91, s. 361 (2).

(3)   An auxiliary source of energy shall be inspected and tested by being operated at regular intervals of not more than seven days to ensure that it works. O. Reg. 213/91, s. 361 (3).

Lube oil discharge

362. (1)   A compressor for a work chamber or an air lock shall be constructed so as to ensure that lubricating oil is not discharged with the air that the compressor supplies. O. Reg. 213/91, s. 362 (1).

Air intake

(2)   The air intake for a compressor shall be located so as to prevent the entry of exhaust gases from internal combustion engines or other contaminants. O. Reg. 213/91, s. 362 (2).

Air quality

363. Air supplied for use in a work chamber or an air lock,

(a)   shall be clean and free from excessive moisture, oil or other contaminants; and

(b)   shall be kept between 10 degrees and 27 degrees celsius, as far as is practicable. O. Reg. 213/91, s. 363.

Air Locks and Work Chambers

364. One air lock shall be provided for each work chamber at a project. O. Reg. 213/91, s. 364.

Design

365. (1) An air lock, including the bulkheads and doors, shall be designed by a professional engineer in accordance with good engineering practice to withstand the pressures to be used in the work chamber and in the air lock. O. Reg. 213/91, s. 365 (1).

Construction

(2) An air lock shall be constructed in accordance with the professional engineer's design drawings for it. O. Reg. 213/91, s. 365 (2).

(3) An air lock used for people,

(a) shall measure at least two metres laterally and vertically;

(b) shall be large enough to accommodate the maximum number of people expected to be in the work chamber without them being in cramped positions;

(c) other than an ancillary air lock that complies with section 367, shall contain a functional and accurate electric time piece, thermometer and pressure gauge. O. Reg. 213/91, s. 365 (3).

Drawings

(4) The constructor shall send to a Director before construction of an air lock begins a copy of the design drawings for the air lock. O. Reg. 213/91, s. 365 (4); O. Reg. 145/00, s. 40; O. Reg. 85/04, s. 24.

(5)   The constructor shall keep at a project a copy of the design drawings for an air lock while the air lock is at the project. O. Reg. 213/91, s. 365 (5).

Separate air locks

366. Separate air locks shall be used for people and for materials,

(a)   if the air lock is in a shaft; or

(b)   where practicable, if the air locks are installed in a tunnel and if the air pressure is likely to exceed 100 kilopascals. O. Reg. 213/91, s. 366.

Ancillary air lock

367. (1)   Every air lock shall have an ancillary air lock that,

(a)   can be pressurized independently of the primary air lock;

(b)   has a door into the primary air lock or into the work chamber; and

(c)   has a door into air at atmospheric pressure. O. Reg. 213/91, s. 367 (1).

(2)   Except in an emergency, a door in an ancillary air lock into air at atmospheric pressure shall be kept open. O. Reg. 213/91, s. 367 (2).

(3)   A vertical air lock in a shaft or pneumatic caisson shall not be used to decompress workers unless a separate worker-lock with its own controls for compression and decompression is provided. O. Reg. 213/91, s. 367 (3).

(4)   An ancillary air lock shall be used to enter the work chamber only,

(a)   when the door between the chamber and the primary air lock is open; and

(b)   when it is impossible or impracticable for the door to be closed. O. Reg. 213/91, s. 367 (4).

(5)   Except in an emergency, an ancillary air lock shall not be used to decompress people. O. Reg. 213/91, s. 367 (5).

Air supply pipes
368. (1)   At least two pipes shall supply air to each work chamber and each air lock. O. Reg. 213/91, s. 368 (1).

(2)   Each of the pipes shall have a valve installed in the vicinity of the compressors to enable one pipe to be disconnected while another pipe remains in service at the work chamber or air lock. O. Reg. 213/91, s. 368 (2).

(3)   The outlet end of a pipe supplying air to a work chamber or an air lock shall have a hinged flap valve. O. Reg. 213/91, s. 368 (3).

Air pressure control
369. (1)   Each work chamber and each air lock, including an ancillary air lock, shall have a means of controlling and of automatically limiting the maximum air pressure in it. O. Reg. 213/91, s. 369 (1).

(2)   The air pressure control mechanism shall be set at a level not greater than,

(a)   for an air lock, the pressure for which the air lock, bulkheads and doors are designed; and

(b) for a work chamber, seventy kilopascals more than the maximum air pressure to be used in the chamber.
O. Reg. 213/91, s. 369 (2).

Gauge, time piece, thermometer

370. At each set of valves controlling the air supply to and discharge from an air lock, there shall be,

(a) a pressure gauge showing the air pressure in the air lock;

(b) a pressure gauge showing the air pressure in the work chamber;

(c) an electric time piece;

(d) a thermometer showing the temperature in the air lock; and

(e) a legible copy of the procedures governing maximum work periods and minimum decompression times for the air lock.
O. Reg. 213/91, s. 370.

Separate valves

371. (1) Separate valves controlling the air supply to and discharge from an air lock shall be provided inside and outside the lock.
O. Reg. 213/91, s. 371 (1).

(2) The valves shall be arranged so that a person can enter or leave the air lock or work chamber if no lock tender is attending the air lock. O. Reg. 213/91, s. 371 (2).

Automatic device

372. If an automatic compression and decompression device is installed in an air lock used for people, the air lock shall have a manual means of controlling the air pressure in the lock. O. Reg. 213/91, s. 372.

Automatic recording gauge

373. (1)   An air lock, other than an ancillary air lock, used for people shall have an automatic recording gauge to permanently record the air pressure in the lock. O. Reg. 213/91, s. 373 (1).

(2)   The gauge shall be a rotating dial or strip-chart rectilinear type. O. Reg. 213/91, s. 373 (2).

(3)   The gauge,

    (a)   shall be installed so that the lock tender cannot see it when at the controls of the air lock;

    (b)   shall indicate the change in air pressure at intervals of not more than five minutes; and

    (c)   shall be kept locked except when the recording paper is being changed. O. Reg. 213/91, s. 373 (3).

(4)   Despite subsection (2) and clause (3) (b), the gauge for an air lock at a work chamber whose air pressure exceeds 100 kilopascals shall be the strip-chart rectilinear type and shall indicate the change in air pressure at intervals of not more than one minute. O. Reg. 213/91, s. 373 (4).

(5)   The recording paper used in a gauge shall be changed every seven days and shall be marked to identify the period of time to which it relates. O. Reg. 213/91, s. 373 (5).

Pressure gauge

374. (1)   An air lock shall have a pressure gauge that can be read from the work chamber and that shows the air pressure in the lock. O. Reg. 213/91, s. 374 (1).

(2)   A pressure gauge, other than a portable pressure gauge, shall have fittings for attaching test gauges to it and shall be tested daily for accuracy. O. Reg. 213/91, s. 374 (2).

Portable pressure gauge, thermometer

375. A work chamber shall contain, in a protective container within fifteen metres of the work face, a portable pressure gauge and a thermometer. O. Reg. 213/91, s. 375.

Unit of pressure

376. (1)   Only one unit of measuring pressure (either kilopascals or pounds per square inch) shall be used on a project. O. Reg. 213/91, s. 376 (1).

(2)   Pressure gauges for decompression equipment and decompression procedures established for a project shall be calibrated using the unit of pressure for the project. O. Reg. 213/91, s. 376 (2).

377. (1)   The door between an air lock and a work chamber shall be kept open,

      (a)   unless the air lock is being used to compress or decompress people or to move materials; or

      (b)   when people are in the work chamber. O. Reg. 213/91, s. 377 (1).

(2)   Clause (1) (a) does not apply with respect to an ancillary air lock. O. Reg. 213/91, s. 377 (2).

Observation window

378. Every air lock door shall have a transparent observation window. O. Reg. 213/91, s. 378.

Seats

379. If practicable, an air lock used for people, other than an ancillary air lock, shall have one seat for each person being decompressed at one time. O. Reg. 213/91, s. 379.

Radiant heat

380. (1)   An air lock in which people are decompressed shall have a means of radiant heat if the air pressure in the lock exceeds 100 kilopascals. O. Reg. 213/91, s. 380 (1).

(2)   The temperature in an air lock used for people shall not exceed 27 degrees celsius. O. Reg. 213/91, s. 380 (2).

Smoke

381. (1)   A smoke line shall be provided from each work face of a work chamber if an air lock or bulkhead is located between the chamber and the surface. O. Reg. 213/91, s. 381 (1).

(2)   Each smoke line shall extend to within fifteen metres of a work face. O. Reg. 213/91, s. 381 (2).

(3)   Each smoke line shall have two quick opening valves at least 100 millimetres in diameter,

   (a)   one located within seventeen metres of the work face; and

   (b)   one located between the air lock closest to the work chamber and the work chamber and within two metres of the air lock. O. Reg. 213/91, s. 381 (3).

(4)   Each smoke line shall be at least 100 millimetres in diameter and shall have a readily-accessible outlet above ground,

    (a)   that has a quick opening valve at least 100 millimetres in diameter;

    (b)   that is clearly marked with a sign stating "SMOKE LINE – TO BE USED ONLY IN CASE OF EMERGENCY"; and

    (c)   that is sealed to prevent the inadvertent opening of the valve. O. Reg. 213/91, s. 381 (4).

(5)   Each smoke line shall extend from inside the work chamber to above ground and shall pass vertically through either the air lock or the bulkhead between the work chamber and air at atmospheric pressure. O. Reg. 213/91, s. 381 (5).

Passage

382. (1)   No bulkhead in a work chamber shall interfere with the free passage from the work face to an air lock of people in a tunnel or shaft. O. Reg. 213/91, s. 382 (1).

(2)   Subsection (1) does not apply with respect to a partial bulkhead in a sub-aqueous tunnel if the bulkhead is designed and placed to trap air so that workers can escape from the tunnel if it is flooded. O. Reg. 213/91, s. 382 (2).

Limits

383. (1)   Except when it is necessary to protect people during an emergency, the pressure in a work chamber shall not exceed 350 kilopascals for more than five minutes. O. Reg. 213/91, s. 383 (1).

(2)   If the pressure in a work chamber exceeds 350 kilopascals for more than five minutes,

    (a)   the superintendent shall promptly notify an inspector by telephone, two-way radio or in person; and

(b) the pressure maintained in the work chamber shall be the least possible pressure required to meet the emergency. O. Reg. 213/91, s. 383 (2).

Temperature

384. (1) Subject to subsection (2), no worker shall work or be permitted to work in a work chamber in which the temperature exceeds the greater of,

(a) 27 degrees celsius; and

(b) the temperature at the entrance to the service shaft above ground. O. Reg. 213/91, s. 384 (1).

(2) No worker shall work or be permitted to work in a work chamber in which the temperature exceeds 38 degrees celsius. O. Reg. 213/91, s. 384 (2).

Water

385. (1) Water on the floor of a work chamber or an air lock shall be drained by a pipe or mop line and, if necessary, a pump. O. Reg. 213/91, s. 385 (1).

(2) A pipe or mop line shall have an inside diameter of at least fifty-one millimetres. O. Reg. 213/91, s. 385 (2).

(3) At least one inlet with a valve to a pipe or mop line for an air lock and work chamber shall be located,

(a) in the air lock;

(b) within fifteen metres of the work face; and

(c) at intervals of not more than thirty metres along the length of the work chamber. O. Reg. 213/91, s. 385 (3).

(4) An inlet shall be diverted downward. O. Reg. 213/91, s. 385 (4).

(5) An outlet from an air lock shall discharge downward under atmospheric air pressure. O. Reg. 213/91, s. 385 (5).

Work Periods and Rest Periods

Work periods

386. (1) Subject to subsection (2), no worker shall,

    (a) work for more than two working periods in any consecutive twenty-four hour period where the maximum air pressure is not greater than 100 kilopascals; or

    (b) work for more than one working period in any consecutive twenty-four hour period where the maximum air pressure is more than 100 kilopascals. O. Reg. 213/91, s. 386 (1).

(2) No worker shall work or be permitted to work more than eight hours in a period of twenty-four hours. O. Reg. 213/91, s. 386 (2).

(3) No lock tender shall work or be permitted to work more than nine hours in a period of twenty-four hours. O. Reg. 213/91, s. 386 (3).

(4) The period between the end of one work period and the beginning of the next for a worker doing manual work under compressed air where the maximum air pressure exceeds 100 kilopascals shall be at least twelve hours. O. Reg. 213/91, s. 386 (4).

Rest periods

387. (1)   A worker who is working in compressed air shall have a rest period of at least,

(a)   ¼ hour, if the worker was working in pressure of 100 kilopascals or less;

(b)   ¾ hour, if the worker was working in pressure greater than 100 kilopascals up to and including 140 kilopascals;

(c)   1½ hours, if the worker was working in pressure greater than 140 kilopascals up to and including 220 kilopascals; or

(d)   two hours, if the worker was working in pressure greater than 220 kilopascals. O. Reg. 213/91, s. 387 (1).

(2)   No worker shall be permitted to perform manual work or engage in physical exertion during a rest period. O. Reg. 213/91, s. 387 (2).

(3)   No worker shall be permitted to leave a project during a rest period. O. Reg. 213/91, s. 387 (3).

Beverages

388. (1)   The employer shall provide, free of charge, sugar and hot beverages for workers working in compressed air to consume during their rest periods. O. Reg. 213/91, s. 388 (1).

(2)   An employer shall keep containers and cups for beverages in a sanitary condition and shall store them in a closed container. O. Reg. 213/91, s. 388 (2).

Lock Tenders

Duties

389. (1) A lock tender shall supervise the controls of an air lock when a worker is about to be, or is being, subjected to compressed air in the air lock or work chamber. O. Reg. 213/91, s. 389 (1).

(2) Subject to subsection (3), a lock tender shall tend only one air lock at a time. O. Reg. 213/91, s. 389 (2).

(3) A lock tender may tend two locks if,

(a) they are in close proximity;

(b) the pressure in each work chamber does not exceed 100 kilopascals; and

(c) only one of the locks is being used to compress or decompress a worker. O. Reg. 213/91, s. 389 (3).

390. (1) A lock tender shall ensure that the requirements of this section are met before a worker enters an air lock. O. Reg. 213/91, s. 390 (1).

(2) A worker shall be examined by a project physician before the worker enters an air lock in preparation for working in compressed air. O. Reg. 213/91, s. 390 (2).

(3) A lock tender shall ensure that any worker who enters the air lock in preparation for working in compressed air has been examined by a physician in accordance with subsection (2). O. Reg. 213/91, s. 390 (3).

(4) The means of air supply, air pressure gauges and controls, lock equipment and other devices necessary for the safe operation of an air lock and the protection of workers shall be in working order. O. Reg. 213/91, s. 390 (4).

391. (1) A lock tender shall increase the air pressure on a worker in an air lock in accordance with this section. O. Reg. 213/91, s. 391 (1).

(2) Air pressure shall be increased uniformly and to no more than thirty-five kilopascals in the first two minutes of application of compressed air. O. Reg. 213/91, s. 391 (2).

(3) Air pressure shall not be increased to more than thirty-five kilopascals until the lock tender ensures that every worker in the air lock is free from discomfort due to air pressure. O. Reg. 213/91, s. 391 (3).

(4) Air pressure shall be increased above thirty-five kilopascals at a uniform rate of not greater than thirty-five kilopascals per minute. O. Reg. 213/91, s. 391 (4).

(5) A lock tender shall observe a worker in an air lock while increasing the air pressure on the worker and, if the worker shows signs of discomfort and the discomfort does not quickly disappear, the lock tender shall gradually decrease the air pressure until the worker reports that the discomfort has ceased or until the air pressure reaches atmospheric pressure. O. Reg. 213/91, s. 391 (5).

392. (1) A lock tender shall decrease the air pressure on a worker in an air lock in accordance with this section and section 395. O. Reg. 213/91, s. 392 (1).

(2) Air pressure shall be decreased uniformly in each of the stages of decompression referred to in section 395. O. Reg. 213/91, s. 392 (2).

(3) A lock tender shall constantly observe a worker in an air lock while decreasing the air pressure on the worker and, if the worker shows signs of discomfort and the discomfort does not quickly

disappear, the lock tender shall gradually increase the air pressure until the worker reports that the discomfort has ceased or until the air pressure equals the pressure in the work chamber. O. Reg. 213/91, s. 392 (3).

393. (1) If a worker in an air lock appears to be suffering from decompression sickness, a lock tender shall notify, and follow the instructions of, a project physician, the superintendent or a person designated by the superintendent. O. Reg. 213/91, s. 393 (1).

(2) If a worker in an air lock appears to be injured or to be unwell from a cause unrelated to air pressure, a lock tender shall notify, and follow the instructions of, a project physician. O. Reg. 213/91, s. 393 (2).

(3) In the circumstances described in subsection (2), a lock tender shall decompress the worker unless otherwise instructed by the project physician. O. Reg. 213/91, s. 393 (3).

Records

394. (1) A lock tender shall record information about the compression and decompression of a worker in an air lock. O. Reg. 213/91, s. 394 (1).

(2) A separate record shall be kept for each air lock and each compression and decompression of a worker. O. Reg. 213/91, s. 394 (2).

(3) The information to be recorded is,

    (a) the description of the air lock;

    (b) the worker's name;

    (c) the time of the beginning and end of each compression or decompression to which the worker is subjected;

    (d)   the pressure and temperature in the air lock before and after each compression or decompression to which the worker is subjected; and

    (e)   a description of any unusual occurrence respecting the worker, the air lock or any related matter. O. Reg. 213/91, s. 394 (3).

(4)   A lock tender shall give the record to the superintendent. O. Reg. 213/91, s. 394 (4).

Decompression Procedures

395. (1)   A worker who has been in air pressure greater than atmospheric air pressure for more than five minutes shall be decompressed down to atmospheric pressure in accordance with this section. O. Reg. 213/91, s. 395 (1).

(2)   Subject to subsection (3), decompression shall be done in accordance with the Tables to this Regulation. O. Reg. 213/91, s. 395 (2).

(3)   The rate of decompression required by subsection (2) may be doubled with respect to a worker if, while performing the work in compressed air, the worker,

    (a)   has not been exposed to air pressure greater than 220 kilopascals;

    (b)   has remained under compressed air for a maximum of thirty minutes; and

    (c)   has not done manual work. O. Reg. 213/91, s. 395 (3).

(4)   Subsection (3) applies only if every worker who is in the air lock,

(a)   meets the requirements of clauses 3 (a), (b) and (c); and

(b)   has previously experienced decompression. O. Reg. 213/91, s. 395 (4).

Posting of Tables

(5)   A copy of the Tables to this Regulation shall be kept posted at a project,

(a)   in each air lock;

(b)   at the controls outside each air lock; and

(c)   in each change room. O. Reg. 213/91, s. 395 (5).

396. A worker who believes he or she has decompression sickness shall promptly notify,

(a)   the superintendent or a project physician; or

(b)   the lock tender, if the worker is under compressed air. O. Reg. 213/91, s. 396.

Report of decompression sickness

397. (1)   The superintendent shall make a report at least once a week to a Director concerning every case of decompression sickness at a project occurring since the previous report, if any. O. Reg. 213/91, s. 397 (1); O. Reg. 145/00, s. 41 (1).

(2)   The superintendent shall promptly make a report by telephone, two-way radio or other direct means to a Director concerning a case of decompression sickness that does not respond to first-aid treatment. O. Reg. 213/91, s. 397 (2); O. Reg. 145/00, s. 41 (2).

(3)   A report under this section shall indicate, for each case of decompression sickness,

    (a)   the air pressure to which the worker was subjected;

    (b)   the length of time the worker was subjected to the air pressure;

    (c)   the nature of the medical treatment given to the worker; and

    (d)   the extent of the worker's recovery. O. Reg. 213/91, s. 397 (3).

DECOMPRESSION TABLE 1 (SECTION 395)

Total decompression time, min

Working pressure kPa	Working period, h									
	0.5	1	1.5	2	3	4	5	6	7	8
10	-	-	-	-	-	1	1	1	1	1
20	-	-	-	-	-	1	1	1	1	1
30	-	-	-	-	-	2	2	2	2	2
40	-	-	-	-	-	2	2	2	2	2
50	-	-	-	-	-	2	2	2	2	2
60	-	-	-	-	-	2	2	2	2	2
70	-	-	-	-	-	8	8	8	8	8
80	-	-	-	-	-	10	10	10	15	20
90	-	-	-	-	-	10	10	20	30	40
100	-	-	-	-	12	13	30	44	-	-
110	-	-	-	-	16	28	47	73	-	-
120	-	-	-	-	25	46	73	108	-	-
130	-	-	-	-	37	65	105	140	-	-
140	-	-	-	27	61	103	-	-	-	-
150	-	-	-	36	77	131	-	-	-	-
160	-	-	-	45	93	152	-	-	-	-
170	-	-	-	55	110	175	-	-	-	-
180	-	-	34	65	132	-	-	-	-	-
190	-	28	42	77	154	-	-	-	-	-
200	-	29	47	88	175	-	-	-	-	-
210	-	33	56	101	197	-	-	-	-	-
220	-	36	64	114	-	-	-	-	-	-
230	-	39	72	131	-	-	-	-	-	-
240	-	44	80	148	-	-	-	-	-	-
250	30	51	90	164	-	-	-	-	-	-
260	32	56	101	-	-	-	-	-	-	-
270	34	62	111	-	-	-	-	-	-	-
280	35	67	125	-	-	-	-	-	-	-
290	37	73	139	-	-	-	-	-	-	-
300	40	78	155	-	-	-	-	-	-	-
310	42	90	-	-	-	-	-	-	-	-
320	43	95	-	-	-	-	-	-	-	-
330	46	103	-	-	-	-	-	-	-	-
340	48	113	-	-	-	-	-	-	-	-
350	50	122	-	-	-	-	-	-	-	-

O. Reg. 213/91, Table 1.

DECOMPRESSION TABLE 2 (SECTION 395)

Working pressure, kPa	Working period, h	Stage No.	Pressure reduction, kPa From	To	Time in stage, min	Pressure reduction rate, min/10 kPa	Total time decompress., min
10	4-8	1	10	0	1.0		1.0
20	4-8	1	20	0	1.0		1.0
30	4-8	1	30	0	1.0		1.0
40	4-8	1	40	0	2.0		2.0
50	4-8	1	50	0	2.0		2.0
60	4-8	1	60	0	2.0		2.0
70	4-8	1	70	0	2.0		2.0
80	4-8	1	80	40	1.0	0.33	
		2	40	30	1.0	1	
		3	30	30	5.0		
		4	30	0	1.0		8.0
90	5	1	90	45	1.5	0.33	
		2	45	30	1.5	1	
		3	30	30	6.0		
		4	30	0	1.0		10
	6	1	90	45	1.5	0.33	
		2	45	30	1.5	1	
		3	30	30	6.0		
		4	30	0	1.0		10
	7	1	90	45	1.5	0.33	
		2	45	30	1.5	1	
		3	30	30	11.0		
		4	30	0	1.0		15
	8	1	90	45	1.5	0.33	
		2	45	30	1.5	1	
		3	30	30	16.0		
		4	30	0	1.0		20
100	4	1	100	50	2	0.33	
		2	50	30	2	1	
		3	30	30	5		
		4	30	0	1		10
	5	1	100	50	2	0.33	
		2	50	30	2	1	
		3	30	30	5		
		4	30	0	1		10

DECOMPRESSION TABLE 2 (cont'd)

Working pressure, kPa	Working period, h	Stage No.	Pressure reduction, kPa From	To	Time in stage, min	Pressure reduction rate, min/10 kPa	Total time decompress., min
100	6	1	100	50	2	0.33	
		2	50	30	2	1	
		3	30	30	15		
		4	30	0	1		20
	7	1	100	50	2	0.33	
		2	50	30	2	1	
		3	30	30	25		
		4	30	0	1		30
	8	1	100	50	2	0.33	
		2	50	30	2	1	
		3	30	30	35		
		4	30	0	1		40
110	3	1	110	55	2	0.33	
		2	55	30	3	1	
		3	30	30	6		
		4	30	0	1		12
	4	1	110	55	2	0.33	
		2	55	30	3	1	
		3	30	30	7		
		4	30	0	1		13
	5	1	110	55	2	0.33	
		2	55	30	3	1	
		3	30	30	24		
		4	30	0	1		30
	6	1	110	55	2	0.33	
		2	55	30	3	1	
		3	30	30	38		
		4	30	0	1		44
120	3	1	120	60	2	0.33	
		2	60	30	3	1	
		3	30	30	10		
		4	30	0	1		16
	4	1	120	60	2	0.33	
		2	60	30	3	1	
		3	30	30	22		
		4	30	0	1		28
	5	1	120	60	2	0.33	
		2	60	30	3	1	
		3	30	30	41		
		4	30	0	1		47

DECOMPRESSION TABLE 2 (cont'd)

Working pressure, kPa	Working period, h	Stage No.	Pressure reduction, kPa		Time in stage, min	Pressure reduction rate, min/10 kPa	Total time decom-press., min
			From	To			
120	6	1	120	60	2	0.33	
		2	60	30	6	2	
		3	30	30	64		
		4	30	0	1		73
130	3	1	130	65	3	0.33	
		2	65	30	4	1	
		3	30	30	17		
		4	30	0	1		25
	4	1	130	65	3	0.33	
		2	65	30	4	1	
		3	30	30	38		
		4	30	0	1		46
	5	1	130	65	3	0.33	
		2	65	30	7	2	
		3	30	30	62		
		4	30	0	1		73
	6	1	130	65	3	0.33	
		2	65	30	14	4	
		3	30	30	90		
		4	30	0	1		108
140	3	1	140	70	3	0.33	
		2	70	30	4	1	
		3	30	30	29		
		4	30	0	1		37
	4	1	140	70	3	0.33	
		2	70	30	6	1.5	
		3	30	30	55		
		4	30	0	1		65
	5	1	140	70	3	0.33	
		2	70	30	12	3	
		3	30	30	89		
		4	30	0	1		105
	6	1	140	70	3	0.33	
		2	70	30	20	5	
		3	30	30	116		
		4	30	0	1		140
150	2	1	150	75	3	0.33	
		2	75	30	5	1	
		3	30	30	18		
		4	30	0	1		27

DECOMPRESSION TABLE 2 (cont'd)

Working pressure, kPa	Working period, h	Stage No.	Pressure reduction, kPa From	To	Time in stage, min	Pressure reduction rate, min/10 kPa	Total time decom- press., min
150	3	1	150	75	3	0.33	
		2	75	30	7	1.5	
		3	30	30	50		
		4	30	0	1		61
	4	1	150	75	3	0.33	
		2	75	30	9	2	
		3	30	30	90		
		4	30	0	1		103
160	2	1	160	80	3	0.33	
		2	80	30	5	1	
		3	30	30	27		
		4	30	0	1		36
	3	1	160	80	3	0.33	
		2	80	30	10	2	
		3	30	30	63		
		4	30	0	1		77
	4	1	160	80	3	0.33	
		2	80	30	25	5	
		3	30	30	102		
		4	30	0	1		131
170	2	1	170	85	3	0.33	
		2	85	45	4	1	
		3	45	30	5	3	
		4	30	30	32		
		5	30	0	1		45
	3	1	170	85	3	0.33	
		2	85	45	6	1.5	
		3	45	30	6	4	
		4	30	30	77		
		5	30	0	1		93
	4	1	170	85	3	0.33	
		2	85	45	12	3	
		3	45	30	18	12	
		4	30	30	118		
		5	30	0	1		152
180	1.5	1	180	90	3	0.33	
		2	90	45	5	1	
		3	45	30	5	3	
		4	30	30	20		
		5	30	0	1		34

DECOMPRESSION TABLE 2 (cont'd)

Working pressure, kPa	Working period, h	Stage No.	Pressure reduction, kPa From	To	Time in stage, min	Pressure reduction rate, min/10 kPa	Total time decompress., min
180	2	1	180	90	3	0.33	
		2	90	45	5	1	
		3	45	30	5	3	
		4	30	30	41		
		5	30	0	1		55
	3	1	180	90	3	0.33	
		2	90	45	7	1.5	
		3	45	30	9	6	
		4	30	30	90		
		5	30	0	1		110
	4	1	180	90	3	0.33	
		2	90	45	14	3	
		3	45	30	23	15	
		4	30	30	134		
		5	30	0	1		175
190	1	1	190	95	4	0.33	
		2	95	50	5	1	
		3	50	30	6	3	
		4	30	30	12		
		5	30	0	1		28
	1.5	1	190	95	4	0.33	
		2	95	50	5	1	
		3	50	30	6	3	
		4	30	30	26		
		5	30	0	1		42
	2	1	190	95	4	0.33	
		2	95	50	7	1.5	
		3	50	30	6	3	
		4	30	30	47		
		5	30	0	1		65
	3	1	190	95	4	0.33	
		2	95	50	9	2	
		3	50	30	16	8	
		4	30	30	102		
		5	30	0	1		132
200	1	1	200	100	4	0.33	
		2	100	50	5	1	
		3	50	30	6	3	
		4	30	30	13		
		5	30	0	1		29

DECOMPRESSION TABLE 2 (cont'd)

Working pressure, kPa	Working period, h	Stage No.	Pressure reduction, kPa From	To	Time in stage, min	Pressure reduction rate, min/10 kPa	Total time decompress., min
200	1.5	1	200	100	4	0.33	
		2	100	50	5	1	
		3	50	30	6	3	
		4	30	30	31		
		5	30	0	1		47
	2	1	200	100	4	0.33	
		2	100	50	8	1.5	
		3	50	30	8	4	
		4	30	30	56		
		5	30	0	1		77
	3	1	200	100	4	0.33	
		2	100	50	15	3	
		3	50	30	20	10	
		4	30	30	114		
		5	30	0	1		154
210	1	1	210	105	4	0.33	
		2	105	55	5	1	
		3	55	30	8	3	
		4	30	30	15		
		5	30	0	1		33
	1.5	1	210	105	4	0.33	
		2	105	55	5	1	
		3	55	30	8	3	
		4	30	30	38		
		5	30	0	1		56
	2	1	210	105	4	0.33	
		2	105	55	8	1.5	
		3	55	30	10	4	
		4	30	30	65		
		5	30	0	1		88
	3	1	210	105	4	0.33	
		2	105	55	15	3	
		3	55	30	30	12	
		4	30	30	125		
		5	30	0	1		175
220	1	1	220	110	4	0.33	
		2	110	55	6	1	
		3	55	30	8	3	
		4	30	30	17		
		5	30	0	1		36

DECOMPRESSION TABLE 2 (cont'd)

Working pressure, kPa	Working period, h	Stage No.	Pressure reduction, kPa From	To	Time in stage, min	Pressure reduction rate, min/10 kPa	Total time decompress., min
220	1.5	1	220	110	4	0.33	
		2	110	55	9	1.5	
		3	55	30	10	4	
		4	30	30	40		
		5	30	0	1		64
	2	1	220	110	4	0.33	
		2	110	55	9	1.5	
		3	55	30	13	5	
		4	30	30	74		
		5	30	0	1		101
	3	1	220	110	4	0.33	
		2	110	55	17	3	
		3	55	30	38	15	
		4	30	30	137		
		5	30	0	1		197
230	1	1	230	115	4	0.33	
		2	115	60	6	1	
		3	60	30	9	3	
		4	30	30	19		
		5	30	0	1		39
	1.5	1	230	115	4	0.33	
		2	115	60	9	1.5	
		3	60	30	9	3	
		4	30	30	49		
		5	30	0	1		72
	2	1	230	115	4	0.33	
		2	115	60	9	1.5	
		3	60	30	18	6	
		4	30	30	82		
		5	30	0	1		114
240	1	1	240	120	4	0.33	
		2	120	60	6	1	
		3	60	30	9	3	
		4	30	30	24		
		5	30	0	1		44
	1.5	1	240	120	4	0.33	
		2	120	60	9	1.5	
		3	60	30	12	4	
		4	30	30	54		
		5	30	0	1		80

DECOMPRESSION TABLE 2 (cont'd)

Working pressure, kPa	Working period, h	Stage No.	Pressure reduction, kPa From	To	Time in stage, min	Pressure reduction rate, min/10 kPa	Total time decom- press., min
240	2	1	240	120	4	0.33	
		2	120	60	12	2	
		3	60	30	24	8	
		4	30	30	90		
		5	30	0	1		131
250	0.5	1	250	125	5	0.33	
		2	125	65	6	1	
		3	65	30	11	3	
		4	30	30	7		
		5	30	0	1		30
	1	1	250	125	5	0.33	
		2	125	65	6	1	
		3	65	30	11	3	
		4	30	30	28		
		5	30	0	1		51
	1.5	1	250	125	5	0.33	
		2	125	65	9	1.5	
		3	65	30	14	4	
		4	30	30	61		
		5	30	0	1		90
	2	1	250	125	5	0.33	
		2	125	65	12	2	
		3	65	30	28	8	
		4	30	30	102		
		5	30	0	1		148
260	0.5	1	260	130	5	0.33	
		2	130	65	7	1	
		3	65	30	11	3	
		4	30	30	8		
		5	30	0	1		32
	1	1	260	130	5	0.33	
		2	130	65	7	1	
		3	65	30	11	3	
		4	30	30	32		
		5	30	0	1		56
	1.5	1	260	130	5	0.33	
		2	130	65	10	1.5	
		3	65	30	18	5	
		4	30	30	67		
		5	30	0	1		101

DECOMPRESSION TABLE 2 (cont'd)

Working pressure, kPa	Working period, h	Stage No.	Pressure reduction, kPa From	To	Time in stage, min	Pressure reduction rate, min/10 kPa	Total time decompress., min
260	2	1	260	130	5	0.33	
		2	130	65	13	2	
		3	65	30	35	10	
		4	30	30	110		
		5	30	0	1		164
270	0.5	1	270	135	5	0.33	
		2	135	70	7	1	
		3	70	30	12	3	
		4	30	30	9		
		5	30	0	1		34
	1	1	270	135	5	0.33	
		2	135	70	7	1	
		3	70	30	16	4	
		4	30	30	33		
		5	30	0	1		62
	1.5	1	270	135	5	0.33	
		2	135	70	10	1.5	
		3	70	30	20	5	
		4	30	30	75		
		5	30	0	1		111
280	0.5	1	280	140	5	0.33	
		2	140	70	7	1	
		3	70	30	12	3	
		4	30	30	10		
		5	30	0	1		35
	1	1	280	140	5	0.33	
		2	140	70	7	1	
		3	70	30	16	4	
		4	30	30	38		
		5	30	0	1		67
	1.5	1	280	140	5	0.33	
		2	140	70	11	1.5	
		3	70	30	32	8	
		4	30	30	76		
		5	30	0	1		125
290	0.5	1	290	145	5	0.33	
		2	145	75	7	1	
		3	75	30	14	3	
		4	30	30	10		
		5	30	0	1		37

DECOMPRESSION TABLE 2 (cont'd)

Working pressure, kPa	Working period, h	Stage No.	Pressure reduction, kPa From	To	Time in stage, min	Pressure reduction rate, min/10 kPa	Total time decompress., min
290	1	1	290	145	5	0.33	
		2	145	75	7	1	
		3	75	30	18	4	
		4	30	30	42		
		5	30	0	1		73
	1.5	1	290	145	5	0.33	
		2	145	75	11	1.5	
		3	75	30	36	8	
		4	30	30	86		
		5	30	0	1		139
300	0.5	1	300	150	5	0.33	
		2	150	75	8	1	
		3	75	30	14	3	
		4	30	30	12		
		5	30	0	1		40
	1	1	300	150	5	0.33	
		2	150	75	8	1	
		3	75	30	18	4	
		4	30	30	46		
		5	30	0	1		78
	1.5	1	300	150	5	0.33	
		2	150	75	15	2	
		3	75	30	36	8	
		4	30	30	98		
		5	30	0	1		155
310	0.5	1	310	155	6	0.33	
		2	155	80	8	1	
		3	80	30	15	3	
		4	30	30	12		
		5	30	0	1		42
	1	1	310	155	6	0.33	
		2	155	80	12	1.5	
		3	80	30	20	4	
		4	30	30	51		
		5	30	0	1		90
320	0.5	1	320	160	6	0.33	
		2	160	80	8	1	
		3	80	30	15	3	
		4	30	30	13		
		5	30	0	1		43

DECOMPRESSION TABLE 2 (cont'd)

Working pressure, kPa	Working period, h	Stage No.	Pressure reduction, kPa From	To	Time in stage, min	Pressure reduction rate, min/10 kPa	Total time decompress., min
320	1	1	320	160	6	0.33	
		2	160	80	12	1.5	
		3	80	30	20	4	
		4	30	30	56		
		5	30	0	1		95
330	0.5	1	330	165	6	0.33	
		2	165	85	8	1	
		3	85	30	17	3	
		4	30	30	14		
		5	30	0	1		46
	1	1	330	165	6	0.33	
		2	165	85	12	1.5	
		3	85	30	22	4	
		4	30	30	62		
		5	30	0	1		103
340	0.5	1	340	170	6	0.33	
		2	170	85	9	1	
		3	85	30	17	3	
		4	30	30	15		
		5	30	0	1		48
	1	1	340	170	6	0.33	
		2	170	85	13	1.5	
		3	85	30	28	5	
		4	30	30	65		
		5	30	0	1		113
350	0.5	1	350	175	6	0.33	
		2	175	90	9	1	
		3	90	30	18	3	
		4	30	30	16		
		5	30	0	1		50
	1	1	350	175	6	0.33	
		2	175	90	13	1.5	
		3	90	30	30	5	
		4	30	30	72		
		5	30	0	1		122

O. Reg. 213/91, Table 2.

Form 1

Occupational Health and Safety Act

RECORD OF COMPRESSED AIR WORKER

Name .... Age ....

Address ....

Social Insurance Number [SIN] ____ — ____ — ____

File No. .... Location (Municipality) ....

Project ....

Constructor ....

Employer ....

Previous Compressed Air Experience ....

Pre-Employment Medical Examination ....

Date .... Accept .... Reject .... Signature .... M.D.

SUBSEQUENT MEDICAL EXAMINATIONS

	Date	Accept	Reject	Signature - M.D.		Date	Accept	Reject	Signature - M.D.
1					7				
2					8				
3					9				
4					10				
5					11				
6					12				

O. Reg. 213/91, Form 1

Approximate Imperial Equivalents to SI Metric Values

Users are reminded that the Imperial measures provided in this chart are *not* precise Metric equivalents and are provided for convenience only. For precise measurements and to ensure compliance, please refer to the SI metric values found in the legislation itself.

In the first column, reference is made to the section in which a SI metric value is given; the second column shows this value; the third column shows the approximate Imperial equivalent for this SI metric value.

List of Symbols and Abbreviations

°C	degrees celsius
°F	degrees Fahrenheit
fpm	feet per minute
fps	feet per second
ft	feet
ft.lb	foot-pounds
gal	gallon
HP	horsepower
in.	inches
J	joules
kN	kilonewtons
kN/m^2	kilonewtons per square metre
kPa	kilopascals
kW	kilowatts
lb	pound
min	minute
mm	millimetre
mph	miles per hour
psf	pounds per square foot
psi	pounds per square inch
psia	pounds per square inch absolute
psig	pounds per square inch gauge
sq ft	square feet

Section	SI Metric Value	Approx. Imperial Equivalent
1(1)	6800 kilograms	15,000 lbs
	37.8 degrees celsius	100°F
	275 kilopascals	40 psia
	90 kilometres per hour	56 mph
6(1)(b)	7.5 metres	25 ft
6(1)(c)	four metres	13 ft
	thirty square metres	300 sq ft
6(1)(d)	three metres	10 ft
	7.5 metres	25 ft
6(1)(g)	300 metres	1,000 ft
	1.2 metres	4 ft
	thirty metres	100 ft
7	1.2 metres	4 ft
11(1) 1.	three metres	10 ft
23(2)(a)	125 joules	167 ft.lb
23(2)(b)	1.2 kilonewtons	270 lb force
26	3 metres	10 ft
	1.2 metres	4 ft
26.3(1)	2.4 metres	8 ft
26.3(2)2. v.	2.4 kilopascals	50 psf
26.3(4)2.	450 newtons	101 lb force
26.3(4)3.	0.9 metres	3 ft
	1.1 metres	3 ft 7 in.

Section	SI Metric Value	Approx. Imperial Equivalent
26.3(4)4.	100 millimetres 89 millimetres	4 in. 3 1/2 in.
26.3(4)5.	300 millimetres	1 ft
26.3(5)1.	675 newtons	152 lb force
26.3(5)2.	450 newtons	101 lb force
26.3(5)3.	450 newtons	101 lb force
26.3(5)4.	225 newtons	51 lb force
26.3(6)	2.4 metres	8 ft
26.3(7)3.	38 millimetres 89 millimetres 2.4 metres	1 1/2 in. 3 1/2 in. 8 ft
26.3(7)4.	38 millimetres 89 millimetres	1 1/2 in. 3 1/2 in.
26.3(8)1.	10 millimetres	2/5 in.
26.3(8)3.	2.4 metres 9 metres	8 ft. 29 ft 6 in.
26.5(1)(b)	0.6 metres	2 ft
26.5(3)	0.6 metres	2 ft
26.6(5)	8 kilonewtons	1,800 lb force

Section	SI Metric Value	Approx. Imperial Equivalent
26.7(2)1.	8 kilonewtons	1,800 lb force
26.7(2)2.	6 kilonewtons	1,350 lb force
26.7(2)3.	6 kilonewtons	1,350 lb force
26.7(2)5.	2 kilonewtons	450 lb force
27(3)(a)	fifteen metres	50 ft
29(4)	9.5 millimetres	3/8 in.
	180 metres	591 ft
29(5)	180 metres	591ft
29(6)	3 kilometres	1.86 miles
29(7)	9 metres	29 ft 6 in.
32(2)(a)(ii)	2.4 kilonewtons per square metre	50 psf
34(2)	2.4 kilonewtons per square metre	50 psf
35(5)(b)	100 millimetres	4 in.
35(5)(c)	1.2 metres	4 ft
40(1)	1.8 metres	6 ft
42(4)	three metres	10 ft
43(1)	100 metres	300 ft

Section	SI Metric Value	Approx. Imperial Equivalent
44(2)	150 millimetres	6 in.
52(3)	300 square metres	3,000 sq ft
56	84 metres 1890 litres per minute 450 kilopascals	276 ft 416 gal/min 65 psi
57(3)(a)	twenty-three metres	75 ft
57(3)(b)	900 millimetres 300 millimetres	3 ft 1 ft
57(5)(a)	thirty-eight millimetres	1 1/2 in.
57(9)	30 centimetres 90 centimetres	1 ft 3 ft
57(10)(b)	38 millimetres	1 1/2 in.
64(1)	4.5 metres	15 ft
64(3)(a)	2.4 metres	8 ft
64(3)(b)	1.1 metres	3 ft 7 in.
64(3)(c)	2.4 kilonewtons per square metre	50 psf
64(3)(f)	one metre	3 ft 3 in.
65	1.8 metres	6 ft
67(1)	30 kilometres per hour	19 mph

Section	SI Metric Value	Approx. Imperial Equivalent
68 1.	450 millimetres 1.2 metres	1 ft 6 in. 4 ft
68 2.	six millimetres	1/4 in.
68 3.	150 millimetres	6 in.
68 4.	317 millimetres 120 millimetres	12 1/2 in. 4 3/4 in.
69(3)	90 kilometres per hour	56 mph
69.1(1)2.	5 centimetres 500 square centimetres 570 square centimetres	2 in. 77 1/2 sq in. 88 sq in.
69.1(1)3.	225 millimetres	8 3/4 in.
69.1(4)	50 square centimetres	7 3/4 sq in.
73(2)(b)	2.4 kilonewtons per square metre	50 psf
73(4)	460 millimetres	1 ft 6 in.
74(1)(b)	nineteen millimetres thirty-eight millimetres 500 millimetres	1 in. nominal 1 1/2 in. 1 ft 6 in.
74(2)(b)	thirty-eight millimetres 300 millimetres	1 1/2 in. 1 ft
75(2)(b)	nine metres	30 ft

Section	SI Metric Value	Approx. Imperial Equivalent
76(1)	4.8 kilonewtons per square metre	100 psf
77(2)(a)	500 millimetres	1 ft 8 in.
77(2)(d)	4.5 metres	15 ft
77(4)	thirty-eight millimetres eighty-nine millimetres	1 1/2 in. 3 1/2 in.
78(2)(b)	300 millimetres	1 ft
78(2)(c)	300 millimetres	1 ft
78(3)(a)	five metres	16 ft
78(3)(b)	six metres	20 ft
78(3)(c)	nine metres	30 ft
78(3)(d)	fifteen metres	50 ft
78(3)(e)	twenty metres	66 ft
80(a)	900 millimetres	3 ft
80(b)	150 millimetres	6 in.
81(2)(a)	400 millimetres 610 millimetres	1 ft 4 in. 2 ft
81(2)(b)(i)	thirty-eight millimetres eighty-nine millimetres 5.8 metres	1 1/2 in. 3 1/2 in. 19 ft

Section	SI Metric Value	Approx. Imperial Equivalent
81(2)(b)(ii)	thirty-eight millimetres 140 millimetres 5.8 metres	1 1/2 in. 5.51 in. 19 ft
81(3)(a)(i)	nineteen millimetres sixty-four millimetres 400 millimetres	1 in. nominal 2.52 in. 1 ft 4 in.
81(3)(a)(ii)	nineteen millimetres eighty-nine millimetres 400 millimetres 610 millimetres	1 in. nominal 3.5 in. 1 ft 4 in. 2 ft
81(3)(b)	nineteen millimetres	1 in. nominal
82(a)	thirty-eight millimetres 140 millimetres	1 1/2 in. 5.51 in.
82(b)(i)	thirty-eight millimetres eighty-nine millimetres	1 1/2 in. 3 1/2 in.
82(b)(iii)	nineteen millimetres	1 in. nominal
82(c)	1.5 metres two metres	5 ft 6 ft 6 in.
84(1)(b)	9 metres	29 1/2 ft
84(1)(d)	three metres 2.2 metres 90 centimetres	10 ft 7 ft 3 ft
84(1)(e)	90 centimetres	3 ft
84(1)(f)	15 centimetres	5.91 in.
89(1)(d)	three metres	10 ft

Section	SI Metric Value	Approx. Imperial Equivalent
106(1.1)2.	5 centimetres	2 in.
	500 square centimetres	77 1/2 sq in.
	570 square centimetres	88 1/2 sq in.
106(1.1)3.	225 millimetres	8 3/4 in.
106(1.4)	50 square centimetres	7 3/4 sq in.
119(1)(a)	seventy-five millimetres	3 in.
119(2)(a)	22 newtons	5 lb force
119(3)	ninety metres per second	300 fps
	two metres	6 1/2 ft
128(4)(a)	twenty-two kilonewtons	5,000 lbs
128(4)(b)	16.7 kilonewtons	3,800 lbs
129(3)	2.4 metres	8 ft
130(1)(a)	fifteen metres	50 ft
130(1)(b)	ten metres	30 ft
133(2)	3.7 metres	12 ft
134(1)(b)	2.4 kilonewtons per square metre	50 psf
134(2)	2.2 kilonewtons	500 lb
135(1)(a)	460 millimetres	1 ft 6 in.
135(1)(b)	2.4 metres	8 ft

Section	SI Metric Value	Approx. Imperial Equivalent
135(2)(b)	forty-eight millimetres 248 millimetres	1.89 in. 9.76 in.
135(2)(c)	2.1 metres	7 ft
135(2)(d)	150 millimetres 300 millimetres	6 in. 12 in.
136(3)	one metre	3 ft 3 in.
137(10)(a)	ninety metres	300 ft
138(2)	150 millimetres 450 millimetres	6 in. 1 ft 6 in.
138(4)	1.6 millimetres thirty-eight millimetres	0.63 in. 1 1/2 in.
139(1)	525 kilograms	1,160 lbs
140(1)	600 millimetres 250 millimetres	2 ft 10 in.
140(2)	nine millimetres	3/8 in.
142(1)	seventy-five millimetres	3 in.
144(1)(b)	1.3 kilonewtons	300 lb
150(1)	7,260 kilograms	16,000 lb
168(2)(b)(i)	one millimetre nineteen millimetres	3/64 in. 3/4 in.

Section	SI Metric Value	Approx. Imperial Equivalent
168(2)(b)(ii)	two millimetres nineteen millimetres twenty-nine millimetres	1 1/6 in. 3/4 in. 1 1/8 in.
168(2)(b)(iii)	three millimetres twenty-nine millimetres	3/32 in. 1 1/8 in.
171(2)	100 millimetres 300 millimetres	4 in. 1 in.
186(1)	3 metres 4.5 metres 6 metres	10 ft 15 ft 20 ft
200(1)	eight metres	26 ft
200(2)	eight metres	26 ft
203(2)(c)	one kilometre	5/8 mile
204(2)(a)	7.5 metres	25 ft
204(2)(b)	150 millimetres	6 in.
204(4)	one metre	3 ft 3 in.
207(1)	two metres	6 ft 6 in.
207(2)	1.1 metres	3 ft 7 in.
208(2)	two metres	6 ft 6 in.
211(2)(a)	three metres	10 ft
219	2.4 metres	8 ft
231	450 millimetres	1 ft 6 in.

Section	SI Metric Value	Approx. Imperial Equivalent
233(1)	one metre	3 ft 3 in.
233(4)	2.4 metres 1.1 metres	8 ft 3 ft 7 in.
234(2)(a)	1.2 metres	4 ft
234 (2(e)	1.2 metres	4 ft
235(2)	six metres 3.6 metres	20 ft 12 ft
237(2)(c)	3.6 metres	12 ft
237(2)(d)	3.6 metres	12 ft
238(1) (Shoring and Timbering Table appears on next page)	ten millimetres	3/4 in.
241(1)	0.3 metres	1 ft
241(3)	0.5 metres	20 in.
247(1)	1.2 metres	4 ft
247(2)(a)	sixty centimetres 1.2 metres	23.6 in. 4 ft
247(2)(c)	100 millimetres	4 in.
249(1)(c)	thirty metres	100 ft
251(1)	1.5 metres	5 ft
252(1)(a)	fifty-one millimetres	2 in.
253(1)(a)	fifty-one millimetres	2 in.
253(1)(b)	forty-five metres	150 ft

TABLE
Section 238   EXCAVATION SHORING AND TIMBERING (APPROXIMATE IMPERIAL SIZES)

COLUMN 1		COLUMN 2	COLUMN 3				COLUMN 4
			STRUTS				
			WIDTH OF TRENCH AT STRUT LOCATION		STRUT SPACING		
EXCAVATION DEPTH	SOIL TYPE	SHEATHING	6 ft. to 12 ft.	Up to 6 ft.	Vertical	Horizontal	WALES
10 ft. or less	1	2" x 8" at 4' o/c	8" x 8"	6" x 6"	4 ft.	*8 ft.	*8" x 8"
	2	2" x 8" at 4' o/c	8" x 8"	6" x 6"	4 ft.	*8 ft.	*8" x 8"
	3	2" x 8" with 1/2" gap	8" x 8"	8" x 8"	4 ft.	8 ft.	10" x 10"
	4	3" x 8" with 1/2" gap	10" x 10"	8" x 8"	4 ft.	8 ft.	12" x 12"
Over 10 ft. to 15 ft.	1	2" x 8" with 1/2" gap	8" x 8"	6" x 6"	4 ft.	8 ft.	8" x 8"
	2	2" x 8" with 1/2" gap	8" x 8"	8" x 8"	4 ft.	8 ft.	10" x 10"
	3	2" x 8" with 1/2" gap	10" x 10"	10" x 10"	4 ft.	8 ft.	10" x 10"
Over 15 ft. to 20 ft.	4	3" x 8" with 1/2" gap	12" x 12"	12" x 12"	4 ft.	8 ft.	12" x 12"
Over 20 ft. to 25 ft.	1	2" x 8" with 1/2" gap	8" x 8"	8" x 8"	4 ft.	8 ft.	8" x 8"
	2	2" x 8" with 1/2" gap	10" x 10"	10" x 10"	4 ft.	8 ft.	10" x 10"
	3	2" x 8" with 1/2" gap	12" x 12"	12" x 12"	4 ft.	8 ft.	12" x 12"

*Note: For trenches to 10 ft. deep in soil Types 1 and 2, the wales can be omitted if the struts are used at 4 ft. horizontal spacings.

Section	SI Metric Value	Approx. Imperial Equivalent
254(1)(a)	thirty millimetres	1 1/4 in.
254(1)(c)	twenty-three metres	75 ft
254(2)	forty-six metres	150.9 ft
260(3)(a)(i)	ten square metres	100 sq ft
260(3)(a)(ii)	one square metre	10 sq ft
260(3)(d)	27 degrees celsius	80°F
266(1)	forty-five metres	150 ft
266(6)	100 metres	300 ft
266(7)	100 metres 150 metres	300 ft 500 ft
266(8)	150 metres	500 ft
270(1)	twenty-three metres	75 ft
270(3)(d)	thirty metres	100 ft
272	six metres	20 ft
273(7)	450 millimetres thirteen millimetres	1 ft 6 in. 1/2 in.
278(2)	six metres fifteen metres	20 ft 50 ft
278(2)(a)	2.4 metres	8 ft

Section	SI Metric Value	Approx. Imperial Equivalent
	1.5 metres	5 ft
278(2)(b)	5.7 square metres	50 sq ft
279(2)	1.2 metres	4 ft
280(1)	1.2 metres	4 ft
281(1)	six metres 3.6 metres	20 ft 12 ft
281(1)(a)	fifty-one millimetres 152 millimetres	2 in. 5.98 in.
281(2)(a)(i)	152 millimetres 2.7 metres	5.98 in. 9 ft
281(2)(a)(ii)	203 millimetres 2.7 metres 4.3 metres	8 in. 9 ft 14 ft
281(2)(a)(iii)	254 millimetres 4.3 metres six metres	10 in. 14 ft 20 ft
281(2)(b)	1.2 metres	4 ft
282(1)	1.1 metres	3 ft 7 in.
282(2)	2.4 metres	8 ft
282(2)(b)	thirty-eight millimetres 140 millimetres 2.4 metres	1 1/2 in. 5.5 in. 8 ft

Section	SI Metric Value	Approx. Imperial Equivalent
286(1)	six metres	20 ft
286(1)(a)	4.5 metres	15 ft
286(3)	750 mm	2 ft 5.25 in.
287(1)	six metres	20 ft
287(3)	fifty-one millimetres ten millimetres	2 in. 1/2 in.
288(1)	six metres	20 ft
288(2)	200 millimetres	8 in.
288(2)(a)	fifty millimetres 1.8 metres	2 in. 6 ft
288(2)(b) 300(1)	thirty-eight millimetres thirty metres	1 1/2 in. 100 ft
300(4)	thirty metres	100 ft
302(1)(a)	1.8 metres	6 ft
302(2)(a)	thirty-eight millimetres	1 1/2 in.
302(2)(b)	fifty millimetres 1.8 metres	2 in. 6 ft
302(3)	600 millimetres	2 ft
303(3)(a)	1.2 metres	4 ft

Section	SI Metric Value	Approx. Imperial Equivalent
303(5)	0.5 metres per second	100 fpm
306(2)	760 millimetres	2 ft 6 in.
306(3)	450 millimetres	1ft 6 in.
306(4)	sixty metres	200 ft
313(2)	300 millimetres	1 ft
317	4.5 metres	15 ft
319(1)(c)	six kilometres per hour	4 mph
322(b)	7.5 metres	25 ft
339(2)	fifty millimetres	2 in.
351(5)	350 kilopascals	50 psig
356(2)	520 kilopascals	75 psig
357(1)	1.8 metres	6 ft
357(5)(a) 357(7)	seventy kilopascals 18 degrees celsius	10 psig 65°F
358(2)(a)	100 kilopascals	14 psig
358(2)(b)	100 kilopascals	14 psig
359(3)(b)	100 kilopascals	14 psig
363(b)	10 degrees celsius 27 degrees celsius	50°F 80°F

Section	SI Metric Value	Approx. Imperial Equivalent
365(3)(a)	two metres	6 ft 6 in.
366(b)	100 kilopascals	14 psig
369(2)(b)	seventy kilopascals	10 psig
373(4)	100 kilopascals	14 psig
375	fifteen metres	50 ft
380(1)	100 kilopascals	14 psig
380(2)	27 degrees celsius	80°F
381(2)	fifteen metres	50 ft
381(3)	100 millimetres	4 in.
381(3)(a)	seventeen metres	56 ft
381(3)(b)	two metres	6 ft 6 in.
381(4)	100 millimetres	4 in.
381(4)(a)	100 millimetres	4 in.
383(1)	350 kilopascals	50 psig
383(2) 384(1)(a)	350 kilopascals 27 degrees celsius	50 psig 80°F
384(2)	38 degrees celsius	100°F
385(2)	fifty-one millimetres	2 in.

Section	SI Metric Value	Approx. Imperial Equivalent
385(3)(b)	fifteen metres	50 ft
385(3)(c)	thirty metres	100 ft
386(1)(a)	100 kilopascals	14 psig
386(1)(b)	100 kilopascals	14 psig
386(4)	100 kilopascals	14 psig
387(1)(a)	100 kilopascals	14 psig
387(1)(b)	100 kilopascals 140 kilopascals	14 psig 20 psig
387(1)(c)	140 kilopascals 220 kilopascals	20 psig 32 psig
387(1)(d)	220 kilopascals	32 psig
389(3)(b)	100 kilopascals	14 psig
391(2)	thirty-five kilopascals	5 psig
391(3)	thirty-five kilopascals	5 psig
391(4)	thirty-five kilopascals thirty-five kilopascals per minute	5 psig 5 psig/min
395(3)(a)	220 kilopascals	32 psig

Section 395 - Decompression Table A1 (Approx. Imperial Equivalents)

Total Decompression Time, Min.

Working Pressure Psig	Working period, H									
	0.5	1	1.5	2	3	4	5	6	7	8
2						1	1	1	1	1
4						1	1	1	1	1
6						2	2	2	2	2
8						2	2	2	2	2
10						2	2	2	2	2
12						8	8	8	8	8
14						10	10	15	20	25
16					12	13	29	43		
18					17	33	53	88		
20					33	59	96	129		
22				29	61	101	142			
24				40	81	133				
26			31	52	105	166				

Section 395 - Decompression Table A1 (Approx. Imperial Equivalents)

Total Decompression Time, Min.

Working period, H

Working Pressure Psig	0.5	1	1.5	2	3	4	5	6	7	8
28		26	41	66	133					
30		30	50	80	161					
32		33	62	96	188					
34		39	73	116						
36		46	85	142						
38	29	53	98	165						
40	32	61	112							
42	35	69	131							
44	38	81	158							
46	40	91								
48	42	100								
50	45	111								

Decompression Table A2 (Approx. Imperial Equivalents)

Working Pressure, psig	Working Period, h	Stage No.	Pressure Reduction, psig From	Pressure Reduction, psig To	Time In Stage, min	Pressure Reduction Rate, min/psi	Total Time Decompress., min
2	4-8	1	2	0	1.0		1.0
4	4-8	1	4	0	1.0		1.0
6	4-8	1	6	0	2.0		2.0
8	4-8	1	8	0	2.0		2.0
10	4-8	1	10	0	2.0		2.0
12	4-8	1	12	6	1.0		8.0
		2	6	4	1.0		
		3	4	4	5.0	0.2	
		4	4	0	1.0	0.5	
14	4	1	14	7	1.5		10
		2	7	4	1.5		
		3	4	4	6.0	0.2	
		4	4	0	1.0	0.5	
	5	1	14	7	1.5		10
		2	7	4	1.5		
		3	4	4	6.0	0.2	
		4	4	0	1.0	0.5	

Decompression Table A2 (Approx. Imperial Equivalents)							
Working Pressure, psig	Working Period, h	Stage No.	Pressure Reduction, psig		Time In Stage, min	Pressure Reduction Rate, min/psi	Total Time Decompress., min
			From	To			
14	6	1	14	7	1.5	0.2	15
		2	7	4	1.5	0.5	
		3	4	4	11.0		
		4	4	0	1.0		
	7	1	14	7	1.5	0.2	20
		2	7	4	1.5	0.5	
		3	4	4	16.0		
		4	4	0	1.0		
	8	1	14	7	1.5	0.2	25
		2	7	4	1.5	0.5	
		3	4	4	21.0		
		4	4	0	1.0		
16	3	1	16	8	2	0.2	12
		2	8	4	2	0.5	
		3	4	4	7		
		4	4	0	1		
	4	1	16	8	2	0.2	13
		2	8	4	2	0.5	
		3	4	4	8		
		4	4	0	1		

Decompression Table A2 (Approx. Imperial Equivalents)

Working Pressure, psig	Working Period, h	Stage No.	Pressure Reduction, psig		Time In Stage, min	Pressure Reduction Rate, min/psi	Total Time Decompress., min
			From	To			
16	5	1	16	8	2	0.2	29
		2	8	4	2	0.5	
		3	4	4	24		
		4	4	0	1		
	6	1	16	8	2	0.2	43
		2	8	4	2	0.5	
		3	4	4	38		
		4	4	0	1		
18	3	1	18	9	2	0.2	17
		2	9	4	3	0.5	
		3	4	4	11		
		4	4	0	1		
	4	1	18	9	2	0.2	33
		2	9	4	3	0.5	
		3	4	4	27		
		4	4	0	1		
	5	1	18	9	2	0.2	53
		2	9	4	5	1.0	
		3	4	4	45		
		4	4	0	1		

Decompression Table A2 (Approx. Imperial Equivalents)

Working Pressure, psig	Working Period, h	Stage No.	Pressure Reduction, psig		Time In Stage, min	Pressure Reduction Rate, min/psi	Total Time Decompress., min
			From	To			
18	6	1	18	9	2	0.2	88
		2	9	4	10	2.0	
		3	4	4	75		
		4	4	0	1		
20	3	1	20	10	2	0.2	33
		2	10	4	3	0.5	
		3	4	4	27		
		4	4	0	1		
	4	1	20	10	2	0.2	59
		2	10	4	6	1.0	
		3	4	4	50		
		4	4	0	1		
	5	1	20	10	2	0.2	96
		2	10	4	12	2.0	
		3	4	4	81		
		4	4	0	1		
	6	1	20	10	2	0.2	129
		2	10	4	18	3.0	
		3	4	4	108		
		4	4	0	1		

Decompression Table A2 (Approx. Imperial Equivalents)

Working Pressure, psig	Working Period, h	Stage No.	Pressure Reduction, psig		Time In Stage, min	Pressure Reduction Rate, min/psi	Total Time Decompress., min
			From	To			
22	2	1	22	11	3	0.2	
		2	11	6	3	0.5	
		3	6	4	4	2.0	29
		4	4	4	18		
		5	4	0	1		
	3	1	22	11	3	0.2	
		2	11	6	3	0.5	
		3	6	4	4	2.0	61
		4	4	4	50		
		5	4	0	1		
	4	1	22	11	3	0.2	
		2	11	6	5	1.0	
		3	6	4	6	3.0	101
		4	4	4	86		
		5	4	0	1		
	5	1	22	11	3	0.2	
		2	11	6	10	2.0	
		3	6	4	12	6.0	142
		4	4	4	116		
		5	4	0	1		

Decompression Table A2 (Approx. Imperial Equivalents)

Working Pressure, psig	Working Period, h	Stage No.	Pressure Reduction, psig From	Pressure Reduction, psig To	Time In Stage, min	Pressure Reduction Rate, min/psi	Total Time Decompress., min
24	2	1	24	12	3	0.2	40
		2	12	6	3	0.5	
		3	6	4	4	0.2	
		4	4	4	29		
		5	4	0	1		
	3	1	24	12	3	0.2	81
		2	12	6	6	1.0	
		3	6	4	6	3.0	
		4	4	4	65		
		5	4	0	1		
	4	1	24	12	3	0.2	133
		2	12	6	12	2.0	
		3	6	4	12	6.0	
		4	4	4	105		
		5	4	0	1		
26	1.5	1	26	13	3	0.2	31
		2	13	7	3	0.5	
		3	7	4	6	2.0	
		4	4	4	18		
		5	4	0	1		

Decompression Table A2 (Approx. Imperial Equivalents)

Working Pressure, psig	Working Period, h	Stage No.	Pressure Reduction, psig From	To	Time In Stage, min	Pressure Reduction Rate, min/psi	Total Time Decompress., min
26	2	1	26	13	3	0.2	52
		2	13	7	3	0.5	
		3	7	4	6	2.0	
		4	4	4	39		
		5	4	0	1		
	3	1	26	13	3	0.2	105
		2	13	7	6	1.0	
		3	7	4	12	4.0	
		4	4	4	83		
		5	4	0	1		
	4	1	26	13	3	0.2	166
		2	13	7	12	2.0	
		3	7	4	30	10.0	
		4	4	4	120		
		5	4	0	1		
28	1	1	28	14	3	0.2	26
		2	14	7	4	0.5	
		3	7	4	6	2.0	
		4	4	4	12		
		5	4	0	1		

Decompression Table A2 (Approx. Imperial Equivalents)

Working Pressure, psig	Working Period, h	Stage No.	Pressure Reduction, psig		Time In Stage, min	Pressure Reduction Rate, min/psi	Total Time Decompress., min
			From	To			
28	1.5	1	28	14	3	0.2	41
		2	14	7	4	0.5	
		3	7	4	6	2.0	
		4	4	4	27		
		5	4	0	1		
	2	1	28	14	3	0.2	66
		2	14	7	7	1.0	
		3	7	4	9	3.0	
		4	4	4	46		
		5	4	0	1		
	3	1	28	14	3	0.2	133
		2	14	7	14	2.0	
		3	7	4	15	5.0	
		4	4	4	100		
		5	4	0	1		
30	1	1	30	15	3	0.2	30
		2	15	8	4	0.5	
		3	8	4	8	2.0	
		4	4	4	14		
		5	4	0	1		

Decompression Table A2 (Approx. Imperial Equivalents)

Working Pressure, psig	Working Period, h	Stage No.	Pressure Reduction, psig		Time In Stage, min	Pressure Reduction Rate, min/psi	Total Time Decompress., min
			From	To			
30	1.5	1	30	15	3	0.2	50
		2	15	8	4	0.5	
		3	8	4	8	2.0	
		4	4	4	34		
		5	4	0	1		
	2	1	30	15	3	0.2	80
		2	15	8	7	1.0	
		3	8	4	12	3.0	
		4	4	4	57		
		5	4	0	1		
	3	1	30	15	3	0.2	161
		2	15	8	14	2.0	
		3	8	4	32	8.0	
		4	4	4	111		
		5	4	0	1		
32	1	1	32	16	4	0.2	33
		2	16	8	4	0.5	
		3	8	4	8	2.0	
		4	4	4	16		
		5	4	0	1		

Decompression Table A2 (Approx. Imperial Equivalents)

Working Pressure, psig	Working Period, h	Stage No.	Pressure Reduction, psig From	To	Time In Stage, min	Pressure Reduction Rate, min/psi	Total Time Decompress., min
32	1.5	1	32	16	4	0.2	62
		2	16	8	8	1.0	
		3	8	4	8	2.0	
		4	4	4	41		
		5	4	0	1		
	2	1	32	16	4	0.2	96
		2	16	8	8	1.0	
		3	8	4	12	3.0	
		4	4	4	71		
		5	4	0	1		
	3	1	32	16	4	0.2	188
		2	16	8	16	2.0	
		3	8	4	40	10.0	
		4	4	4	127		
		5	4	0	1		
34	1	1	34	17	4	0.2	39
		2	17	9	4	0.5	
		3	9	4	10	2.0	
		4	4	4	20		
		5	4	0	1		

Decompression Table A2 (Approx. Imperial Equivalents)

Working Pressure, psig	Working Period, h	Stage No.	Pressure Reduction, psig		Time In Stage, min	Pressure Reduction Rate, min/psi	Total Time Decompress., min
			From	To			
34	1.5	1	34	17	4	0.2	73
		2	17	9	8	1.0	
		3	9	4	10	2.0	
		4	4	4	50		
		5	4	0	1		
	2	1	34	17	4	0.2	116
		2	17	9	8	1.0	
		3	9	4	25	5.0	
		4	4	4	78		
		5	4	0	1		
36	1	1	36	18	4	0.2	46
		2	18	9	5	0.5	
		3	9	4	10	2.0	
		4	4	4	26		
		5	4	0	1		
	1.5	1	36	18	4	0.2	85
		2	18	9	9	1.0	
		3	9	4	15	3.0	
		4	4	4	56		
		5	4	0	1		

Decompression Table A2 (Approx. Imperial Equivalents)

Working Pressure, psig	Working Period, h	Stage No.	Pressure Reduction, psig		Time In Stage, min	Pressure Reduction Rate, min/psi	Total Time Decompress., min
			From	To			
36	2	1	36	18	4	0.2	142
		2	18	9	18	2.0	
		3	9	4	25	5.0	
		4	4	4	94		
		5	4	0	1		
38	0.5	1	38	19	4	0.2	29
		2	19	10	5	0.5	
		3	10	4	12	2.0	
		4	4	4	7		
		5	4	0	1		
	1	1	38	19	4	0.2	53
		2	19	10	5	0.5	
		3	10	4	12	2.0	
		4	4	4	31		
		5	4	0	1		
	1.5	1	38	19	4	0.2	98
		2	19	10	9	1.0	
		3	10	4	18	3.0	
		4	4	4	66		
		5	4	0	1		

Decompression Table A2 (Approx. Imperial Equivalents)

Working Pressure, psig	Working Period, h	Stage No.	Pressure Reduction, psig		Time In Stage, min	Pressure Reduction Rate, min/psi	Total Time Decompress., min
			From	To			
38	2	1	38	19	4	0.2	165
		2	19	10	18	2.0	
		3	10	4	36	6.0	
		4	4	4	106		
		5	4	0	1		
40	0.5	1	40	20	4	0.2	32
		2	20	10	5	0.5	
		3	10	4	12	2.0	
		4	4	4	10		
		5	4	0	1		
	1	1	40	20	4	0.2	61
		2	20	10	5	0.5	
		3	10	4	18	3.0	
		4	4	4	33		
		5	4	0	1		
	1.5	1	40	20	4	0.2	112
		2	20	10	10	1.0	
		3	10	4	24	4.0	
		4	4	4	73		
		5	4	0	1		

Decompression Table A2 (Approx. Imperial Equivalents)

Working Pressure, psig	Working Period, h	Stage No.	Pressure Reduction, psig From	Pressure Reduction, psig To	Time In Stage, min	Pressure Reduction Rate, min/psi	Total Time Decompress., min
42	0.5	1	42	21	5	0.2	35
		2	21	11	5	0.5	
		3	11	4	14	2.0	
		4	4	4	10		
		5	4	0	1		
	1	1	42	21	5	0.2	69
		2	21	11	5	0.5	
		3	11	4	21	3.0	
		4	4	4	37		
		5	4	0	1		
	1.5	1	42	21	5	0.2	131
		2	21	11	10	1.0	
		3	11	4	35	5.0	
		4	4	4	80		
		5	4	0	1		
44	0.5	1	44	22	5	0.2	38
		2	22	11	6	0.5	
		3	11	4	14	2.0	
		4	4	4	12		
		5	4	0	1		

Decompression Table A2 (Approx. Imperial Equivalents)

Working Pressure, psig	Working Period, h	Stage No.	Pressure Reduction, psig From	Pressure Reduction, psig To	Time In Stage, min	Pressure Reduction Rate, min/psi	Total Time Decompress., min
44	1	1	44	22	5	0.2	81
		2	22	11	11	1.0	
		3	11	4	21	3.0	
		4	4	4	43		
		5	4	0	1		
	1.5	1	44	22	5	0.2	158
		2	22	11	22	2.0	
		3	11	4	35	5.0	
		4	4	4	95		
		5	4	0	1		
46	0.5	1	46	23	5	0.2	40
		2	23	12	6	0.5	
		3	12	4	16	2.0	
		4	4	4	12		
		5	4	0	1		
	1	1	46	23	5	0.2	91
		2	23	12	11	1.0	
		3	12	4	24	3.0	
		4	4	4	50		
		5	4	0	1		

Working Pressure, psig	Working Period, h	Stage No.	Pressure Reduction, psig		Time In Stage, min	Pressure Reduction Rate, min/psi	Total Time Decompress., min
			From	To			
48	0.5	1	48	24	5	0.2	42
		2	24	12	6	0.5	
		3	12	4	16	2.0	
		4	4	4	14		
		5	4	0	1		
	1	1	48	24	5	0.2	100
		2	24	12	12	1.0	
		3	12	4	24	3.0	
		4	4	4	58		
		5	4	0	1		
50	0.5	1	50	25	5	0.2	45
		2	25	13	6	0.5	
		3	13	4	18	2.0	
		4	4	4	15		
		5	4	0	1		
	1	1	50	25	5	0.2	111
		2	25	13	12	1.0	
		3	13	4	27	3.0	
		4	4	4	66		
		5	4	0	1		

Index to the
Occupational Health and Safety Act

Section

Section

Section

A-6

Section

Critical injury or death,
investigation by joint committee .... 9(31)
health and safety representative .... 8(14)
notice of .... 51(1)

Crown, application of Act to .... 2(1)
liability in tort of .... 65(2)

Dangerous circumstances, defined .... 44(1)
where not applicable .... 44(2)

Delegation, by Chief Prevention Officer 7.7
Deputy Minister 5
Minister 5, 22.9

Deputy Minister, appointment of inspectors by .... 6(1)
defined .... 1(1)
delegation of powers by 5

Designated entities 22.5
effect of designation 22.6
advice to Minister .... 22.7(3)
appointment of administrator 22.8
compliance and monitoring of designated entities ....22.7(1)
failure to comply .... 22.6(3)
government directives .... 22.6(2)
Minister direct designated entity ....22.6(1)
report on compliance of designated entities
to Minister ....22.7(2)
eligible for grant .... 22.5(1)
amendment to standard ....22.5(7)
compliance date for amended standard ....22.5(8)
designation by Minister ....22.5(2)
duty to comply ....22.5(6)

Section

Section

Section

Section

Section

INDEX
to
Construction Projects Regulation

Section

Section

Section

Section

Professional Engineer

Section

Tables

Telephone/Telephone System

Section

REGULATIONS THAT DIRECTLY AFFECT THE OCCUPATIONAL HEALTH AND SAFETY ACT

[Confined Spaces; Critical Injury Defined; Inventory of Agents; Joint Health and Safety Committees; Occupational Health and Safety Awareness and Training; Offices of the Worker and Employer Advisers; and Unilateral Work Stoppage]

Confined Spaces
O. Reg. 632/05
as amended by O. Reg. 23/09, O. Reg. 492/09, O. Reg. 95/11

Definitions

1.   In this Regulation,

"acceptable atmospheric levels" means that,

(a)   the atmospheric concentration of any explosive or flammable gas or vapour is less than,

(i)   25 per cent of its lower explosive limit, if paragraph 1 of subsection 19 (4) applies,

(ii)   10 per cent of its lower explosive limit, if paragraph 2 of subsection 19 (4) applies,

(iii)   5 per cent of its lower explosive limit, if paragraph 3 of subsection 19 (4) applies,

(b)   the oxygen content of the atmosphere is at least 19.5 per cent but not more than 23 per cent by volume,

(c) in the case of a workplace that is not a project, the exposure to atmospheric contaminants does not exceed any applicable limit set out in Regulation 833 of the Revised Regulations of Ontario, 1990 (Control of Exposure to Biological or Chemical Agents) made under the Act or Ontario Regulation 490/09 (Designated Substances) made under the Act, and

(d) in the case of a workplace that is a project, if atmospheric contaminants, including gases, vapours, fumes, dusts or mists are present, their concentrations do not exceed what is reasonable in the circumstances for the protection of the health and safety of workers;

"adequate", when used in relation to a procedure, plan, material, device, object or thing, means that it is,

(a) sufficient for both its intended and its actual use, and

(b) sufficient to protect a worker from occupational illness or occupational injury;

"adequately" has a meaning that corresponds to the meaning of "adequate";

"assessment" means an assessment of hazards with respect to one or more confined spaces in a workplace, as described in section 6;

"atmospheric hazards" means,

(a) the accumulation of flammable, combustible or explosive agents,

(b) an oxygen content in the atmosphere that is less than 19.5 per cent or more than 23 per cent by volume, or

    (c)   the accumulation of atmospheric contaminants, including gases, vapours, fumes, dusts or mists, that could,

        (i)   result in acute health effects that pose an immediate threat to life, or

        (ii)   interfere with a person's ability to escape unaided from a confined space;

"cold work" means work that is not capable of producing a source of ignition;

"confined space" means a fully or partially enclosed space,

    (a)   that is not both designed and constructed for continuous human occupancy, and

    (b)   in which atmospheric hazards may occur because of its construction, location or contents or because of work that is done in it;

"emergency work" means work performed in connection with an unforeseen event that involves an imminent danger to the life, health or safety of any person;

"hot work" means work that is capable of producing a source of ignition;

"lead employer" means an employer who contracts for the services of one or more other employers or independent contractors in relation to one or more confined spaces that are located,

    (a)   in the lead employer's own workplace, or

    (b)   in another employer's workplace;

"plan" means a plan for one or more confined spaces in a workplace, as described in section 7;

"program" means a program for one or more confined spaces in a workplace, as described in section 5;

"purging" means displacing contaminants from a confined space;

"related work" means work that is performed near a confined space in direct support of work inside the confined space. O. Reg. 632/05, s. 1; O. Reg. 492/09, s. 1, 2; O. Reg. 95/11, s. 1.

Application
2.   Subject to section 3, this Regulation applies to all workplaces to which the Occupational Health and Safety Act applies. O. Reg. 632/05, s. 2.

Exceptions
3.   (1)   This Regulation does not apply to work performed underwater by a diver during a diving operation as defined in Ontario Regulation 629/94 (Diving Operations) made under the Act.

(2)   Sections 4 to 7 and 9 to 21 of this Regulation do not apply to emergency work performed by,

   (a)   a firefighter as defined in subsection 1 (1) of the Fire Protection and Prevention Act, 1997; or

   (b)   a person who,

      (i)   holds a certificate under the Technical Standards and Safety Act, 2000 designating him or her as a gas technician, and

      (ii)   is working under the direction of a fire department, as defined in the Fire Protection and Prevention Act, 1997.

(3)   A worker described in subsection (2) who performs emergency work shall be adequately protected by,

      (a)   personal protective equipment, clothing and devices provided by the worker's employer;

      (b)   training under section 8 provided by that employer; and

      (c)   written procedures and other measures developed by that employer. O. Reg. 632/05, s. 3; O. Reg. 23/09, s. 1; O. Reg. 95/11, s. 2.

Confined spaces with multi-employer involvement

4.   (1)   This section applies if the workers of more than one employer perform work in the same confined space or related work with respect to the same confined space.

(2)   Before any worker enters the confined space or begins related work with respect to the confined space, the lead employer or, in the case of a project, the constructor, shall prepare a co-ordination document to ensure that the duties imposed on employers by sections 5 to 7, 9 to 12 and 14 to 20 are performed in a way that protects the health and safety of all workers who perform work in the confined space or related work with respect to the confined space.

(3)   Without restricting the generality of subsection (2), in the case of a workplace that is not a project, the co-ordination document may provide for the performance of a duty or duties referred to in that subsection by one or more employers on behalf of one or more other employers, with respect to some or all of the workers.

(4) A copy of the co-ordination document shall be provided to,

    (a) each employer of workers who perform work in the same confined space or related work with respect to the same confined space;

    (b) in the case of a workplace that is not a project, the joint health and safety committee or health and safety representative, if any, for each employer of workers who perform work in the same confined space or related work with respect to the same confined space; and

    (c) in the case of a workplace that is a project, the joint health and safety committee or health and safety representative, if any, for the project. O. Reg. 632/05, s. 4; O. Reg. 95/11, s. 3.

Program

5. (1) If a workplace includes a confined space that workers may enter to perform work, the employer shall ensure that a written program for the confined space is developed and maintained in accordance with this Regulation before a worker enters the confined space.

(2) A program described in subsection (1) may apply to one or more confined spaces.

(3) In the case of a workplace that is not a project, the program described in subsection (1) shall be developed and maintained in consultation with the joint health and safety committee or the health and safety representative, if any.

(4)   A program described in subsection (1) shall be adequate and shall provide for,

    (a)   a method for recognizing each confined space to which the program applies;

    (b)   a method for assessing the hazards to which workers may be exposed, in accordance with section 6;

    (c)   a method for the development of one or more plans, in accordance with section 7;

    (d)   a method for the training of workers, in accordance with section 8 or section 9.1, as the case may be; and

    (e)   an entry permit system that sets out the measures and procedures to be followed when work is to be performed in a confined space to which the program applies.

(5)   In the case of a workplace that is not a project, the employer shall provide a copy of the program to the joint health and safety committee or the health and safety representative, if any.

(6)   In the case of a workplace that is a project, the employer shall provide a copy of the program to the constructor, who shall provide a copy of it to the project's joint health and safety committee or the health and safety representative, if any.

(7)   The employer or constructor, as the case may be, shall ensure that a copy of the program is available to,

    (a)   any other employer of workers who perform work to which the program relates; and

    (b)   every worker who performs work to which the program relates, if the workplace has no joint health and safety committee or health and safety representative. O. Reg. 95/11, s. 4.

Assessment

6.   (1)   Before any worker enters a confined space, the employer shall ensure that an adequate assessment of the hazards related to the confined space has been carried out.

(2)   The assessment shall be recorded in writing and shall consider, with respect to each confined space,

    (a)   the hazards that may exist due to the design, construction, location, use or contents of the confined space; and

    (b)   the hazards that may develop while work is done inside the confined space.

(3)   The record of the assessment may be incorporated into an entry permit under section 10.

(4)   If two or more confined spaces are of similar construction and present the same hazards, their assessments may be recorded in a single document, but each confined space shall be clearly identified in the assessment.

(5)   The employer shall appoint a person with adequate knowledge, training and experience to carry out the assessment and shall maintain a record containing details of the person's knowledge, training and experience.

(6)   The assessment shall contain the name of the person who carries out the assessment.

(7)   The person shall sign and date the assessment and provide it to the employer.

(8)   On request, the employer shall provide copies of the assessment and of the record mentioned in subsection (5) to,

  (a)   the joint health and safety committee or the project's joint health and safety committee, as the case may be, or the health and safety representative, if any; or

  (b)   every worker who performs work to which the assessment relates, if the workplace has no joint health and safety committee or health and safety representative.

(9)   The employer shall ensure that the assessment is reviewed as often as is necessary to ensure that the relevant plan remains adequate. O. Reg. 632/05, s. 6; O. Reg. 95/11, s. 5.

Plan
7.   (1)   Before any worker enters a confined space, the employer shall ensure that an adequate written plan, including procedures for the control of hazards identified in the assessment, has been developed and implemented by a competent person for the confined space.

(2)   The plan may be incorporated into an entry permit under section 10.

(3)   The plan shall contain provisions for,

  (a)   the duties of workers;

  (b)   co-ordination in accordance with section 4, if applicable;

  (c)   on-site rescue procedures, in accordance with section 11;

(d)   rescue equipment and methods of communication, in accordance with section 12;

(e)   personal protective equipment, clothing and devices, in accordance with section 13;

(f)   isolation of energy and control of materials movement, in accordance with section 14;

(g)   attendants, in accordance with section 15;

(h)   adequate means for entering and exiting, in accordance with section 16;

(i)   atmospheric testing, in accordance with section 18;

(j)   adequate procedures for working in the presence of explosive or flammable substances, in accordance with section 19; and

(k)   ventilation and purging, in accordance with section 20.

(4)   One plan may deal with two or more confined spaces that are of similar construction and present the same hazards as identified by the assessment.

(5)   The employer shall ensure that the plan is reviewed as often as is necessary to ensure that it remains adequate. O. Reg. 632/05, s. 7.

Hazard recognition and other general training — workplaces other than projects

8.   (0.1) This section does not apply to workplaces that are projects.

(1)   Every worker who enters a confined space or who performs related work shall be given adequate training for safe work practices for working in confined spaces and for performing related work, including training in the recognition of hazards associated with confined spaces.

(2)   The employer shall appoint a person with adequate knowledge, training and experience to conduct the training.

(3)   The employer shall ensure that training under this section is developed in consultation with the joint health and safety committee or the health and safety representative, if any.

(4)   The employer shall ensure that training under this section is reviewed, in consultation with the joint health and safety committee or the health and safety representative, if any, whenever there is a change in circumstances that may affect the safety of a worker who enters a confined space in the workplace, and in any case at least once annually.

(5)   The employer shall maintain up-to-date written records showing who provided and who received training under this section, the nature of the training and the date when it was provided.

(6)   The records may be incorporated into an entry permit under section 10.

(7)   Training under this section may be combined with training under section 9. O. Reg. 632/05, s. 8; O. Reg. 95/11, s. 6.

Plan-specific training — workplaces other than projects

9. (0.1) This section does not apply to workplaces that are projects.

(1) The employer shall ensure that every worker who enters a confined space or who performs related work,

    (a) receives adequate training, in accordance with the relevant plan, to work safely and properly; and

    (b) follows the plan.

(2) The employer shall maintain up-to-date written records showing who provided and who received training under this section, and the date when it was provided.

(3) The records may be incorporated into an entry permit under section 10.

(4) Training under this section may be combined with training under section 8. O. Reg. 632/05, s. 9; O. Reg. 95/11, s. 7.

Training — projects

9.1 (1) This section applies only to workplaces that are projects.

(2) The employer shall ensure that every worker who enters a confined space or who performs related work receives adequate training to perform the work safely, in accordance with the relevant plan.

(3) Training under subsection (2) shall include training in,

    (a) the recognition of hazards associated with confined spaces; and

    (b) safe work practices for working in confined spaces and for performing related work.

(4)   The employer shall maintain up-to-date written records showing who provided and who received training under this section and the date when it was provided.

(5)   The employer shall provide the training records under subsection (4) to the project's joint health and safety committee or health and safety representative, if any, on request.

(6)   The records may be incorporated into an entry permit under section 10. O. Reg. 95/11, s. 8.

Entry permits

10. (1)   The employer shall ensure that a separate entry permit is issued each time work is to be performed in a confined space, before any worker enters the confined space.

(2)   An entry permit shall be adequate and shall include at least the following:

1.   The location of the confined space.
2.   A description of the work to be performed there.
3.   A description of the hazards and the corresponding control measures.
4.   The time period for which the entry permit applies.
5.   The name of the attendant described in section 15.
6.   A record of each worker's entries and exits.
7.   A list of the equipment required for entry and rescue, and verification that the equipment is in good working order.
8.   Results obtained in atmospheric testing under section 18.
9.   If the work to be performed in the confined space includes hot work, adequate provisions for the hot work and corresponding control measures.

(3)   Before each shift, a competent person shall verify that the entry permit complies with the relevant plan.

(4)   The employer shall ensure that the entry permit, during the time period for which it applies, is readily available to every person who enters the confined space and to every person who performs related work with respect to the confined space. O. Reg. 632/05, s. 10.

On-site rescue procedures

11.   (1)   The employer shall ensure that no worker enters or remains in a confined space unless, in accordance with the relevant plan, adequate written on-site rescue procedures that apply to the confined space have been developed and are ready for immediate implementation.

(2)   Before a worker enters a confined space, the employer shall ensure that an adequate number of persons trained in the matters listed in subsection (3) are available for immediate implementation of the on-site rescue procedures mentioned in subsection (1).

(3)   The persons shall be trained in,

   (a)   the on-site rescue procedures mentioned in subsection (1);

   (b)   first aid and cardio-pulmonary resuscitation; and

   (c)   the use of the rescue equipment required in accordance with the relevant plan. O. Reg. 632/05, s. 11.

Rescue equipment and methods of communication

12.   (1)   The employer shall ensure that the rescue equipment identified in the relevant plan is,

   (a)   readily available to effect a rescue in the confined space;

(b)   appropriate for entry into the confined space; and

(c)   inspected as often as is necessary to ensure it is in good working order, by a person with adequate knowledge, training and experience who is appointed by the employer.

(2)   The inspection under clause (1) (c) shall be recorded in writing by the person, and the record of the inspection may be incorporated into the entry permit under section 10.

(3)   The employer shall establish methods of communication that are appropriate for the hazards identified in the relevant assessment, and shall make them readily available for workers to communicate with the attendant described in section 15. O. Reg. 632/05, s. 12.

Personal protective equipment, clothing and devices
13.   The employer shall ensure that each worker who enters a confined space is provided with adequate personal protective equipment, clothing and devices, in accordance with the relevant plan. O. Reg. 632/05, s. 13.

Isolation of energy and control of materials movement
14.   The employer shall, in accordance with the relevant plan, ensure that each worker entering a confined space is adequately protected,

(a)   against the release of hazardous substances into the confined space,

(i)   by blanking or disconnecting piping, or

(ii)   if compliance with subclause (i) is not practical in the circumstances for technical reasons, by other adequate means;

    (b)   against contact with electrical energy inside the confined space that could endanger the worker,

        (i)   by disconnecting, de-energizing, locking out and tagging the source of electrical energy, or

        (ii)   if compliance with subclause (i) is not practical in the circumstances for technical reasons, by other adequate means;

    (c)   against contact with moving parts of equipment inside the confined space that could endanger the worker,

        (i)   by disconnecting the equipment from its power source, de-energizing the equipment, locking it out and tagging it, or

        (ii)   if compliance with subclause (i) is not practical in the circumstances for technical reasons, by immobilizing the equipment by blocking or other adequate means; and

    (d)   against drowning, engulfment, entrapment, suffocation and other hazards from free-flowing material, by adequate means. O. Reg. 632/05, s. 14; O. Reg. 23/09, s. 2.

Attendant

15. (1) Whenever a worker is to enter a confined space, the employer shall ensure that an attendant,

    (a)   is assigned;

    (b)   is stationed outside and near,

        (i)   the entrance to the confined space, or

      (ii)   if there are two or more entrances, the one that will best allow the attendant to perform his or her duties under subsection (2);

  (c)   is in constant communication with all workers inside the confined space, using the means of communication described in the relevant plan; and

  (d)   is provided with a device for summoning an adequate rescue response.

(2)   The attendant shall not enter the confined space at any time and shall, in accordance with the relevant plan,

  (a)   monitor the safety of the worker inside;

  (b)   provide assistance to him or her; and

  (c)   summon an adequate rescue response if required. O. Reg. 632/05, s. 15.

Means for entering and exiting

16.   An adequate means for entering and exiting shall be provided for all workers who enter a confined space, in accordance with the relevant plan. O. Reg. 632/05, s. 16.

Preventing unauthorized entry

17.   If there is a possibility of unauthorized entry into a confined space, the employer, or in the case of a project, the constructor, shall ensure that each entrance to the confined space,

  (a)   is adequately secured against unauthorized entry; or

  (b)   has been provided with adequate barricades, adequate warning signs regarding unauthorized entry, or both. O. Reg. 632/05, s. 17; O. Reg. 95/11, s. 9.

Atmospheric testing

18. (1)   The employer shall appoint a person with adequate knowledge, training and experience to perform adequate tests as often as necessary before and while a worker is in a confined space to ensure that acceptable atmospheric levels are maintained in the confined space in accordance with the relevant plan.

(2)   If the confined space has been both unoccupied and unattended, tests shall be performed before a worker enters or re-enters

(3)   The person performing the tests shall use calibrated instruments that are in good working order and are appropriate for the hazards identified in the relevant assessment.

(4)   The employer shall ensure that the results of every sample of a test are recorded, subject to subsection (5).

(5)   If the tests are performed using continuous monitoring, the employer shall ensure that test results are recorded at adequate intervals.

(6)   The tests shall be performed in a manner that does not endanger the health or safety of the person performing them.

(7)   In this section,

"sample" means an individual reading of the composition of the atmosphere in the confined space;

"test" means a collection of samples. O. Reg. 632/05, s. 18.

Explosive and flammable substances

19. (1)   This section applies only in respect of atmospheric hazards described in clause (a) of the definition of "atmospheric hazards" in section 1.

(2)   The employer shall ensure that this section is complied with, by ventilation, purging, rendering the atmosphere inert or other adequate means, in accordance with the relevant plan.

(3)   The employer shall ensure that no worker enters or remains in a confined space that contains or is likely to contain an airborne combustible dust or mist whose atmospheric concentration may create a hazard of explosion.

(4)   The employer shall ensure that no worker enters or remains in a confined space that contains or is likely to contain an explosive or flammable gas or vapour, unless one of the following applies:

1.   The worker is performing only inspection work that does not produce a source of ignition. In the case of an explosive or flammable gas or vapour, the atmospheric concentration is less than 25 per cent of its lower explosive limit, as determined by a combustible gas instrument.

2.   The worker is performing only cold work. In the case of an explosive or flammable gas or vapour, the atmospheric concentration is less than 10 per cent of its lower explosive limit, as determined by a combustible gas instrument.

3. The worker is performing hot work. All the following conditions are satisfied:

    i. In the case of an explosive or flammable gas or vapour, the atmospheric concentration is less than 5 per cent of its lower explosive limit, as determined by a combustible gas instrument.

    ii. The atmosphere in the confined space does not contain, and is not likely to contain while a worker is inside, an oxygen content greater than 23 per cent by volume.

    iii. The atmosphere in the confined space is monitored continuously.

    iv. The entry permit includes adequate provisions for hot work and corresponding control measures.

    v. An adequate warning system and exit procedure are provided to ensure that workers have adequate warning and are able to exit the confined space safely if either or both of the following occur:

        A. In the case of an explosive or flammable gas or vapour, the atmospheric concentration exceeds 5 per cent of its lower explosive limit.

        B. The oxygen content of the atmosphere exceeds 23 per cent by volume.

(5) Subsections (3) and (4) do not apply if,

  (a) the atmosphere in the confined space,

    (i) has been rendered inert by adding an inert gas, and

        (ii)   is monitored continuously to ensure that it remains inert; and

    (b)   a worker entering the confined space uses,

        (i)   adequate respiratory protective equipment,

        (ii)   adequate equipment to allow persons outside the confined space to locate and rescue the worker if necessary, and

        (iii)   such other equipment as is necessary to ensure the worker's safety.

(6)   The equipment mentioned in subclauses (5) (b) (i), (ii) and (iii) shall be inspected by a person with adequate knowledge, training and experience, appointed by the employer, and shall be in good working order before the worker enters the confined space. O. Reg. 632/05, s. 19; O. Reg. 23/09, s. 3.

Ventilation and purging

20.   (1)   This section applies only in respect of atmospheric hazards described in clause (b) or (c) of the definition of "atmospheric hazards" in section 1.

(2)   If atmospheric hazards exist or are likely to exist in a confined space, the confined space shall be purged, ventilated or both, before any worker enters it, to ensure that acceptable atmospheric levels are maintained in the confined space while any worker is inside.

(3)   If mechanical ventilation is required to maintain acceptable atmospheric levels, an adequate warning system and exit procedure shall also be provided to ensure that workers have adequate warning of ventilation failure and are able to exit the confined space safely.

(4)   If compliance with subsection (2) is not practical in the circumstances for technical reasons,

> (a)   compliance with subsection (3) is not required; and
>
> (b)   a worker entering the confined space shall use,
>
>> (i)   adequate respiratory protective equipment,
>>
>> (ii)   adequate equipment to allow persons outside the confined space to locate and rescue the worker if necessary, and
>>
>> (iii)   such other equipment as is necessary to ensure the worker's safety.

(5)   The equipment mentioned in subclauses (4) (b) (i), (ii) and (iii) shall be inspected by a person with adequate knowledge, training and experience, appointed by the employer, and shall be in good working order before the worker enters the confined space. O. Reg. 632/05, s. 20.

Records

21.   (1)   In the case of a workplace that is not a project, the employer shall retain every assessment, plan, co-ordination document under section 4, record of training under subsection 8 (5) or 9 (2), entry permit under section 10, record of an inspection under subsection 12 (2) and record of a test under section 18, including records of each sample, for the longer of the following periods:

1. One year after the document is created.

2. The period that is necessary to ensure that at least the two most recent records of each kind that relate to a particular confined space are retained.

(2) In the case of a workplace that is a project, the constructor or employer, as the case may be,

(a) shall keep available for inspection at the project every assessment, plan, co-ordination document under section 4, record of training under subsection 9.1 (4), entry permit under section 10, record of an inspection under subsection 12 (2) and record of a test under section 18, including records of each sample; and

(b) shall retain the documents described in clause (a) for one year after the project is finished.

(3) If section 4 applies,

(a) the documents described in subsection (1) shall be retained by the employer responsible for creating them; and

(b) the documents described in clause (2) (a) shall be retained by the constructor or employer, as the case may be, responsible for creating them. O. Reg. 95/11, s. 10.

Critical Injury – Defined
R.R.O. 1990, Regulation 834

1.   For the purposes of the Act and the Regulations, "critically injured" means an injury of a serious nature that,

> (a)   places life in jeopardy;
>
> (b)   produces unconsciousness;
>
> (c)   results in substantial loss of blood;
>
> (d)   involves the fracture of a leg or arm but not a finger or toe;
>
> (e)   involves the amputation of a leg, arm, hand or foot but not a finger or toe;
>
> (f)   consists of burns to a major portion of the body; or
>
> (g)   causes the loss of sight in an eye.

R.R.O. 1990, Reg. 834, s. 1.

Inventory of Agents or Combinations of Agents
for the Purpose of Section 34 of the Act
R.R.O. 1990, Regulation 852,
as amended by O. Reg. 517/92

1. The Ministry of Labour hereby adopts, as an inventory of agents or combinations of agents that are not new biological or chemical agents or combinations of such agents for the purpose of section 34 of the Act, the Chemical Substances Initial Inventory including the User Guides and Indices and Trademarks and Product Names reported in conjunction therewith of May, 1979, together with the Cumulative Supplement to the Initial Inventory of June, 1980, published by the Administrator of the Environmental Protection Agency of the United States of America under The Toxic Substances Control Act (P.L. 94-469). R.R.O. 1990, Reg. 852, s. 1.

2. Inquiries concerning Inventory and Cumulative Supplement may be addressed to:

Inventory of Agents
Occupational Health and Safety Branch
Ministry of Labour
505 University Avenue 19th Fl
Toronto ON M7A 1T7

O. Reg. 517/92, s. 1.

Joint Health and Safety Committees -
Exemption from Requirements
O. Reg. 385/96 as amended by O. Reg. 131/98

1. In this Regulation,

    "ordinary worker" does not include a participant in community participation under the Ontario Works Act, 1997;

    "volunteer worker" means a worker who performs work or supplies a service but who receives no monetary compensation for doing so other than an allowance for expenses or an honorarium. O. Reg. 385/96, s. 1; O. Reg. 131/98, s. 1.

2. A workplace at which fewer than 20 ordinary workers are regularly employed is exempted from clause 9 (2) (a) of the Act. O. Reg. 385/96, s. 2.

3. A project at which fewer than 20 ordinary workers are regularly employed is exempted from clause 9 (2) (a) of the Act. O. Reg. 385/96, s. 3.

4. The following workplaces are exempt from subsection 9 (12) of the Act:

    1. A workplace at which fewer than 20 ordinary workers (who are not volunteer workers) are regularly employed.

    2. A project at which fewer than 50 ordinary workers (who are not volunteer workers) are regularly employed. O. Reg. 385/96, s. 4.

Occupational Health and Safety Awareness and Training
O. Reg. 297/13

Basic Occupational Health and Safety Awareness Training

Basic occupational health and safety awareness training — workers

1. (1)   An employer shall ensure that a worker who performs work for the employer completes a basic occupational health and safety awareness training program that meets the requirements set out in subsection (3) as soon as practicable.

(2)   Subsection (1) does not apply if,

(a)   the worker previously completed a basic occupational health and safety awareness training program and provides the employer with proof of completion of the training; and

(b)   the employer verifies that the previous training meets the requirements set out in subsection (3).

(3)   A basic occupational health and safety awareness training program for workers must include instruction on the following:

1.   The duties and rights of workers under the Act.

2.   The duties of employers and supervisors under the Act.

3.   The roles of health and safety representatives and joint health and safety committees under the Act.

4.   The roles of the Ministry, the Workplace Safety and Insurance Board and entities designated under section

22.5 of the Act with respect to occupational health and safety.

5. Common workplace hazards.

6. The requirements set out in Regulation 860 (Workplace Hazardous Materials Information System (WHMIS)) with respect to information and instruction on controlled products.

7. Occupational illness, including latency.

Basic occupational health and safety awareness training — supervisors

2. (1) An employer shall ensure that a supervisor who performs work for the employer completes a basic occupational health and safety awareness training program that meets the requirements set out in subsection (3) within one week of performing work as a supervisor.

(2) Subsection (1) does not apply if,

(a) the supervisor previously completed a basic occupational health and safety awareness training program and provides the employer with proof of completion of the training; and

(b) the employer verifies that the previous training meets the requirements set out in subsection (3).

(3) A basic occupational health and safety awareness training program for supervisors must include instruction on the following:

1. The duties and rights of workers under the Act.

2. The duties of employers and supervisors under the Act.

3. The roles of health and safety representatives and joint health and safety committees under the Act.

4. The roles of the Ministry, the Workplace Safety and Insurance Board and entities designated under section 22.5 of the Act with respect to occupational health and safety.

5. How to recognize, assess and control workplace hazards, and evaluate those controls.

6. Sources of information on occupational health and safety.

Exemptions

3. (1) The requirements set out in section 1 do not apply to an employer with respect to a supervisor if,

(a) before this Regulation came into force, the supervisor was performing work as a supervisor for the employer; and

(b) the employer verifies that, before this Regulation came into force, the supervisor completed a basic occupational health and safety awareness training program that meets the requirements set out in subsection 2 (3).

(2) The requirements set out in section 1 do not apply to an employer with respect to a worker or supervisor if,

(a) another employer was exempt with respect to the worker or supervisor under subsection (1); and

(b) the worker or supervisor provides the employer with proof of the exemption.

Record of training

4.　(1)　An employer shall maintain a record of the basic occupational health and safety awareness training required by sections 1 and 2 that is completed by workers and supervisors who perform work for the employer.

(2)　An employer shall maintain a record of workers and supervisors who perform work for the employer in respect of whom the employer is exempt under section 3.

(3)　If a worker or supervisor completes a training program under subsection 1 (1) or 2 (1), the employer shall, at the request of the worker or supervisor, provide the worker or supervisor with written proof of completion of the training.

(4)　If an employer is exempt with respect to a supervisor under subsection 3 (1), the employer shall, at the request of the supervisor, provide the supervisor with written proof of the exemption.

(5)　If, within six months of a worker or supervisor no longer performing work for an employer, the worker or supervisor requests a written proof described in subsection (3) or (4), the employer shall provide the worker or supervisor with the requested written proof.

Certification Training

Certification training

5.　(1)　An employer shall carry out the training programs necessary to enable a committee member to become a certified member, and the programs must be selected in accordance with the training and other requirements established by the Chief Prevention Officer under section 7.6 of the Act.

(2)   For greater certainty, in subsection (1),

"carry out" includes paying for the training.

Offices of the Worker and Employer Advisers
O. Reg. 33/12

Functions of the Offices of the Worker and Employer Advisers

1.   (1)   For the purposes of Part VI (Reprisals by Employer Prohibited) of the Act, the functions of the Office of the Worker Adviser are to educate, advise and represent in proceedings before the Board workers who are not members of a trade union.

(2)   For the purposes of Part VI (Reprisals by Employer Prohibited) of the Act, the functions of the Office of the Employer Adviser are to educate, advise and represent in proceedings before the Board employers that have fewer than 50 employees. O. Reg. 33/12, s. 1.

Unilateral Work Stoppage
[Criteria to be Used and Other Matters to be Considered by the Board under Subsection 46 (6) of Act]
O. Reg. 243/95
as amended by O. Reg. 22/09

1.   For the purpose of subsection 46 (6) of the Act, the following criteria are prescribed for determining whether the constructor or employer has demonstrated a failure to protect the health and safety of workers:

1.   The record of accidents, deaths, injuries and work related illnesses in the workplace.

2. The constructor's or employer's occupational health and safety policies and the length of time they have been in place.

3. The training, communications and programs established to implement the policies under paragraph 2, and the length of time they have been in place.

4. The constructor's or employer's health and safety record under the Act, including,

   i. complaints made to the Ministry of Labour against the constructor or employer,

   ii. work refusals under section 43 of the Act,

   iii. the Board's or adjudicators' decisions under section 46 of the Act,

   iv. work stoppages under sections 45 and 47 of the Act,

   v. the results of inspections conducted by the Ministry,

   vi. convictions for contraventions of the Act or the regulations made under it,

   vii. the record of compliance with inspectors' orders.

5. Any other factors that it is reasonable to consider in the circumstances. O. Reg. 243/95, s. 1; O. Reg. 22/09, s. 2.

2. The following matters are prescribed as matters to be considered by the Board in deciding upon an application under section 46:

1. Any previous occasion on which the Board or an adjudicator found under that section that the procedure for stopping work set out in section 45 of the Act would not be sufficient to protect the constructor's or employer's workers.

2. The constructor's or employer's course of conduct with respect to the establishment and operation of the committee and the appointment and certification of its members.

3. A pattern, if any, of the constructor or employer dealing in bad faith with the committee.

4. The nature and extent of the health and safety hazards at the workplace, including the risks they pose and whether adequate measures have been established to respond to them.

5. If the measures established to respond to the health and safety hazards are not adequate, the length of time that would be required to establish adequate measures and the degree of intervention by an inspector that would be necessary.

6. Any other matters that it is reasonable to consider in the circumstances. O. Reg. 243/95, s. 2; O. Reg. 22/09, s. 3.

Regulations made under the
Occupational Health and Safety Act
Revised Statutes of Ontario, 1990, Chapter O.1

July 1, 2014

A.   Safety Regulations

Construction Projects:	O. Reg. 213/91, as amended by O. Reg. 631/94, O. Reg. 143/99, O. Reg. 571/99, O. Reg. 145/00, O. Reg. 527/00, O. Reg. 85/04, O. Reg. 627/05, O. Reg. 628/05; O. Reg. 443/09, O. Reg. 96/11, O. Reg. 88/13.
Industrial Establishments:	R.R.O. 1990, Reg. 851, as amended by O. Reg. 516/92, O. Reg. 630/94, O. Reg. 230/95, O. Reg. 450/97, O. Reg. 144/99, O. Reg. 284/99, O. Reg. 528/00, O. Reg. 488/01, O. Reg. 280/05, O. Reg. 629/05, O. Reg. 565/06, O. Reg. 179/07, O. Reg. 494/09, O. Reg. 420/10, O. Reg. 98/11.
Mines and Mining Plants:	R.R.O. 1990, Reg. 854, as amended by O. Reg. 583/91, O. Reg. 584/91, O. Reg. 171/92, O. Reg. 384/92, O. Reg. 571/92, O. Reg. 693/92, O. Reg. 60/94, O. Reg. 779/94, O. Reg. 68/96, O. Reg. 272/97, O. Reg. 236/99, O. Reg. 486/99, O. Reg. 174/01, O. Reg. 251/01, O. Reg. 291/02, O. Reg. 31/04, O. Reg. 630/05, O. Reg. 84/07, O. Reg. 496/09, O. Reg. 99/11 O. Reg. 296/11, O. Reg. 92/13, O. Reg. 34/14.
Critical Injury – Defined:	R.R.O. 1990, Reg. 834.
Diving Operations:	O. Reg. 629/94, as amended by O. Reg. 155/04, O. Reg. 32/14.

Farming Operations	O. Reg. 414/05, as amended by O. Reg. 90/13.
Firefighters – Protective Equipment:	O. Reg. 714/94, as amended by O. Reg. 449/97, O. Reg. 80/02, O. Reg. 24/09, O. Reg. 480/10.
Health Care and Residential Facilities:	O. Reg. 67/93 as amended by O. Reg. 142/99, O. Reg. 631/05, O. Reg. 25/09, O. Reg. 495/09, O. Reg. 94/10, O. Reg. 97/11, O. Reg. 169/11, O. Reg. 89/13.
Needle Safety	O. Reg. 474/07, as amended by O. Reg. 317/08, O. Reg. 439/09.
Occupational Health and Safety Awareness and Training:	O. Reg. 297/13.
Oil and Gas-Offshore:	R.R.O. 1990, Reg. 855, as amended by O. Reg. 566/06, O. Reg. 421/10.
Roll-Over Protective Structures:	R.R.O. 1990, Reg. 856.
Teachers:	R.R.O. 1990, Reg. 857.
University Academics and Teaching Assistants:	R.R.O. 1990, Reg. 858.
Window Cleaning:	R.R.O. 1990, Reg. 859, as amended by O. Reg. 523/92.

B. Designated Substances

Asbestos on Construction Projects and in Buildings and Repair Operations:	O. Reg. 278/05, as amended by O. Reg. 493/09, O. Reg. 422/10, O. Reg. 479/10.
Designated Substances:	O. Reg. 490/09, as amended by O. Reg. 259/10, O. Reg. 148/12.

C.   General

Biological or Chemical Agents, Control of Exposure to:	R.R.O. 1990, Reg. 833, as amended by O. Reg. 513/92, O. Reg. 597/94, O. Reg. 388/00, O. Reg. 100/04, O. Reg. 16/05, O. Reg. 77/05, O. Reg. 177/05, O. Reg. 607/05, O. Reg. 83/07, O. Reg. 248/08, O. Reg. 491/09, O. Reg. 419/10, O. Reg. 149/12.
Workplace Hazardous Materials Information System:	R.R.O. 1990, Reg. 860, as amended by O. Reg. 36/93.

D.   Hazardous Physical Agents

X-Ray Safety:	R.R.O. 1990, Reg. 861.

E.   Regulations that Directly Affect/Impact the Act

Confined Spaces:	O. Reg. 632/05, as amended by O. Reg. 23/09, O. Reg. 492/09 O. Reg. 95/11.
Inventory of Agents or Combinations of Agents for the Purpose of Section 34 of the Act:	R.R.O. 1990, Reg. 852, as amended by O. Reg. 517/92.
Joint Health & Safety Committees- Exemption from Requirements:	O. Reg. 385/96, as amended by O. Reg. 131/98.
Offices of the Worker and Employer Advisers:	O. Reg. 33/12.
Unilateral Work Stoppage:	O. Reg. 243/95, as amended by O. Reg. 22/09.

NOTE:

For a complete reference to the Regulations made under the Occupational Health and Safety Act, please see the e-Laws website [http://www.e-laws.gov.on.ca]; Current Consolidated Law contains all of the Statutes and the regulations made under them, while the Legislative Tables contain both a Legislative History Overview and a Detailed Legislative History of Statutes and Regulations.

Ticketing Schedules and Set Fines
relating to occupational health and safety
(information current through July 1, 2014)

NOTE: The Set Fines cited in the following tables do not include the Victim Fine Surcharge. The amount of the VFS is usually 20 per cent of the imposed fine. For example, a $100 fine would result in a $20 surcharge. Fines over $1,000 carry a surcharge of 25 per cent.

Schedule 67
Ontario Regulation 213/91, Construction Projects

Item	Column 1	Column 2/ OHSA section	Set Fine
1.	Worker failing to work in compliance with subsection 26.1 (2) of Ontario Regulation 213/91 by not being adequately protected by fall protection	28 (1) (a)	$295.00
2.	Worker failing to work in compliance with section 115 of Ontario Regulation 213/91 by using loose object as workplace or as support for object	clause 28 (1) (a)	$195.00
3.	Worker having or using stilts or leg extension devices contrary to section 116 of Ontario Regulation 213/91	28 (1) (a)	$195.00
4.	Employer failing to ensure compliance with stilts and leg extension devices requirements in section 116 of Ontario Regulation 213/91	25 (1) (c)	$295.00
5.	Supervisor failing to ensure worker working in compliance with stilts and leg extension devices requirements in section 116 of Ontario Regulation 213/91	27 (1) (a)	$295.00

Item	Column 1	Column 2/ OHSA section	Set Fine
6.	Worker failing to work in compliance with subsection 195.1 (1) of Ontario Regulation 213/91 by using inadequately grounded cord-connected electrical equipment or tools	28 (1) (a)	$195.00

O. Reg. 661/00, s. 1; O. Reg. 444/09, s. 1.

Schedule 67.1
Ontario Regulation 213/91, Construction Projects

Item	Column 1	Column 2	Set Fine
1.	Worker failing to wear protective headwear	section 22	$195.00
2.	Worker failing to wear protective footwear	section 23	$195.00
3.	Worker failing to wear eye protection	section 24	$195.00
4.	Worker failing to use provided protective respiratory equipment	subsection 46 (2)	$195.00
5.	Worker who may be endangered by vehicular traffic failing to wear prescribed garment	section 69.1	$195.00
6.	Operator leaving the controls of machine unattended	section 102	$195.00
7.	Signaller failing to wear prescribed garment	subsections 106 (1.1) - (1.4)	$195.00
8.	Worker failing to wear adequate personal protective equipment while using fastening tool	clause 117 (3) (a)	$195.00
9.	Worker failing to wear adequate eye protection while using fastening tool	clause 117 (3) (b)	$195.00

Item	Column 1	Column 2	Set Fine
10.	Worker failing to wear full body harness connected to fall arrest system while on suspended equipment	subsection 141 (1)	$295.00

O. Reg. 661/00, s. 1.

Sources of the following information:

The schedules are reproduced from Regulation 950 made under the Provincial Offences Act:

http://www.e-laws.gov.on.ca/html/regs/english/elaws_regs_900950_e.htm

The fines are reproduced from the Ontario Court of Justice Set Fines website:

http://www.ontariocourts.on.ca/ocj/en/setfines/

Ministry of Labour – Occupational Health and Safety Contact Information

Call the Ministry of Labour Health and Safety Contact Centre

- Report incidents, critical injuries or fatalities

  If it's an emergency, call 911 immediately

- Report possible unsafe work practices

- General occupational health and safety inquiries

  Ministry of Labour Health and Safety Contact Centre
  Toll-Free: 1-877-202-0008
  TTY: 1-855-653-9260
  Fax: 905-577-1316

Other Ways to Contact the Ministry of Labour

- **E-mail:** webohs@ontario.ca
- **Web:** www.ontario.ca/labour
- **Regional Offices:**
  www.labour.gov.on.ca/english/about/reg_offices.php

Ministry of Labour
Operations Division

400 University Ave
Toronto, Ontario
M7A 1T7

R.S.O. 1990, c. O.1 as amended

O. Reg. 213/91 as amended by
O. Reg. 631/94, O. Reg. 143/99,
O. Reg. 571/99, O. Reg. 145/00,
O. Reg. 527/00, O. Reg. 85/04,
O. Reg. 627/05, O. Reg. 628/05,
O. Reg. 443/09, O. Reg. 96/11,
O. Reg. 88/13.

Remember that while complying with occupational health and safety laws, you are also required to comply with applicable environmental laws.

ISBN 978-1-4606-4185-9   **Rev. 07/14**